KALEIDOSCOPE

AN ANTHOLOGY OF THE PAPERS OF JAMES R MATHERS 1916 – 1986

Social Psychiatrist, Superintendent of Rubery Hill Hospital, Birmingham

Honorary Lecturer in Pastoral Studies,
Theology Department, University of Birmingham

With best wishes

Jean Wilson.

Edited by Michael and Jean Wilson.

Published
by
REARDON PUBLISHING
56, Upper Norwood Street
Cheltenham, GL53 0DU
England
www.reardon.co.uk
email: reardon@bigfoot.com

Copyright © 2003

Edited by Michael and Jean Wilson.

ISBN 1 873877 53 6

Typesetting and Layout
by
N. Reardon

Cover Creation
by
David Wilson

Printed
through
World Print Ltd
Hong Kong

CONTENTS

ACKNOWLEDGEMENTS

At this moment in time the greatest acknowledgement of all must be given to James himself. As I have been reading through these papers time and again the striking thing about them is the freshness of their contribution to our current situation in the 21st. Century. James retired early and quite deliberately gave his time to thinking, reading, writing and speaking as prophetically as he was then able to be: this took considerable self sacrifice on his and Margaret's behalf, both in financial terms and in terms of the gift of his time. Many more people will now, I hope, be enabled to profit from his actions.

Acknowledgement must be given to the Mathers family who have unstintingly given their support to this project. They are happy, in due course, for the Archive of his Papers to be deposited in the Library of the University of Birmingham. Arrangements are in hand for this to happen. Thanks must also be recorded to the Archivist there who has indicated willingness to receive them.

Acknowledgement from us all must also go to Michael Wilson who, in his lifetime was the only man other than James who had actually read all the papers. It was the completion of this task, over many months of great dedication, that enabled him to make the selection of papers you have before you today.

The many, many people, patients, students, staff, family friends and neighbours whom James encountered in his lifetime, with and from whom he learnt so much, also deserve our gratitude.

The compilation of the Memorial Lecture has been an interesting exercise in itself. Faced with a tape recording of the actual Lecture, a transcription of it by another person, (which I scanned into my computer as the basis for the paper) and the script of the Lecture printed in the Pastoral Studies Spring Conference Papers 1987 I had three slightly different versions! What you read here is a fourth version – I have done my best to be faithful both to Professor Dyson's written text and to his spoken word. At best this is illustrative of how other texts from history have been written. . . .

The present Editor of CONTACT has permitted use of the Academic Critique – thank you.

My thanks must also go to Nicholas Reardon of Reardon Publishing, Cheltenham, U.K. who has been extremely helpful in seeing this book through to your bookshelf! And to my son David M. Wilson, who has not only introduced me to Nicholas Reardon, but has kindly given permission for the use of his photograph of James and Margaret Mathers in their garden in Hay-on-Wye on the back of the book.

Jean Wilson
July 2002

ABBREVIATIONS

ACCS	Advisory Commission for Church & Society (Church in Wales)
BBC	British Broadcasting Corporation
BCC	British Council of Churches
BMJ	British Medical Journal
C	Century
CHC	Community Health Council
CIO	Church Information Office
CNS	Central Nervous System
CO	Commanding Officer
Coy	Company
DLT	Darton, Longman & Todd
DPS	Diploma in Pastoral Studies
FCFC	Free Church Federal Council
IRM	Institute of Religion and Medicine
JCH	John Conolly Hospital, Birmingham
LMG	London Medical Group
MDS	Medical Dressing Station
MNO	Mental Nurse Orderly
MO	Medical Officer
MW	Michael Wilson
NAMH	National Association of Mental Health
NHS	National Health Service
OED	Oxford English Dictionary
OUP	Oxford University Press
PT	Physical Training
RAL	Robert A Lambourne
RHB	Regional Hospital Board
RHH	Rubery Hill Hospital, Birmingham
RMO	Regimental Medical Officer
SCM	Student Christian Movement
SPCK	Society for the Propagation of Christian Knowledge
TLS	Times Literary Supplement
UP	University Press
WHO	World Health Organisation
WVS	Women's Voluntary Service

PREFACE

My reasons for publishing a selection of James Mathers' papers are fivefold:

* I am fired by the insights of a lively and imaginative mind.
* His insights into the nature of knowledge, of human relationships, of mental health and human growth and development through community, and of a future Health Service for Britain are as relevant today as when he first wrote them.
* To make a wider selection of his papers available for discussion amongst ordinary people as well as students, church groups and politicians. They are a valuable resource for research.
* The papers not only contain valuable ideas, but contain important local history about the last twenty years of a large asylum for psychiatric patients, now no longer existent.
* It is important to record the wisdom of our present Western culture which is now in decline, so that it may in the long-term of history be available for the foundations of whatever new culture may succeed our own.

I do not propose to make an academic critique of James' papers for two reasons:

Firstly, because his papers were mostly written for *speaking,* and were adapted for various audiences. His lively mind leapt sideways across disciplines to collect stories and illustrations into a patchwork quilt which presented a new and often surprising aspect of supposedly familiar matters.

Secondly, because I am not the right person to do so: James and I share too many of the same 'prejudices'.

James is a man of his time and his language is male-dominated. I have tried to change this where possible, but in many places too much mutilation of the text is involved. I can only ask readers to give James non-judgemental acceptance.

Michael Wilson, August 1998

Michael and I had worked hard together on the production and editing of these papers until September 1998 when Michael himself was diagnosed with a terminal illness. Whilst I shared with him the living - the pregnancy of his dying – this work necessarily went into hibernation. I return to finish the task now according to Michael's wish and his intention was that when eventually published it should appear in our joint names.

Jean Wilson, July 2002

INTRODUCTION TO PAPERS

James' Mathers papers are not terminals but campsites pitched at sunset and struck at dawn in order to travel onwards. He did not hoard his insights, but pursued their consequences into the many areas of life where he roamed.

The speed and restlessness of his thinking made him an essay writer rather than an author of books. Most papers were written for speaking: he preferred talking to writing because he enjoyed the dance of minds in conversation. His conclusions were not as clear as he would have liked, but he suspected there was a price to be paid for clarity - you had probably left something out.

A more logical way of writing would have dampened the energy, the search and the surprising bursts of free association which brought unlikely images together. He was a master of the discussion-starter.

James was a trans-disciplinary thinker. He was educated in Medicine, Psychiatry, Psychotherapy and Biology: but was also knowledgeable in Ethology, Social Work, Pastoral Theology, Group Dynamics, Education and Ethics. There are few writers where you will find a discussion of the behaviour of the Galapagos finches in a paper on idolatry. His metier was making connections: and it is often more helpful to be imaginative rather than right. On the other hand his book reviews were concise, sharp and focussed: his criticisms of the National Health Service and Counselling are still pertinent today. But his pioneering work in the Therapeutic Community approach (139-4 pp. 79-85) to the promotion of health has been virtually overwhelmed by the increasing dualism of Western culture. His vision of wholeness, however, remains part of this culture's wisdom which, hopefully, will pass into the foundations of any new culture that may succeed our present culture's demise.

He was somewhat apologetic for the abundance of his papers, but among the reasons which he gave for exploring and sharing ideas are:

- That one of the main characteristics of a human being is inter-communion: he described human relationships as 'channels of communication' - especially of feelings - between people.

- 'We need to be thinking ahead of our time'.

- "The subject which I have chosen (63 - Healthy Death) is one in which I have no special qualification, and indeed in which I am particularly conscious of my ignorance. I thought that if I undertook to speak about it, it might help me to get my own thoughts in order, and possibly stimulate some fruitful discussion of the matter which would enable me to learn, rather than teach."

- "My aim is to see, not to explain."

- "I like talking with young people."

James was an expressive man who enjoyed the sharing of ideas and the stimulus of discussion with people of varied opinions, occupations and cultures. He visibly brightened when he brought the surprise of insight to himself, to a patient, and to friend or foe. He is a creative thinker who has charted new paths for the human imagination.

In his first essays written in the Far East amid the turmoil of the 1939-45 war, he unfolds a questing mind with a sharp academic intellect that included also the realms of intuition, feeling and imagination. There are clear lines of enquiry which he pursued for the rest of his life: a search for meaning in life, the implications of morale for mental and physical health, the relationship of science and religion, the corporate nature of human beings, and a concern for everyone to grow and develop their God-given selfhood in a common purpose for God's kingdom.

He also shows in these early papers that his theological stance would always be experience-related and rooted in a communal search for truth. He did not speak of his experience in an individual way but, for example, on the Arakan Front in Burma he saw his experience like a continual dance with colleagues, patients, brigade officers and regimental doctors. He was widely knowledgeable, but factual knowledge only interested him in so far as it could be embodied in daily life.

He did not use the Bible in a critical way, but used the gospels particularly as a rich source of images. It was the subject with which he was wrestling, such as health or leadership, that formed the shape of his sermons, with shafts of light from scripture; rather than working from scripture first. James never retired into a religious ghetto where religious language can become divorced from daily life. He was a layman to his fingertips and much in demand for addresses to N.H.S. staff on Hospital Sunday or St Luke's-tide. But he preferred occasions when discussion could follow his address. He abhorred monologues!

His use of language reveals two aspects: often enough he uses words in a factual way where accuracy is important. Papers on 'Crisis Theory' (104) and 'Fear, Anxiety and Group Morale' (2-3) are of this nature. But he also uses language to build relationships between himself and his listeners (or readers) and between one another (for example, 63 Healthy Death). He was a natural community-builder, interpersonal communion was, for James, the essence of being human - a 'biological imperative'.

He spoke to a variety of audiences, both professional and lay, religious and secular. His enjoyment of discussion and feedback made him a leading member of the Institute of Religion and Medicine. This group of professionals, interested in the care of others, included teachers and social workers as well as doctors, nurses and related professions. Their conferences were to hear some of his most exploratory papers (e.g.161 - 1 Too Much Noise Makes You Deaf).

His addresses were akin to evangelism, an invitation to his hearers to change their point of view (*metanoia* - repent!), to explore with him some new way of looking at something familiar: for example, to see the Health Service as an anti-disease service, or to see prayer in terms of communication. His quest for truth was at a deep level of his nature, and he was not satisfied with mere curiosity.

James' approach to education was an open one. He could not help noticing a neglect of the emotional life in our Western educational system because he constantly had to help people who had not learnt to handle their own feelings and grow up emotionally. He called his regular seminars with the post-graduate students of the Diploma in Pastoral Studies Course – 'Kaleidoscope' - after the toy which makes beautiful patterns out of bits of coloured paper, cloth and beads. Whenever you shake the toy, the patterns break up and transform into new patterns. This was the key to James' educational method. He described himself not as a teacher addressing a class face-to-face, but as standing behind a student with his hands on their shoulders, studying the same matter which the student was studying. James was not concerned to 'inform' students, but joined the group as a member and enabled all to contribute their own gifts and knowledge to the human growth and development of the whole group.

In the guide lines to his seminar (242 - Kaleidoscope) which he wrote for the new tutor, when he retired, he described three main areas of discourse: patterns of health and community, the corporate nature of persons as well as individuality, and the importance of the role of amateurs in matters of health, religion and social care - areas too often rigorously patrolled by professionals.

He constantly helped students in their pastoral work to relate to those for whom they cared both objectively and also through participation in their feelings, and their wider relationships with spouse, siblings, friends and neighbours. He was never comfortable with a one-to-one situation but always tried to widen a 'group' of two to include other related people.

In a quest for truth he was unafraid to be wrong, and in his psychiatric work with groups he deliberately learnt to withstand (i.e. to stand with) embarrassment, powerlessness and vulnerability. Bob Lambourne, James Mathers and myself (three medical doctors on the staff of the Theology Department of the University of Birmingham) worked and thought together in the fields of religion and medicine, church, healing and health, doctors and clergy. The interchange of ideas between us means that our writings are interwoven!

James retired at the age of fifty-five "in order to have time to read, think and write". He deliberately set out to change his identity by removing himself from his customary backgrounds of place, work and local church: in effect he laicised himself from his profession and church leadership in order to relate to 'normal, healthy people' as a normal healthy person. He often spoke of this liberating change of perspective. By so doing he explored an important contribution which older retired people can make to society.

Although since his death the explosive development of the Internet has solved the problem of the *collection* of information (the importance of which he had repeatedly emphasised) our current problems are *selection* and *reflection*. It was time to reflect - to think - which James sought in early retirement. He also gave time to selection through his reviews of books, which became a major occupation in his last few years when, because of Margaret's illness, he curbed his travelling and speaking in order to care for her.

An academic critique of James' papers (see pp.322-6) is one part only of an estimate of his thought, inadequate by itself to disclose the fullness of his creativity. His meaning is to be grasped with the intellect only in so far as he was rash enough to write so extensively! It goes beyond analysis in the quality of his personal communion with family, friends, colleagues, students, fellow church members, patients and many 'normal healthy people' who felt enlarged by meeting him. Encounters, which enable a new awareness, enlarge the boundaries of our personal world and reveal a new dimension of truth, are life-giving and transformative.

Because the range of subjects, which James covered in his papers, is so wide I have adopted the following pattern for this selection. I have chosen ten major ideas or insights which James had, and have followed each one, chapter by chapter, into the various contexts of his own and his audiences' knowledge and interests. Thus I have, for example, taken his discovery of the importance of morale for the physical and mental health of soldiers in battle: and I have followed this insight as he worked out its implications in the contexts of health, mental health, hospitals, therapeutic community, residential care in social work, church (sermons, mission, patterns of ministry and pastoral care), marriage, education and the Institute of Religion and Medicine. Thus our minds begin, as it were, at a point and then spiral like a snail shell among ever wider contexts, from self to the marriage relationship, to the family, friends, church congregation, neighbourhood, country, global issues and universe. A new idea could be born at any level and become the explosive point of a new helix.

Because James repeated the same ideas for different audiences, repetition is a particular difficulty for this anthology. I would like a reader, for example, to be able to turn to Chapter 8 and read his paper on Wholeness (121 - 8) without necessarily having mastered the ideas of previous chapters.

Certain ideas such as the distinction between differentiation and specialisation, the implications of Freud's discovery of the transference, and Winnicott's phrase that 'a mother needs to be good enough', recur constantly. If they form a link in the chain of an argument, omission damages the sense. So there is more repetition in the papers than is perhaps ideal in an anthology designed to be read as a whole.

On Friday 27th March 1987 there was a Celebration of the lives of James and Margaret Mathers. It was a threefold event, held in the University of Birmingham. At noon there was a Service of Thanksgiving in the chapel of St Francis Hall (the address is printed on pp.301-306): followed by a meal in which family, friends and students, past and present, could renew their membership one of another. Then Professor Dyson of the University of Manchester gave a Memorial Lecture (pp.307-321) in the Faculty of Arts. And because James and Margaret had given themselves severally and together, to the life of Hay-on-Wye for fifteen years, there was also a Memorial Service in their local parish church of St Mary's in January 1987.

Let the final word be with James:

"Death challenges us to see it as the end we have in view,
not as an overwhelming enemy from whom we should try to escape."

Michael Wilson, Birmingham, 1998

Chapter One

WE-RELATIONSHIPS

We shall live together as one family, or die apart as fools: our life blood flows in one another's veins. Without denying the uniqueness of each individual, James countered the prevailing individualism of Western culture by seeing every person as the centre of a network of human relationships. Our human genius for communication with others is nurtured in the mother/baby relationship, which soundly founds (or twists) our distinctively human ability to love and be loved.

There is hardly a single paper of James' that could not be included in this chapter. But the following selection lays a foundation stone for all subsequent papers. Our mental health, our communal living, our gift for self-sacrifice, our self-identity, our very humanity, depend on we-relationships.

M.W.

HUMAN RELATIONSHIPS

. . . What do we mean by a 'human relationship' anyway? It is probably impossible to define it precisely, but I am going to use it as meaning a *continuing channel of communication between two people*. Generally speaking, the more channels of communication there are between men and women and those with whom they come into contact, the more mentally healthy they are likely to be. Conversely, when we think a person is mentally ill, what we usually mean is that there is some kind of a barrier to communication between them and us - we can't understand what they mean. The channel is blocked up.

What do we mean by *communication*? An SOS signal from the radio operator of a ship doesn't become a communication until it has been received and understood - until its meaning is something we have 'in common' with the sender. Communications are not necessarily made up of words; in fact, words by themselves can be very misleading. When we talk face-to-face with another person we often get a quite different - and nearly always a more accurate - idea of what they mean, than when we only read something they have written. We communicate by our expression and behaviour as well as by words: by what we don't say as well as by what we do say. The most significant communications often scarcely need words at all: two young people in love often talk sheer gibberish. So does a mother talking to her baby.

There must be a *channel* of communication - a two-way flow must be able to take place. The lecturer talking to a lot of people who are half asleep is not likely to be communicating with them, at least not by the subject matter of the talk. When we leave a lecture and talk with our friends in the foyer we can often agree that *the lecturer* was boring, or interesting, or sincere, or muddleheaded; the lecturer has communicated something of their personality to us. But we will have difficulty in finding more than two people who will agree about what was actually said. (Try this for yourself sometime). The two-way channel is best illustrated by the two lovers: he says "Darling" and she replies "Darling" - and we say that they have come to an "understanding".

Our channel of communication must be reasonably *continuing*. If I pass a girl in the street and exchange a smile with her, it isn't necessarily a human relationship. But if I exchange smiles with her every morning it is.

Try to imagine what would happen to us if we tried to do without these continuing channels of communication with other people. It would be like solitary confinement in a prison cell for life. Or, in this respect, like being sent to Coventry forever. In a social sense, a human being is 'nothing but' a knot in a network of personal relationships. Loneliness and isolation are well known to be enemies of mental health. Some people in every generation have sought solitude as a spiritual exercise; but even they have carried with them memories of their friends and their childhood. An infant who had no experience of human relationships could never grow into a human adult.

The New Testament teaches us that the foundation of health, or wholeness, is love. Love is, in fact, the emotion of a human relationship at its most perfect development. At its best, it is the timeless, entirely unselfish feeling which allows of complete mutual understanding and freedom of expression between people. By studying human relationships we are, so to speak, taking a look at the biology of love, surveying its natural history in human beings; and I hope that in so doing we may arrive at a clearer understanding of its implications for us as Christians.

21 - The Search for Mental Health.

THE MOTHER-CHILD RELATIONSHIP

Unlike other baby animals, the human infant has a very limited repertory of instinctive kinds of behaviour - far too few to enable it to survive if left alone within a few weeks of birth. It is dependent on others of its own kind for longer than any other animal. The advantage, which has to be balanced against this apparent disadvantage, is that the human baby has a far wider range of *possible* behaviour than any other animal. Any normal healthy baby, for instance, can be taught to speak any language or dialect under the sun. But it has to be taught - by another, more adult, human being.

It is possible to imagine that a machine could be invented which might take mother's place as far as relieving baby's elementary discomforts is concerned: a sort of robot, which would be 'set off' by baby's cry of distress, and would then try out various ways of relieving it - rocking the cradle, offering a bottle of warm milk, or even (if we let fancy have a loose rein) changing a nappy. Such a machine might possibly keep baby alive for a week or two. But it wouldn't be a very 'responsive' kind of mother-substitute. When baby gurgles happily, it would maintain a stony silence. It wouldn't be able to give a goodnight kiss, or play peep-boo behind its fingers. Baby would never learn to talk, or play. It could never become anything more than another robot, mechanical, lacking all initiative, inhuman. A baby, like the legendary Phoenix, requires to be fed on a rich pabulum from birth, in order that it can become strong and healthy for the later tasks life will require.

A baby has to *learn* to become a human being. It can feel happy or contented or frustrated or angry, just like the rest of us (perhaps more intensely than older people); and, like us, it will show this in it's behaviour. It's behaviour is an attempt to express it's feelings. It is, in fact, a signal, hoisted for mother to see. If it behaves acceptably, it's signal is 'received and understood', and mother responds in a way which shows that she approves. If it behaves otherwise, she either ignores it (if she doesn't understand) or else responds disapprovingly. It isn't always easy to understand a baby, since it can't talk. The person who can understand it best is the one who is always there. And equally, the person who is always there is the one whom the baby finds it easiest to understand. This is why the experts say that even a 'bad' mother (by our own standards of respectability) is better than no mother at all; and that in children's homes and orphanages, there must be continuity in the relationship between the child, and the foster-mother or nurse.

If this continuity is broken - if mother disappears, or is replaced by a stranger, there is a break in the vital channel of communication on which all baby's capacity for learning depends. In point of fact, baby gets frightened if mother doesn't come to reassure it; and this fear, if not quickly dispelled, becomes panic - a catastrophic reaction. We all know what happens in catastrophes - communications break down. At a personal level, we say "it's face was frozen with fear" or "it was too terrified to move". All capacity for self-expression seems to leave us under these conditions. The badly frightened baby stops crying after a while ... we say with exhaustion. But is this exhaustion ever unaccompanied by terror?

Fear is a normal human emotion and has obvious biological value to any animal, living in an environment which contains so many threats to survival. But if panic fear in a human being is aroused by other human beings - or by isolation from other human beings - it is always damaging to mental health and development. Adult memory mercifully blots out recollection of most of our terrors of infancy, but they leave their scars as certainly as a bodily wound does.

The relationship between child and mother (or mother-substitute) is a love-relationship, a continuing channel of two-way communication upon which the whole mental development of the child depends. It is almost never a 'perfect' love-relationship: there is always likely to be some difficulty in mutual sympathy and understanding, if only because no two people express themselves alike and none of us are wholly free of the blind-spots caused by prejudice. But the more love there is in the relationship, the less risk there is of paralysing fear - and when fear is present, there is diminished communication and therefore less possibility of love. Love and fear are perhaps more truly opposite to one another than are love and hate, at least in children. *"There is no fear in love, but perfect love casteth out fear. ... He that feareth is not made perfect in love".*

21 - The Search for Mental Health.

WHO AM I?

. . . With the Incarnation, God became man, and Jesus phrased the question differently. At Caesarea Philippi he said to his disciples *"whom do men say that I am?"* In our time, psychologists have pointed out that for each of us the sense of identity, the sense of who we are, depends in large part upon our being recognised and accepted as unique persons by other persons - and how damaging it is to a man's sense of identity when he is not so recognised! When others speak to us or about us merely as members of impersonal categories, as they so often do - as consumers, or taxpayers, or immigrants, or commuters, for instance - we feel depersonalised, subtly insulted. Often enough our response is to think, or even say, "who the devil do they think we are?"

Whom do men say that I am? The answers Jesus received to his question were all inaccurate - some say John the Baptist, others say Elijah and others Jeremiah or one of the prophets. Perhaps we ought rather to say not wholly inaccurate, but certainly inadequate. When you ask a stranger who he is, he will probably reply in terms of his membership of some group - he comes from a certain town, or is a member of this or that profession. Even his surname indicates membership of a particular family group. (But not his Christian name). Jesus went on to ask the disciples a second question, *"But whom do you say that I am?"* Only one of them - Simon Bar-Jona - replies. The answers to the first question are couched in terms of the past: John the Baptist, Elijah, Jeremiah and the prophets are all dead. So other people confirm my sense of identity (or refuse to confirm it) in terms of my past behaviour, in terms of what I have uttered or outered. But this second question, to which only Simon Bar-Jona responded, refers not to the present arising out of the past, but to the future arising out of the present: *"Thou art the Christ, the son of the living God".* It is not so much that he has reached a conclusion from past evidence; it is that he has recognised something new and unexpected: he has discovered a new man. And Jesus responds *"Blessed are you, Simon Bar-Jona, for flesh and blood have not revealed this to you, but my Father who is in heaven".* This is the creative, personal encounter, in which the true answer to the question "Who am I?" is revealed, paradoxically, by the recognition and confirmation of a totally new identity - for both participants. The man Jesus becomes the Christ, the son of the living God; and Simon Bar-Jona becomes Peter, the rock on which the church is built.

Such truly personal encounters are not part of the public currency of everyday social life. Most of the time we only know *about* people. Really to *know* another person, and face the challenge of a new and unfamiliar identity, a new birth, is something that essentially happens only in the privacy and intimacy of a love relationship. So Jesus charged his disciples to 'tell no-one about him' (Mk 8.30). The beginning of a new thing is always part of a private mystery, shared by very few, to be hidden from public gaze until the proper time comes for it to be shown forth. Modern psychology has little useful to say about new beginnings. They are unpredictable. They cannot be extrapolated from the known facts: flesh and blood cannot reveal them to us. New identities, new beginnings, come from God. The most that man can do is to remove some of the more obvious hindrances to the possibilities of love developing between people, and then to wait in hope and faith.

Who am I? Do we ask this as a scientific question, which can be answered by reference to our past, to our experience which has made us express ourselves in particular kinds of behaviour and words - Whom do men say that I am? Or do we ask it as a question of hope and faith in a future, a question which we can properly address only to those we love - Whom do *you* say that I am?

Perhaps there is a third way in which the question should be put. A person only becomes a person by being in relationship with other persons. Within a love relationship, it is possible for two persons to become 'one flesh'. This means that for them the question is not only "Who am I?" It is now also "Who are *we*?" Every man identifies himself to other people by affirming his one-ness with particular groups of which he is a member. His sense of personal identity, from childhood onward, grows and develops and differentiates, as he becomes able to identify himself with wider and wider groups of other men. To identify himself: to share experience with them, to be at one with them, to commit himself to them - and ultimately, perhaps, to be ready to die for them. But as he matures, he finds that it becomes less important for him to have a strong sense of *individual* identity, to affirm that he is at one with this exclusive group and not with that. As he moves on his Christian journey, outward from his family and outward from his local community and nation, to a recognition of his common humanity with foreigners and those he sees as enemies, he is likely to be assailed by some degree of identity confusion. He is no longer certain who he is or where he belongs. The experience is in fact thrust upon many of us. Even if we are not dispossessed expatriates, the rapid changes of our society and its accepted values means that most of us are already robbed of the familiar background and personal groups which we knew as children. It is hard for most of us to keep contact with the roots of our personal identities. What this seems to imply, if we are to remain healthy and fully human, is that as our ego-identities become less and less important, we need to replace them by successive we-identities, each more comprehensive than its predecessor. Between the egocentric perspective of the infant and the Christocentric perspective of the spiritually mature Christian, lies a continuous series of what we may call socio-centric perspectives, each in turn transcending the limitations and exclusiveness and clarity of definition of the one before. The New Testament contains a number of images of such we-identities. We are members of Christ's body, says St Paul. We are soldiers in Christ's army. We are members one of another. And Jesus prays to his Father *"that they may be one, even as we are one; I in them and thou in me, that they may become perfectly one"*. . . .

. . . Now the scriptures give us plenty of help in understanding how to love our neighbours whom we meet face to face, and this fits in well with the vision of a comprehensive we-identity for Christians. In the relatively small communities of first-century Palestine this is perhaps all we should expect. Certainly, there were strangers to be dealt with, and we are taught to be hospitable toward them. But this implies meeting them face to face, so that they are really potential neighbours. If you meet even your enemy face-to-face, it may be possible to learn to love him.

But in the modern world, the problem is different. Nowadays the Christian's sense of identity is affected by all sorts of people never likely to be met face to face. They include the purveyors of news and advertisement and propaganda, for instance; and those we call 'faceless bureaucrats' who issue instructions and demand that we fill up forms; and as well as these there are peasants and politicians in far-off lands who may see us as oppressors and enemies. These are all strangers to us; and yet they too are God's children and we owe them the same love, and need the same love from them, as we owe to and need from our neighbours. So the question "Who is my Stranger?" has now become an important part of the biblical question, "Who is my neighbour?"

I must leave you with this problem now, though perhaps some of us may discuss it later. It seems to me to be one that God is calling us to explore particularly in this twentieth century. In science, we often find that new discoveries shed fresh light on matters which we had thought we understood. It may be that an exploration of this question, "Who is my stranger?" will provide us with some new answers to our older questions, "Who is my neighbour?" "Who am I?" "Who is the God I worship?"

196 - Who Am I?

AUTHORITY AND POWER

. . . Dictionary definitions of authority are largely couched in terms of power, but the meanings of the word power are various. In any case it is not at all clear that God's or (more particularly) Christ's authority is to be understood as a function of power; on the contrary, he seems to have expressed his authority most convincingly by his refusal to exercise power. Authority and power are distinguishable concepts which do not necessarily go together; and I suggest that, while power exists whether it is recognised or not (i.e. it has an 'objective reality'), authority only exists when it is recognised. Matthew and Mark report that Jesus taught "*as one who had authority, and not as the scribes*". They did not say, as we might have expected, that his authority was greater or more convincing than that of the scribes: they simply refused to recognise the authority which the scribes, their own doctors of the law, would surely have claimed.

The matter may be illuminated if we consider how these concepts may develop in the mind of a child. At birth, the human infant is both physiologically and psycholog-ically 'incomplete', and is thus largely dependent on the sheer physical power and competence of those who care for him. If this parental power is deployed in a manner which more or less satisfies his changing needs (in D .W. Winnicott's phrase, if parents are "good enough"), then as he grows and develops he comes to endow them with authority: that is to say, he authorises or permits them to alter (by their attitudes and behaviour) the view he takes of his existing state.[1] If, when he develops to an age of wilfulness, he refuses to acknowledge their authority, the parents have to fall back on their superior power if they are to exercise control over him.

Once the child has recognised parental authority, it is maintained by a combination of two motives: affection or love, and fear. Families vary in their pattern of social structure between two extremes. At one pole the pattern is *authoritarian*, in which relationships are structured on a model of dominance and submission. The child learns to recognise authority through the threat of punishment. In such a structure, the main focus of his attention will be the threatening parent and the need to maintain a proper distance from him. Physical contact with him is likely to be painful and is best avoided; while the distinction between parental power and authority is difficult or impossible for him to make. As he grows physically stronger, the disproportion between his and his parents' power grows smaller, thus reducing the child's respect for their authority. To the extent that his ideas about God are based on his experience in the family, he is likely to feel that God is (a) powerful and punitive, but (b) at a distance, and therefore (c) possible either to hide from, or ignore, or manipulate.

By contrast, at the other pole the family pattern may best be described as *permissive*. That is to say that parents permit their children a wide range of behaviour before using their power to establish limits. (We misuse the word permissive when we assume it to mean the absence of authority: permissiveness implies the *presence* of one who permits.) In this pattern, the parent maintains control of the child by attracting him, and offering him the comfort of close bodily contact. The absence of threat allows the child's attention to be wide-ranging and exploratory instead of narrowly focused on the parent, so that his intelligence and learning capacity can be more freely deployed. As he grows up, parental power is seen less as a challenge and more as a resource to be shared. Thus a permissive family pattern fosters an image in the child's mind of a God of love rather than wrath, of grace rather than law; and one who is close at hand, immanent as well as transcendent. His power and might are acknowledged but not feared. Of course, the structure of authority in most families lies somewhere between the two extremes thus described.

Many factors could be invoked to explain the lack of respect for authority, human or divine, which we so readily deplore. Let us stay with those which are specially relevant to children. Since the start of the industrial revolution, about two centuries ago, laws against child labour in mines and factories, followed by those establishing compulsory schooling, together with a number of other more recent child-protection measures, have steadily eroded the power which parents can exercise over their offspring, at the same time as they have sought to restrain the abuse of that power. In families where authority and power are poorly distinguished, these laws have therefore also diminished parental authority. But in families where less punitive child-rearing patterns have allowed parental authority to be established through affection rather than fear, the erosion of parental power by external constraints has left parental authority unimpaired. . . .

Reference:

1.   R.A.Lambourne, "Authority, Personal Knowledge and the Therapeutic Relationship", *Contact 25*, (Edinburgh) 1968.

215-2 Authority, Equality and Randomness.

. . . Authority is the outcome of a personal relationship; and personal relationships require that people communicate with one another. We usually think of communication as a matter of words, but there is more to it than that. In fact, all our senses are involved in it. In the earliest communications we experience (at mother/baby level, which are pre-verbal) the important senses are those of touch, and to a lesser extent taste and smell, which give information about the immediate surroundings, rather than those of hearing and vision, which tell us what is going on at a distance. And the patterns of meaning which we learn through touch provide us with a basic structure or scaffolding on which we will later build our understandings of what we see and hear. Children who through brain damage at birth have difficulty in understanding their tactile experience are also handicapped in understanding what they see and hear, and may indeed appear blind and deaf until they have learnt to make sense of what they feel through their skin. So what I am suggesting is that the recognition of authority within a family is primarily based on 'good enough' body contact between parents and children, on cuddling and hand-holding, perhaps spiced with the occasional firmer handling or slap; and only secondarily on the words which are spoken.

Now let me approach the subject from another angle. A child may recognise parental authority through affection or fear, or, of course, a mixture of the two. In general families are so structured as to make one of the two predominate. Now those students of animal behaviour who watch monkeys and apes in their natural state are able to see two distinct patterns of social structure which they describe as *agonistic* or *hedonic*. The agonistic pattern is a dominance/submission model, wherein dominant animals maintain order by threatening those of subordinate rank. This results in each animal's attention being rather narrowly concentrated on keeping a proper distance between him/herself and those above and below him/her in rank. Touching only occurs when he/she fails to keep his/her distance and is then likely to be painful - a blow or a bite. By contrast, in the hedonic pattern, the dominant individual maintains order by displaying attention-seeking behaviour which *attracts* subordinates: they run towards him/her with greeting cries and apparent pleasure. The absence of threat allows attention to be much more wide-ranging and flexible, and the absence of a need to maintain distance results in there being more companionable body contact between them. Naturally, the agonistic pattern is more likely to be seen when the environment is potentially hostile, and the hedonic when threats are less apparent. The agonistic pattern implies that individuals are in a high state of arousal, ready for fight or flight; while the more relaxed hedonic mode allows better for digestion, growth and restorative or recreational activity. Applying these observations to the human family, it seems clear that we should see the hedonic mode as the norm for a nurturing environment, and regard the agonistic as appropriate only for temporary, discontinuous periods of special stress; but of course needing to be exercised or practised in education or play.

If a child is part of a family structure where an agonistic mood predominates, in what we usually call an authoritarian structure, he/she will learn to recognise authority mainly through the threat of punishment. The main focus of his/her attention will be the threatening parent and the need to keep a proper distance from him or her. Physical contact is likely to be painful and is best avoided. And the distinction between parental power and parental authority will be difficult or impossible for him/her to make. As the child grows physically stronger, the disproportion between his/her and his/her parents' power grows less, and this reduces his/her respect for their authority. By contrast, the other pole of the continuum, the family structure will be predominately hedonic and may best be described as permissive: that is to say that parents permit their children a wide range of behaviour before using their power to establish limits. ... In this pattern, the parent keeps control of the child by attracting him/her and offering the comfort of close bodily contact. The absence of threat allows the child's attention to range widely instead of being narrowly focussed on the parent, so that his/her intelligence and learning capacity can be more freely deployed. As he/she grows up, parental power is seen as less of a challenge and more as a resource to be shared, and is recognised as distinct from parental authority, which is acknowledged as a matter of course and scarcely questioned.

A child's ideas about God are inevitably modelled initially on his/her experience of parents. Thus the first characteristic that God will be seen to possess is power. For the child, God is certainly the Almighty. The kind of authority with which he/she then comes to be endowed will depend on the balance of fear and affection evoked by parental authority in the child's mind. If the family structure is authoritarian, he/she is likely to feel that God is punitive as well as powerful, but at a distance, and therefore possible either to hide from, or ignore, or even manipulate. On the other hand, a permissive family pattern fosters the image of a God who is permissive - but not absent; a God of love rather than wrath, of grace rather than law (or as well as law); a God who is close at hand, immanent as well as transcendent. His/her power and might are acknowledged, but not feared.

The distinction between authoritarianism and permissiveness may seem somewhat simplistic unless we take into account the very considerable anxiety and suffering undergone by properly permissive parents. To have children at all is to give hostages to fortune; and to permit them enough freedom to grow in their own way and at their own pace - as God means them to - with all the human risks that this entails, requires a degree of fortitude and patience which we usually attribute only to saints. Disagreements between parents and children about what is and what is not permissible are inevitable - the very stuff of family life. When conflicts arise, how are they to be resolved? The traditional teachings about obedience to commandments and the pardoning of offences imply an essentially authoritarian structure. This is the picture of the God of justice, the lawgiver, the God of wrath. But within a permissive framework, what human experience can provide a model for reconciliation? We are taught that love is patient and keeps no score of wrongs. But children's experience of love can only be very partial: only in maturity can the mutuality of love, and the self-denying element in caring love, be fully understood. It may be relatively easy for the mature parent to forgive - perhaps even before the transgression; but how can the child be brought to repentance, to *metanoia*, the change of mind from past evil? How can he/she be induced to accept that he/she was wrong - or at least, and more realistically, partly wrong?

May it not be that the human experience of close physical body contact, of being touched, of being cuddled, is precisely the element for which we are looking? Conflict implies separating and distancing oneself from the other: reconciliation implies abolishing that distance. I spoke previously of the possibility of experimenting with an image of the incarnate God as being 'good enough', analogous to the image of mother as being just 'good enough' in her child's eyes. Now I seem to be suggesting the image of a God who cuddles. Put like that it sounds absurdly sentimental, but of course it is not meant to be an exclusive image: God has many different faces. It is in Deuteronomy that we read that *"underneath are the everlasting arms"*. Jesus spoke about casting out demons by the *finger* of God; and he invited the doubting Thomas to *touch* his hands and his side. But perhaps the most important Biblical reference to this sort of closeness is an indirect one: the use by Jesus of the name "Abba" - Daddy - in addressing his Father. Liturgiologists are only recently encouraging us to closer physical contact, in the Kiss of Peace; while, of course, the secular appreciation of this blind spot in our understanding of one another is expressed in the 'encounter group' movement. Like the laying on of hands in Christian practice, its significance has been largely narrowed to a therapeutic function, to a putting right what has gone wrong, by specialists, instead of being recognised as a necessary element of growth in all family and social life. Cuddling is, after all, a matter for amateurs, for those who love, rather than for experts.

215-3 Notes on the Development of the Idea of Authority.

THE ART OF MARRIAGE

. . . A successful marriage relationship is, of course, a work of art. It requires the same qualities of aesthetic integrity, strenuous endeavour, and persistence in working through difficulties that are required for the creation of any other work of art. Unlike a painting, or a piece of sculpture, however, it never achieves a static perfection - is never, in some sense, complete; and is never attributable only to the efforts of the two people involved. A marriage is something which can only be successful in a community setting, and the community must take some of the responsibility for its success or failure.

For most people, marriage is the most significant relationship with another human being that they will have. It is not, of course, the most fundamental. The capacity to make relationships is something that develops and differentiates from the moment of birth, and all our experience of relationships has a cumulative effect on any we may make in the future. The fundamental relationship is that of mother and baby. If we regard this as the root of our capacity for relationships, then marriage can be regarded as its flower.
. . .

. . . I feel that one has to stress as fundamental to the marriage relationship its continuity, and the sharing of emotional experience. This is less trite than it sounds when one considers what so frequently happens when a marriage gets into difficulties: it is so easy, when you are annoyed or angry with the other person, *not* to tell him or her what you have been doing or experiencing during the day. Communication between two people needs to be constant and without let or hindrance if the channel is to be kept open. For a successful marriage it is vital not to let the sun go down on your wrath.

When I talk of the sharing of emotional experience I am not thinking so much of sexual experience but of ordinary day-to-day mundane moods and anxieties and curiosities and happinesses. It is, I think, one of the penalties of an academic education that we tend to give undue importance to verbal communication, and to forget that while words are the most delicate and precise means of communication, they are also the most likely to be misused and misunderstood. I don't suppose you will any of you get much good out of this lecture of mine; but I am sure you would have got even less if you had read it without seeing me and noting my gestures and hearing the alterations of my voice and so on. By talking to you face-to-face, I cherish the hope that you will at least understand me better than my words alone could express. Actions, they say, speak louder than words; and in marriage, as in any important relationship, it is not only what you say that matters, but also the way you say it. One is never more than half-aware of the content of any communication within a relationship of this kind. Usually one focuses attention on the words spoken, but its total significance as a communication includes such things as the mood of the speaker, angry or loving, tired or anxious; and the background - words spoken in the bedroom may mean something quite different to the same words spoken in the market place.

Communication always involves two people. Each must foster their capacity for self-expression in terms intelligible to the other; and each must foster the maximum possible sensitivity to the other's meanings. Only by paying a lot of attention, continuously, to these basic principles, can you hope to make a real success of marriage. . . .

. . . It is not within my province to consider courtship; but I should say here that to my mind the only satisfactory basis for a marriage relationship is for each partner to want the marriage so badly that he and she are prepared to give up everything for it - at least, everything as it has been seen by them up to that moment, from an egocentric standpoint. One's standards of values, one's beliefs (which so often are mainly prejudices), one's pet philosophies - all these will require to be looked at afresh after marriage. Even one's ideas of such absolutes as Justice and Truth, and even one's idea of God, should tend to alter and develop and grow again, from the basis of the new experience.

No man is an Island. Only in relationship with others can we become truly human. Selfish behaviour indicates a failure in relationship, and, don't forget, it takes *two* to make a relationship. So an accusation of selfishness is an indication of two people's failure.

To most of us, I suppose, the change of attitude demanded by marriage comes only slowly, and, for many of us if not for all, it comes mainly after marriage. It is a truism that a successful marriage demands an indefinite continuance of courtship; but inasmuch as a readiness to change one's attitude is characteristic of courtship, to meet the wishes of the other, then it is of profound significance. . . .

. . . It will be apparent to you that I believe that a marriage is an act of faith. Intellectually, at least, I believe that one has to take a good deal on trust when one enters such a relationship. I don't mean that one should enter it blindly - very much the reverse. One should look at all possible difficulties with eyes wide open. But having done that, having used one's intellect to its best level, the decision to marry or not remains, and must remain, an affair of the heart rather than the head, so that the solution of the intellectual problems remains a matter for faith.

A healthy marriage is never just a relationship between two people, existing in isolation from the rest of the world. It begins with a public act, duly registered and announced in the public press, signifying that these two persons have taken due notice of the society in which they live, and are prepared, to a greater or lesser extent, to accept the rules and sanctions of this society, to take on their share of its responsibilities and to receive in return the benefits which it offers them. In particular, it signifies that they are accepting their right to have children, to perpetuate their society. Regarded in this light, you will understand that one of the worst possible attitudes towards marriage is that which regards it as ideal to get away from other people - to "keep yourselves to yourselves". Not every marriage will be blest with children; but the hope that two people can be self-sufficient and exist only for each other, in isolation from the rest of the community, is vain and unhealthy - egocentricity carried to a higher degree.

Of course, two people in love will be scarcely aware of the rest of the world. The social significance of marriage is a lesson which one should study before courtship and return to some six months after marriage: between whiles most couples are virtually inaccessible to this point of view. The most obvious practical illustration of the wider relationships involved in marriage is that of the prospective in-laws. The best guarantee that an individual will make a happy marriage is that his or her parents were happily married. It is a rash man who does not study his wife's parents before proposing. He may not have to live with them, but he will have to live with their prejudices and beliefs about a thousand and one every day matters for a long time. It is only a half-truth to say "It's the girl I want to marry, not her parents". For instance, the only experience of bringing up children which a young wife has had will be that which she received herself: her way of bringing up her first born will either be similar, if she approved of her own upbringing, or a reaction against her own, if she hated it. Neither alternative is likely to tally at all closely with the patterns with which her husband is acquainted. After the first child, subsequent additions to the family are rather more fortunate as the parents have some joint experience to go on.

Clearly, the arrival in the family of children brings with it a whole series of opportunities for the parents to re-examine their remaining prejudices and blind spots, and deepen the channel of communication which constitutes their own relationship. Also, the same readiness to give up everything, which we found necessary at the beginning of marriage has to be invoked afresh. To have a child is to give a hostage to fortune. It is an act of faith. People say that having children may well be put off for a year or two - because otherwise they "tie a young couple down". Indeed they do. Youth of any age must be served. But it is a service which brings with it new degrees of freedom. . . .

. . . The sexual adjustment of the partners in a marriage is not its most important aspect, although so much attention is focussed on it. The background - the continuing channel of communication which we have talked about - is of far greater significance and deserves much more attention than it frequently gets. Lerv - the starry-eyed state which the pop-singers are so much preoccupied with - is not, biologically speaking, continuous. It comes, and, often enough, it goes again. It has the same relation to marriage as a taper has to a lantern: it is difficult to get the marriage going without it, but, once it is going, it is of minor significance - pretty enough in the gloaming, but not powerful enough to live by.

The acute attack of sexual love does however find its fulfilment in the sexual act, and brings to what has hitherto been a purely physiological release of bodily tension, entirely egocentric and autoerotic, an immensely deeper meaning. Within marriage, the sexual act is enabled to become the most delicate, precise, and specific means of communication between two people that they will ever experience. Note that I say it is enabled to do so, not that it usually does. The marriage relationship is one of maturity, and it contains within itself elements from all other significant relationships in the individual's past. All husbands make demands for mother-love from their wives at times - for instance when they are sick. This is a fact of life which in no way debases the marriage relationship. Similarly, sexual activity within marriage must be expected to recapitulate many elements from the individual's past sexual experience, so that at times it may seem autoerotic, at others mere lust, and at others only a way of escape from the pressing problems of reality. None of these should be regarded as debasing the relationship in any essential way. They are only deplorable when they replace the fully mature act of mutual self-giving. Thus it is understandable that the perfect sexual experience is a rarity, even within a satisfactory marriage. So long as we do not live in a perfect society, anxieties and past sins and guilt are the lot of every one of us, and they are bound to affect the most delicate relationship of all. For some people, sexual adjustment is more difficult to achieve than for others. But relative failure in this respect need not stop the development of a perfectly satisfactory love relationship in marriage. Many people achieve new depths of mutual sexual understanding after five and even ten years of married life. . . .

. . . The physiological differences, however, point to a much more important psychological problem which has to be faced in marriage: that of the differing roles of the partners. Preconceived ideas of the manly man and the womanly woman are dangerous. Clinical psychology reveals a more or less continuous spectrum of masculine and feminine *traits* in all human beings at some level of the personality; and successful marriage seems to depend upon assortative mating - the unconscious skill with which couples choose each other to ensure that their respective personality traits are complementary to each other. The man who loves cooking, and arranging the flowers, matters which some people regard as essentially feminine occupations - is quite as likely to make a successful marriage as he who plays rugger on Saturday afternoons and spends an hour each evening at the local. Assortative mating can be relied upon, usually, to see that the former selects a wife with whom he will not have to quarrel as to who uses the gas-cooker; and that the latter will wed someone who likes washing muddy shirts.

It must be remembered that the human capacity for adaptation to different roles is far greater than the limits imposed by physiological make-up. Margaret Mead[1] has a chapter heading in her book *Male and Female* – 'Human Fatherhood is a Social Invention'. She points out that communities have been known in which the natural father is not the head of the family; and that humankind is alone among the higher mammals in that the male of the species accepts a nurturing (as opposed to a simply protective) role as regards children. This is a matter of social tradition rather than a biological imperative. Even among women, for whom the biological imperative to nurture their young might be thought to limit adaptability, cultural pressures can bring about such extremes as the handing over of the new-born baby to a wet-nurse by a healthy mother; the denial of maternity implicit in the breastless women's fashions of the 1920s; and, at the other extreme, we can find societies where children of three or even four years old are still allowed to suckle at the breast.

The technological revolution of our times is bringing with it, inevitably, a sense of confusion as to the roles of the man and the woman in marriage. The increasing tendency for the woman to remain a wage-earner after marriage, the decrease in domestic drudgery resulting from improvements in the design of homes and kitchens; even the whole apparatus of the Welfare State, with its provision of facilities for child care and upbringing, and of hospitals where healthy women can go to have their babies - as if normal childbirth were a disease - all these factors have a major impact on traditional concepts of the woman's role in the home. So does the immensely powerful agency of modern mass advertising, and the use of the hidden persuader.

Inasmuch as these factors relieve a married couple of their biological responsibility for nurturing their own children, they are likely to induce anxiety and guilt, and to disrupt, to some extent, the marriage relationship. With increasing anxiety of this kind comes the tendency which I have already deplored, to keep yourselves to yourselves, and to try to solve all the emotional problems of family life within the four walls of the small modern house or flat. It cannot work. It makes for what Durkheim described as the "atomisation of society", and ends in what he called a "dust of individuals". The solutions of the problems of relationship within marriage can only be worked out in the relationships of the couple to the wider society; and the TV, the newspaper and the telephone cannot adequately maintain these wider relationships. Face-to-face contact is essential.

I hope I have said enough to indicate to you that the success of a marriage depends almost as much upon the society in which it occurs as upon the partners themselves. You will realise that since the partners are themselves constituent members of their society, what I have said in no sense diminishes their overall responsibility for marriage, but rather increases it. It is a question of being prepared to alter the standpoint from which you try to assess the truth of the total situation: the appropriate behaviour of a member of a society being that which is in the best interest of all its members.

My insistence upon the need to extend one's face-to-face relationships with other people does not mean that I believe the good life to approximate to that which I imagine obtains in a Holiday Camp. Healthy emotional development requires plenty of opportunity for privacy and even solitude. But most people in our society, for the reasons I have already outlined, tend to maintain a distressingly large part of their lives "defensively private". It is in this area, of course, that the psychiatrist has to work, and is, at all events, likely to realise how unnecessary, as well as unwise, it is for people to keep so many of their attitudes and beliefs 'incommunicado'. It isn't necessary, even if it were possible, to pour every triviality into the channel of communication which constitutes a relationship: what *is* necessary is that the channel should be kept wide and clear so that what needs to flow along it can do so smoothly. . . .

. . . Finally, to summarise. The marriage relationship is, for most of humanity, the keystone of the arch of all relationships. It cannot exist except as part of a social fabric with which it is intimately interwoven. Like all relationships, it is essentially a channel of communication that must be continuously used if it is to be kept clear. It requires those qualities of sympathy and freedom of self-expression and persistence, and patience and unselfishness and courage, which are subsumed under the heading of love. In a changing world, each new marriage is a significant social experiment; traditions and precedents are likely to be unreliable guides, and it is important to go back to first principles, repeatedly and frequently, if mistakes are to be avoided.

Marriage is a love-relationship, and, as such, it partakes of the nature of God, and gives us deeper insight into God's nature - whether we acknowledge God's presence or not.

Reference:
1.   M. Mead, **Male and Female,** (Pelican Books), 1962.

25 - The Art of Marriage.

REVIEW: THE CAPACITY TO LOVE

. . . The author writes of the human experience of love as it develops from early infancy: *"the first attachment of love we make is with our mother"*; " *Freud said that God is the projected father, the universal neurosis. If anything, he is the loving mother"*. And it is only by the third year that the child is able to internalise mother, and *"the first steps are taken to love and be loved in the absence of the beloved"*. So here are two major psychological findings that need to be harmonised with theological doctrine: that our first experience of God - non-verbal but tactile, olfactory and visual - is with a maternal rather than a paternal figure. And that it is only when we are about three years old that we can experience love as God - whom we cannot see or touch and who is physically absent. Thus the question arises: is it possible for those whose experience of mother-love is impaired at the non-verbal and tactile level to develop a healthy understanding of the love of God? The book does not really tackle this fundamental question although it is implied by its title. . . .

. . . The injunction to be perfect in Matthew 5.48 is described as 'a command - not a request' and is interpreted as addressed to the individual as if he were a social isolate. But surely what we are to seek is a corporate perfection, since we are inescapably related to one another: it must be sought in other selves as much as in our own; and at any moment on the human journey the individual self has to accommodate to others as best it can – *"that they all may be one"* - as Jesus had to do during his working lifetime.

Since the author is clearly aware of the overriding importance of relationships - the whole book shows that - it is a pity that he limits his considerations to the traditional individualist frame of reference. Notions of wholeness, perfection, suffering and anxiety take on a new depth of significance, both theologically and otherwise, when considered from a corporate stance. Suffering and anxiety are part of emotional life, and one thing that psychology has long known is that emotions tend to spread, unconsciously, as if by contagion, from one person to another. To talk of suffering, anxiety and anger as if they do not usually have a vicarious significance (and often of course a vicarious origin) is like using one eye to see when binocular vision is available. Dr. Dominian talks of dependence and independence - even of 'mature dependence' - but never of *inter*dependence; yet the very fact of relationship, from infancy onwards, cries out for its acknowledgement. . . .

265 - Review : Jack Dominian, The Capacity to Love.

LETTER: HOMOSEXUALITY

Dear Editors,

Perhaps the most surprising thing about the report of the Working Party on Homosexual Relationships[1] is the chairman's statement that it was unanimous. One can only suppose that it was a unanimity of exhaustion from trying to reconcile the irreconcilable attitudes of some of its members. Taken as a whole the report displays a degree of neurotic ambivalence and indecisiveness, which would surely have incapacitated any of the working party as individuals. One thing seems certain: that it will bring no moral support to Christian homosexuals. Any crumbs of comfort they may have thought to find will turn to ashes in their mouths as they realize the report's timid acquiescence in the prejudice of the heterosexual majority against them.

I use the word prejudice advisedly. It means an opinion or judgement which injures a person by disregarding their rights. The report tries to distinguish between being a victim of prejudice and *'the experience of alienation and rejection which may come to any member of a minority living in a society which does not cater for his needs'* (16). This will not do. A society, which deliberately fails to cater for the needs of its minority members, *is* prejudiced. What is in question here is what the rights and needs of homosexuals actually are, and in what respects the majority's refusal to meet them can be justified.

Before commenting on biblical and theological issues, two questions arise. First, is there evidence that the behaviour and attitudes of the homosexual minority are injurious to the community as a whole? In common with other authorities, the Working Party was unable to find any - except inasmuch as it accepts the majority prejudice (184). Although the report makes a proper distinction between the homosexual orientation and homosexual behaviour, it confuses them again when speaking of homosexual relations (117) and unions (255). There are two basic components in human sexuality: the earlier to develop is the appetite for stimulation of certain areas of the body surface, which reaches consummation in 'tension release'; and the other, which develops rather later, is the appetite for unguarded intimacy with another person, which looks for and sometimes finds its consummation in a love relationship marked by mutual candour, respect, and care expressed in a total self-giving. In sexual maturity there is a degree of integration of the two appetites, and in a healthy relationship (admittedly hard to achieve) the sensual appetite comes to serve and be subordinate to the other. Both play their parts in heterosexual as well as homosexual relationships; and it is widely known (though less often made explicit) that *most* genital activity, even in the best of marriages, is motivated by the desire for tension release on the part of one or both partners, rather than by the urge to procreate. The Working Party might well have found more to say about over-indulgence of the sensual appetite which (when divorced from a love relationship) is likely to be exploitative of others. Undisciplined lust is as undesirable in homosexual as in heterosexual encounters. But apart from this consideration there is no evidence that homosexual behaviour or orientation harm the community or individuals within it. They are neither pathological nor, in view of their high incidence, ought they to be termed abnormal. They are simply non-procreative elements in the wide spectrum of variety characteristic of human sexuality.

That being so, the second question is: how can reconciliation be fostered between the majority and its homosexual minority? The report mentions both the hostility of the majority and the irrational nature of most of it; it somewhat naively expresses surprise at its extent and vehemence (223, 226); and yet it makes no coherent attempt to grapple with it and even (231, 252) appears to condone it. The absence of a real discussion of majority prejudice and the part it plays in maintaining homosexuality as a 'problem' is perhaps the gravest shortcoming of the report. There is, for instance, no mention of the well-known observation that it is often those who repress or fail to acknowledge residual homosexuality in their own make-up who are most zealous in their condemnation of it in others.

The survey of the biblical evidence I find tortuous and it does not appear to reach a conclusion. Here is a contrasting statement based on a study of the same texts as those considered by the Working Party:

> *Nowhere is homosexual behaviour referred to as between people of the same sex who genuinely care for and pledge themselves each to the other; on the contrary, the homosexual behaviour which is specified or implied comes commonly under one or more of three headings: prosti-tution, sexual assault, or plain sensuality of the sort which was and indeed is common among people of no particular high moral insight or belief; and who were (and are) not necessarily homosexual in terms of emotional relationships but in response to plain sexual appetite.*[2]

If not conclusive, this statement at least has the merit of clarity.

As a medically trained layman, my criticisms in this letter have been directed at the groundwork of the report rather than its theological or pastoral conclusions, but I will permit myself one theological observation. It is that in my understanding of the gospel, the care of, and respect for, minorities who feel themselves to be alienated or oppressed is a prime responsibility of the Christian church. In the present context, the implication of Matthew 25, 35-40 is that Christ himself is present in the man or woman of homosexual orientation, and indeed in the man or woman behaving homosexually. In any discussion of homosexuality among Christians, it is an observation to be borne in mind.

References:
1. *Homosexual Relationships: A Contribution to Discussion:* Report to the General Synod, (Board for Social Responsibility), 1979.
2. Leonard. Barnett,, **Homosexuality: Time to Tell the Truth**, (Gollancz), 1975.
178 - 2 Homosexuality, Letter to the Editor of <u>Theology.</u>

ON BEING HUMAN

Human beings can only be understood in a social context.

The scientific approach sees them as a complex arrangement of atoms and molecules, cells and organs, or as a piece of self-regulating machinery; and in either of these ways an account can be given which is congruent with the laws of physics - provided the organism is observed in a 'closed system'.

This is ultimately unsatisfying because - at least in imagination - healthy people refuse to accept the limitation implied in a 'closed system' (the sick dog will lie down in a corner of the cage, but the healthy dog seeks every avenue of escape - and if he can't escape, he becomes sick). In fact, it is a conception of human beings arrived at by abstracting them from their proper context.

The psychologist sees people as social mammals. Like other social mammals, they are under a biological imperative to *express* their emotions, and to respond sympathetically (literally with fellow feeling) to emotions expressed by their neighbours. When one dog barks, all the dogs bark. . . .

. . . Try and imagine human beings abstracted from all human relationships - and from the memory of them. What is left? In an important sense, the human "self" *is* their relationship - there's nothing left of them without it.

The young child says to his mother (at the dawn of self consciousness):-

Who am I?	You are John.
Why am I John?	Because we called you that when you were born.
Why was I born?	Because Daddy loved Mummy and *we* wanted a little baby.

This illustrates the way in which it is part of every individual's deepest experience of him/herself, that he/she has no omnipotent self-determination - he/she is created, named, and their early experience is determined - by *others*. All they can do is to react against what they are by *denying* their own experience; or accepting what they are by *affirming* it. Most of us do something between the two. . . .

42 - What is Man?

PERSONAL - SOCIAL SPACE

. . . We have to rediscover the significance of human *interdependence* with the rest of creation. Human beings cannot, indeed, survive if they continue to destroy the ecosystem of which they are a part. So, as God's stewards on earth, beyond the question 'can *man* survive?', we have to ask ourselves 'in what way can *the whole creation* survive on this earth?' The recent paperback[1] by Barbara Ward and Rene Dubos called *'Only One Earth,'* is subtitled 'The Care and Maintenance of a Small Planet' - a phrase which seems to acknowledge a more comprehensive understanding of stewardship. Our responsibility is wider than human beings; and there are grounds which the Christian must consider for regarding the human species as currently the most dangerous pollutant of all.

The rate of world population growth frightens us. But we don't really know what is tolerable overcrowding for the human species. Among other animal species, social and biological breakdown occurs at levels of population density which impose no strain on resources necessary for biological health such as food. The critical levels apparently depend on *social perception* of crowding rather than on material resources. But among human beings, the technology of affluence has brought more of us nearer to one another than ever before in history: telephones, television, automobiles and aircraft combine to give us an illusory freedom to range more widely, while actually they increase our sense of being crowded instead of diminishing it. Look at the congestion of our transport systems and the daily bombardment of our perceptual apparatus by the mass media. A rising standard of living, as we understand it at present, would sooner or later make even a static population perceive itself as overcrowded, with the results (which we are already beginning to see) of social and mental breakdown. To my mind, it is more urgent that we should constructively re-evaluate our ideas of personal-social space, or 'territory', than that we should worry about the population explosion. We must reformulate our ideas about personal freedom - about the social areas in which we feel free to move. A possible start would be to work out what it really means to worship a God 'whose *service* is perfect freedom'. . . .

Reference:
1.   Barbara Ward and Rene Dubos, **Only One Earth**, (Penguin), 1972.

123 - Review: Can Man Survive?

SOCIAL STRUCTURE

1.   The structures of human societies all depend upon our innate tendency to *pay attention to a central figure*: i.e. we organise ourselves *centripetally.*

2.   There are two modes of such organisation:

a)   the 'agonistic': in which the central figure is respected for his capacity to make a *threatening* display. An agonistic structure means that everyone knows his place, and keeps appropriate distances between himself and his superiors and subordinates. The social structure is strongly rank-ordered and rigid, like that of classical bureaucracy.

b)   the 'hedonic': in this mode the central figure draws attention to himself by some form of display which is not threatening and which evokes a *greeting* response from others. Thus it makes for 'contact behaviour' - and what Desmond Morris[1] calls 'social grooming' (*Naked Ape*, p.200) - rather than keeping distances. It is far more fluid, allows greater flexibility of attention within the group and thus greater opportunities for playing, learning, and co-operating with one another.

3. These two modes result in different styles for the central figure: in the agonistic society he will be 'rex', who maintains order; while in the hedonic society he will be 'dux', the leader who inspires others to follow him - the 'charismatic' figure.

4. But the charismatic type of leadership has its own dangers: the leadership may become tyrannical while the followers may (usually do) become idolatrous - according the charismatic leader superhuman powers and allowing themselves to drift or be driven into a passive-dependent position which is dehumanising and alienating - and irresponsible.

5. The creative response of Jesus to this dilemma of charismatic leadership was to insist upon its *diffusion throughout the followers without denying its validity*. He refused to accept a crown (remaining 'dux' rather than 'rex'); when he washed the disciples' feet he said *"If I your Lord and master do this, you should also do it to one another"*, he symbolically shared his charisma in the Last Supper; and in his resurrection he re-embodied his charisma in them, as St. Paul explains in his doctrine of the resurrected Body of Christ.

6. Furthermore during his life Jesus laid special emphasis upon *peripheral* members of society as those who carry his charisma: e.g. in the beatitudes; and in the story of the sheep and the goats, *"Lord when saw we thee hungry or thirsty or a stranger or naked or ill or in prison? ..."*

7. I think this points to the idea that the peripheral members of a society, while usually 'despised and rejected' by those more centrally placed, do have a special role to play in determining which way the society will move. They are like the scouts or the spies who move ahead, and to the flanks of an army who play a much greater part in the 'dux' function than seems to be commonly recognised by theorists.

8. This 'Christian' technique of turning the 'centric' society inside out was embodied in the early church (Acts 2-14) but got lost as the Establishment took over, feeling the pull of its unregenerate tendency towards centricity.

9. Centric types of organisation seem appropriate when either survival is threatened from outside (in which case the agonistic mode may be needed e.g. in the army); or in order to carry out routine 'service' social functions, largely automatic and therefore relatively 'absent-minded' (in which case the hedonic mode should evolve more often than it does).

10. But at times of rapid social change, there is an increased need for charismatic leadership, which soon has to choose either to revert to a hierarchic, 'rex' type of structure; or to maintain its creative and innovative potential by turning itself inside out, distributing the charisma, refusing to allow the leadership *function* to be embodied in social *structure* - and, I think, paying particular attention to the peripheral members of the organisation.

11. This kind of 'unstructured social structure' is rare and precarious - perhaps because it depends on sacrificial love, which can be shown, even if not recognised, by non-Christians. A current example is perhaps the 'therapeutic

community' approach to the care of the mentally ill, deprived children, drug addicts and prisoners. But it does not follow that it has no relevance for those who are not (yet) labelled as sick!

Reference:

1.　Desmond Morris, **The Naked Ape,** (Jonathon Cape), 1967.

122 - Notes on Centripetal and Peripheral forms of Social Organisation.

FORGIVENESS OF SIN

. . . Sometimes as a psychiatrist I am asked to see, say, a murderer. As together we tease out the strands of their life history, as I try to imagine myself in their shoes at the various crisis points of their life, I become increasingly aware that were I placed in similar circumstances, I might easily have done the same things myself. I say to myself "There but for the grace of God goes James Mathers". So although the murderer alone has to take the responsibility for doing the murder, we find that we share a similar capacity for sinfulness. Furthermore, if out of the life-story they tell me, I try to see which other people who have influenced them might reasonably be 'blamed for having caused them to stumble along to their present catastrophe' - I find that so many people are involved that one can only say "we are all involved" - the whole community, both in this generation and preceding ones. And I am a member of the community. So I also share their guilt. And thus it becomes apparent that we all - all human beings - share, to some degree, in the sins of one another, whether through ignorance or unwittingly or otherwise. We may judge the scientists who did the research which led to the atom bomb to be less guilty than those who ordered it to be dropped. But they certainly acted in a way which made the ultimate sin more likely, and are therefore guilty in some degree. We all, unwittingly but inevitably, cause our brothers and sisters to stumble. And we all need forgiveness, not only from God but from one another. . . .

75-1 Forgiveness of Sin.

GROUP BEHAVIOUR

There is a paradox contained in the notion of 'social science' which we do well to recognise. To study a matter scientifically is to adopt a detached and dispassionate attitude towards it. This works well enough when we study aspects of the non-human world; but the social sciences deal with human beings. To be detached and dispassionate about one's fellow-men is to cut oneself off from them, even if only for a time; and such an affirmation of separateness carries an implication that one is either being antisocial, or asocial, or, perhaps, superhuman and god-like.

Anecdotal reports of group behaviour which give an indication that the reporter was a participating member of the group studied, sharing in its experience, usually seem more convincing than those written by the detached observer who watched his group through a one-way screen. The former may lack clarity of definition and completeness, and their objectivity may be in doubt, but the participant speaks with a special authority. Rather than dispassionate detachment, the virtue, which the participant observer has to cultivate, is best described as 'controlled emotional involvement'. This means that he has to learn how to remain sensitive to the feelings and emotions which continually eddy and flow among any group of people. He has to allow himself to feel them, to recognise that he feels them, and yet not be carried away by them.

This kind of skill stems from that of the psychoanalyst. When Freud began his work, he tried to achieve scientific detachment in his dealings with patients; but from time to time he recognised the significance of what he called transference and counter-transference; he was in fact acting as a participant observer in a group - a group of two; and the consequent replacement of detachment by controlled emotional involvement accounts for much of the suspicion that 'orthodox' scientists still often have for psycho-analysis and its derivatives.

Much writing by psychoanalysts still suffers by being couched in language which implies that the therapist tries to be detached and dispassionate. The analyst will say that his job is to explore the patient's *"inner world"*, or that he regards *"subjective experience as a central object of study,"[1]* without making it clear that the analyst's inner world and subjective experience is inevitably explored and studied at one and the same time. But it is.

I am inclined to believe that we will not make very much further progress in the understanding of man until participant observation and controlled emotional involvement, rather than detachment, becomes accepted as the normal method of study for the serious student. Man is a group animal, and the study of his behaviour in groups or as an individual (when he is still a group animal even if other members of the group are absent) - is only of value inasmuch as it gives us clues to his experience. The question we so often ask, *"what is man?"*, is a question which we can only begin to answer by reference to the meaning of those experiences which the questioner shares with other men. As Theodore Newcomb says, *"it is meanings, not the words and gestures which are their vehicles, which are the essence of communication."* [2]

Only when we have established that it is man's *experience* which is our primary concern, and which we can only begin to know about if we share in it, are we ready to make use of the objective study of behaviour. Only in this context can the social scientist provide tools which enable us to explore some limited aspects of shared experience with a precision and particularity which we would not otherwise obtain. If he examines behaviour reflecting experiences which neither he nor we have shared, his work is of no more than suggestive value, feeding our imagination and fantasy. Quantitative results - the 'hard facts' of much research effort are an irrelevance, except to the man who wants to manipulate or control people's behaviour without understanding them.

However, when the social scientist studies the behaviour of people whose experience he has shared and therefore respects, much of value may emerge. Personal freedom and integrity (perhaps another word for the same thing) depend upon the harmonious functioning of a multitude of determinisms and automatisms, and strict scientific method can tell us about these parts of a whole. But it cannot tell us about the whole, because its method is analytic. It inevitably tends to ignore integrity and limit freedom.

In the field of pastoral care, it would seem wise to give primary emphasis to the viewpoint of the participant observer rather than that of the orthodox scientist. In this field, we ought to be more concerned with the sharing of experience, the exchange of meanings between people, ourselves and others, than we are with controlling behaviour.

The British Council of Churches Working Party report on 'Pastoral Care and the Training of Ministers' talks of the pastoral role as one of *"leadership in the context of partnership."*[3] The phrase is a valuable one. Do we want to understand group behaviour because we see ourselves, in the pastoral situation, as being potential leaders of groups? The lesson we have to remember, over and over again, is that you can't be a good group leader unless you exercise your capacity for being a good group member. This is not an easy lesson to remember. Even when it receives intellectual assent, a moment's reflection will recall many situations where the leader's detachment from his group was much more evident than his membership of it. When we focus attention upon the problems of the leader, those of the followers inevitably remain out of focus in the background. What I am asserting is that there is an indivisible organic relation between the two, that he who leads at any given moment is *primarily* a group member, and cannot safely be thought about in abstraction from this context.

W.R. Bion has reflected deeply upon group experience.[4] He considers that every individual man is essentially "groupish" however isolated he may appear to be; but that there are certain kinds of experience and behaviour of individuals which only become manifest, or potentially manifest, when he is seen as a member of a group. Thus part of the native endowment of a human being is to be dependent upon a leader, to fight or flee from an enemy, and to pair with another human being in the hope of producing a new leader in the future. These are social potentialities of experience, deeply unconscious and probably mutually exclusive at any one time. At any rate, Bion claims to find evidence from the behaviour of any gathered group of people that they are unwittingly, or at least tacitly, acting upon one or other of these three 'basic assumptions' - the group behaves as if it wishes to be dependent on a leader, or to define an enemy from whom it can flee or whom it can fight; or it allows two of its members to pair and waits for the unborn leader to emerge. This unconscious activity of the group has a dreamlike inconsequentiality and disregard of time. The basic assumption will apparently spontaneously change from one of the three to another, sometimes rapidly and sometimes slowly. No one of them is likely to stay manifest indefinitely, because the very fact that the group is manifesting one assumption means that within each individual member the other two are being frustrated. . . .

. . . Inherent in the idea of a group of persons as an organism, is the implication that it has a natural history: it comes to birth, develops to what maturity it can, and then becomes senescent and dies - though sometimes it develops structural rigidities which delay recognition of its death, at the cost of depersonalising the relationships between its members. But a healthy group, in its maturity, can undergo a process of rebirth, by the influx of new members or new ideas or experience; and this can give it continuity if the purpose for which it exists has continuing validity. This is analogous to the survival of a family through the generations despite the death or emigration of its component members. . . .

References:
1. C. Rycroft, **Psychoanalysis Observed,** (Constable), London, 1966, p.10.
2. T.M.Newcomb, 'Autistic Hostility and Social Reality', <u>Human Relations</u>, 1947, Vol.1, No.1. p.73.
3. BCC Working Party, *'Pastoral Care and the Training of Ministers'*, (BCC) London, 1968.
4. W.R.Bion, **Experiences in Groups**, (Tavistock Publications), 1961.
89 - The use of Understanding of Group Behaviour in Pastoral Care.

SOLIDARITY

... The desire for order in society always seems to have led to the excommuni-cation or rejection of the sick, the poor, the delinquent and the mad. Even modern societies seek to isolate such social misfits by confining them in institutions. But in doing so, we hide ourselves from the realisation that it is *our* badness, *our* sickness, which is being confined or rejected. We forget that we are the community, the social organism, and that the sickness of individuals is our sickness. If the cells of my stomach are diseased, it is I that am sick. So the task of the suffering servant is to bring good tidings to the afflicted, to bind up the broken-hearted - showing them that the community cares, not out of pity alone, but because if it is to be truly healthy, it must care for *all* its members: the 'greatest good of the greatest number' is not good enough. ...

85 - Pastoral.

WE - IDENTITY

... In the light of more corporate concepts of health, we can begin to understand that a person's progress toward maturity of personality involves from their earliest years a recurrent moving outward from the infantile centre of experience: their ego-identity, almost from the moment that they first become aware of it, evolves into a shared 'we-identity' - shared with those with whom they choose to identify - mother, parents, family; and this 'we-identity' is in turn differentiated into ever-enlarging social contexts, of school, occupation, community and nation. Surely, these multiple we-identities wax and wane in importance, and some have to be given up altogether. At times of stress or in ill health, the best of us tend to regress to a simpler sense of personal identity: maturity comes upon us as a tide rolls in from the sea, masked by the continual accession and recession of the waves. But in the light of this we can see how the healthy person is called upon to die a little death repeatedly and continually, to lose each successive self in order that a more mature and comprehensive self may be born. So we discover that the gospel injunction to let the self be lost in order to find the true self is not a sudden, all-or-none commandment so much as a statement of the law of healthy growth of personality. ...

103 - The Pastoral Role – A Psychiatrist's View.

THE ART OF MEDICINE.

. . . Most of us know that a good physician can help a patient just by being near them - a social visit without prescription or pill - or merely holding the hand of someone in pain. These things come into the art of medicine too. So does the passive (or apparently passive) listening of the psychiatrist when the patient is first seen. These kinds of procedures have a value in *raising morale* - they have a moral significance. They give the patient a *sense of security*, a feeling that their troubles are *shared*, a feeling that someone else is working with them. Whether or not such measures have a direct effect on the patient's vitality - whether in fact vitality, the capacity for life, can be transferred from one person to another in this way, I don't know. Certainly the physician or therapist (who may merely be a friend) often feels that virtue goes out of them on these occasions, and the patients often feel, or show in their behaviour, that they have greater strength to face their difficulties or pain than they had before; but I don't think the process is measurable.

Even if the process is not susceptible of scientific validation, there are some points about it which are beyond doubt. Firstly, by this type of morale-raising or moral treatment, a patient can become healthier, more nearly 'whole' than they were before, without any medical intervention by physical means, and *without special attention being paid to the particular part of them which was damaged.* Secondly, this kind of help can only be given to a patient who has *'faith'* in the physician. This faith need not be explicitly expressed (as in the case of a sick child), and it need not necessarily imply previous acquaintance with the therapist. It may be - in fact probably always is - fundamentally a more or less unconscious and irrational feeling on the patient's part, though patients will often rationalise their faith in a doctor subsequently. Thirdly, faith in the therapist does not depend upon their technical skill as a scientist, but upon *qualities of personality* which the patient perceives intuitively: they feel that, in relation to their sick self, the therapist is a 'good' person: whatever they mean by 'good' it means there is some *moral evaluation* of the therapist's personality.

It follows that a therapist's success or failure with this method of treatment depends very much more upon what *they are* than upon what *they do*.

This is not an original observation and may appear trite; but I have taken time to work up to it so that I can now point out that this 'art' of medicine may have its technical secrets just as much as the science of medicine has; even though artistic techniques may be more difficult to learn and practise than scientific ones.

Undergraduate training in medicine is almost wholly concerned with science, and orthodox medicine taken by and large, makes no demands that a therapist should *be* a certain kind of person; only that they should *do* certain kinds of things. The only people concerned with healing who take a direct interest in the personality of the therapist are the *psychoanalysts*, and those who are concerned with healing in the *religious* sense. Even of these, the psychoanalysts are concerned to be as scientific as possible, which means that they only concern themselves with the negative aspects of healing - the removal of hindrances and limitations to proper functioning - the removal of *barriers to communication* between people and within people - not with what is communicated.

The artistic, creative, synthesising interest in human beings is in fact wholly a moral or religious interest. **. . .**

10 - The Art of Medicine.

THE FAMILY

. . . Teaching hospitals in our culture take no account of families but only of individuals. The family doctor is - almost by definition - excluded from them unless he dons a disguise and accepts a subservient role as a clinical assistant in some specialty or other. What *do* we mean by the family? In a primitive society it will mean a tribe or clan. One of the dictionary meanings is that of a household, including slaves and servants. Dr. Edmund Leach recently talked of the *"monogamous, neolocal nuclear family"*[13] as if it typified our society - and commented *"Far from being the basis of the good society, the family, with its narrow privacy and tawdry secrets, is the source of all our discontents."*[12]

If we turn to the way that the term is actually used by psychiatrists, we find that Laing and Esterson, reporting on interviews with members of the families of schizophrenics, include among them in-laws, general practitioners, an employer and a headmistress.[10] Professor Russell Davis, talking of the family from the child's point of view, includes neighbours and family friends in his description.[16] So in practice we seem to make more use of the primitive, inclusive concept rather than the modern 'nuclear family' idea.

In spite of this vagueness and uncertainty about its limits, we should be in no doubt that a family is something very different from a random population as understood by the statistician. However transient membership may be, however little choice we may have as to which family we will enter, or how long we will stay with it, the family has a firm reality about it: it is a group of people who are held together by unconscious bonds of attraction to one another, stimulating and responding to one another, whether in love, hate, anger, or even fear, in a way that is different from that in which they respond to outsiders. Members of a family think of themselves as 'us', different from 'them'. . . .

. . . Although your teachers in hospital will no doubt acknowledge that patients have families, they are unlikely to have given the concept any more serious significance than that of a mere appendage to the individual patient. They may talk of the family 'background' to a patient's condition: access to it is through the entry under 'next-of-kin' on the admission card. Its further investigation is delegated to an ancillary - the hospital's social worker. The family as an organism is never the focus of the clinical scientist's attention. R.D.Laing says: *"The group looked at from the outside comes into view as a social object, lending by its appearance and by the apparent processes that go on inside it, credence to the organismic illusion. This is a mirage; as one approaches closer there is no organism anywhere."*[8] In this he is mistaken. The group, typically the family, is undoubtedly a social organism. It is an identifiable living entity with a history. Laing is misled by his nearness to the families he investigates. In fact, in his therapeutic efforts, he gets so close to the family that he becomes temporarily a member of it. And for him to say that the family as organism is a mirage is as unreasonable as it would be for a microbiologist to examine each cell in my body, to agree that each cell was alive, and then to conclude that, as a whole, our life is an illusion. . . .

. . . The family is *not* just a background to the patient and his illness; it is the social organism of which the patient is a part. The disorder which he presents may be no more than a symptom of the family's illness; and I don't need to tell you how wary one has to be of treating symptoms when our diagnosis of the underlying disease is incomplete.

Perhaps my insistence on the importance of the family as the organism you may be called upon to treat is particularly threatening to orthodox medical prejudices. So often, when discussing ethical dilemmas in medicine for instance, we talk of the 'doctor-patient relationship' as sacrosanct - implying that family and social considerations are either of secondary importance or someone else's worry. What I am asserting is that this traditional doctrine is often used as an evasion: that very often you *cannot* do the best for your patient unless you focus your clinical attention on the family, and accord the patient a status as part of a whole, rather than as a whole person with a rather tiresome background. This idea is threatening not only because it attacks tradition, but for practical reasons too: it is relatively easy for the doctor to assert his moral dominance over a single patient in his consulting room or clinic; but it is very much more difficult to maintain this stance when faced by a group of relatives who have not accepted the status of patient. We have to learn how to function from a position of weakness, which doesn't come easily to the professional man. . . .

. . . Now let us consider what happens when a family finds that one of its members is behaving in an unintelligible way. If it is a child who is presented to the doctor, he may quickly discern that the real trouble lies in mother's anxiety.[1] Paediatricians and child psychiatrists are prone to say "there are no anxious children, only anxious mothers". At the child guidance clinic, the so-called mentally afflicted child may be allowed to play for an hour, with the psychiatrist; while the real work is done by the social worker in another room, with mother. At the end of the process, of course, it is the psychiatrist who gets the credit for having cured the child.

But in other cases, the family may not seek outside help, or may not find it if they do seek it. Then they will try to deal with their rising anxiety by the use of some of the mental mechanisms familiar to us in the psychopathology of individuals - for instance, by denial or projection. The young schizophrenic may become more odd and bizarre in behaviour while parents continue to assure themselves and kindly enquirers that he is a model boy who never gives them a moment's unease. As the situation becomes worse, the family closes its ranks and retreats behind its defences. When the anxiety grows too great to be denied, projection is called into play and the school is blamed, or the doctor, or some other outside agency.

Such mechanisms are unlikely to be effective for long, if only because they do nothing toward solving the real problem, of restoring communication and adjustment between family and sufferer. At some stage, the family's anxiety and guilt is likely to be projected inward, so to speak, on to the sufferer himself, since he is the *'locus minoris resistentiae';* so that he becomes labelled as bad as well as mad. This of course creates a vicious circle; and it is most likely to be broken by the sufferer leaving the family in a crisis of mutual rejection - either to mental hospital against his will or elsewhere. The family amputates the member in whom the badness and illness has become localised.

This process of extrusion by scapegoating gives the family respite from its immediate anxiety, but it is not often the optimal solution. Misunderstandings are unresolved, barriers to communication are intensified, and guilt feelings persist. . . .

References:
1.   M. Balint, **The Doctor, His Patient and the Illness,** (Pitman Medical), London, 1957, p.34.
8.   R.D.Laing, **Politics of Experience,** (Penguin), 1977, p.73.
10. R.D.Laing & A. Esterson, **Sanity, Madness and the Family**, (London), 1964, Vol.1 Families of Schizophrenics, pp. 255 – 267.
12. E.R.Leach, <u>The Listener</u>, November 1967, vol.78, no.2018, p.695.
13. E.R.Leach, <u>The Observer</u>, 31st. December 1967, p.10.
16. D. Russell Davis, <u>American Journal of Psychiatry</u>, September 1967, 124.3, p.98.

83 - The Family of the Mentally Afflicted Patient.

. . . Almost any client you see is in relationship with someone, be it family, or work group, or whatever; and the client's arrival in your consulting room is probably significant not only to them, but to their 'group'. So when you find yourself confused in the one-to-one encounter you may get a lot of help if you can get the client to bring a friend or neighbour. Quite possibly the friend will know them from quite a different point of view to your own. And once you begin shifting from being a participant in a group of two (client and counsellor) to participating in the larger group which constitutes the client's immediate social context, you will become aware of a whole new range of factors which bear upon the client's problem - and some of them may be more modifiable or flexible than the client's personality structure. You may begin to see how your client is being cast in the role of scapegoat for the misdoings or shortcomings of the other members of their group. Quite often this kind of client has been regarded as the 'black sheep' for so long that they have come to believe it themselves, and act in a way which verifies the group opinion of them. Or you may be able to see how the balance of emotional stresses between other members of their group has recently altered in a way which has imposed a greater stress on your client, but which has been unrecognised by any of those concerned until you point it out to them. When you do, it helps them to put the problem with which they presented you back into its social context, and may reduce the anxiety to manageable levels.

This shift of the focus of attention - from the individual in front of you to the group of which they are (or ought naturally to be) a member, is not an easy one for us to make. Most counsellors, like doctors, have been brought up to believe that there is something special and exclusive about the one-to-one relationship. It is hedged around with all sorts of rationalisations about privacy and confidentiality. Of course, these are very important, but they are often used as defence mechanisms. So long as we stick to the one-to-one situation, we can generally feel 'in control' of the situation. We sit one side of the table, and the client, knowing their place, sits the other. In the group situation this feeling of being in control is very much impaired. The client is defined - or self-defined - as in need of assistance, and authorises the counsellor to try and provide it; but the other members of their group may not give the counsellor this authority, and so we have to walk delicately in our approach to them, accepting our powerlessness to alter the situation -without losing our nerve and walking out of it. (The midwife is similarly powerless to bear the mother's baby). . . .

100 - Serious Personality Disorders and the Lay Counsellor.

MENTAL HEALTH AND MENTAL ILLNESS

. . . It was the failure of the orthodox medical approach to cure hysteria, of course, which led Freud to make his first attempts at psychoanalysis. Freud himself was essentially scientific in his approach, but his discovery of the pathological significance of emotional conflict, and of the fact of 'transference' - the patient's ability to transfer the feelings they have, or had, for one person, on to another - has led to the development of a completely different approach to the diagnosis and treatment of mental disorder. Psychoanalysis has proved to be so difficult and time-consuming that its value as a method of treatment for individuals is limited. But its effect on our understanding of mental disorder has been, and still is, under-rated.

Perhaps the critical difference between it and orthodox medicine is that it altered the focus of the doctor's attention from the disease from which the patient suffers, to the person of the patient. Having done that, it then accepts as having a particular sort of validity, the patient's unmeasurable and entirely subjective statements about their *feelings*. It does not, of course, accept them at their face value. If a patient says "I loathe and detest that person", then the psychiatrist observes primarily the intensity and appro- priateness of the emotion expressed. Whilst remaining quite open-minded and unconvinced about 'that man' they feel entitled to say that this patient has a good deal of hostile emotion to deal with.

Psychoanalysis thus makes a scientific study of the patient's pattern of emotional relationships with other people, and thus gave birth to the study of Human Relationships between people in general - not only patients considered as individuals; and it is this field of study which is most relevant to problems of mental health as opposed to mental illness, though of course the two are as intimately linked as are physical health and physical illness. . . .

. . . We have seen that in order to achieve therapy and prevention, it may be necessary to alter the focus of attention from the individual to the group of which the patient is at present a member. Let us therefore consider the mental hospital itself, as being the most intractable group with which the psychiatrist has to deal.

Traditionally, people were admitted to an asylum because their behaviour and capacity for communication with those around them was defective in some way. Because their friends could not understand the sufferer, and were therefore unable to predict what they were likely to do next, they became frightened of them, and had them 'put away', as the expression was. The asylum was expected to isolate them from the community, who were thus able to feel secure again. What happened within the high walls of the asylum, they felt, was something better not thought about. What did in fact happen, more or less inevitably, was that the asylum followed the patterns of the other 'long-stay' institutions of its day: it became a cross between a prison and the workhouse. As a result of this, aggravated by the inability of the patients to express themselves in understandable terms, one tended to get a strongly authoritarian culture pattern within the hospital: doctors issued orders to 'attendants' (people with a vocation for nursing tended to keep well away from such places), and attendants obeyed the doctors - and the patients had to fit in to this set-up as best they could. The inability of the acutely disturbed patient to communicate, would, under this system, inevitably result in a disregard of any communications they might make when they were better and more settled. In fact, the only communications from patients which were easily understood and unequivocal were attempts to escape from the place or to commit suicide; and the asylum, both in terms of its architecture and its system of nursing practice responded in an inhibitory fashion to both these aims.

All through the history of lunacy practice in this country and others there were sporadic attempts by outstanding people to combat the evils implicit in this authoritarian pattern. Most such attempts were successful for a time, and many left their mark in widely accepted if minor administrative and nursing improvements. However, so long as there was no widely recognised basis for the understanding of patients' communications, such efforts did not lead to any major revolution in the care of the mentally ill in general.

As some of the implications of Psychoanalysis became clear, however, people began to appreciate the pathogenic effect of isolation from the community, and of the loss of the sense of personal identity, which constituted the 'meaning' of the authoritarian culture-pattern to most patients. It became clear, in fact, that the curtailment of individual liberty in the interests of security tended to make the mentally sick worse rather than better. . . .

11 - Mental Health and Mental Illness.

ON LOSING ONE'S LIFE

. . . It may be that death always appears quite meaningless unless it is seen in the context of a 'we-identity'. To love someone is to die a little, for loving always carries the threat of parting. Every time we move from ego-identity to a we-identity, or from a lesser we-identity to a greater, we lose part of ourselves, just as the body loses some cells as it grows others. Grief is the price we have to pay for love. As we grow out of childhood into maturity, we have continually to be sacrificing parts of ourselves which hitherto we have valued, in order to make room for new possibilities. *"By gaining his life a man will lose it; by losing his life for my sake, he will gain it"* (Matt 10, 39*).

Partial death - failure. No doubt being able to endure and transcend the experience of failure and weakness is very important. But to speak of it in such terms is to suggest that it is an enemy and evil. It isn't always evil. In infancy, mother does everything for her child. But, as he begins to grow up, there come moments when she will - more or less deliberately - fail to solve the child's problems for him, to enable him to learn how to solve them for himself.

In my work in a mental hospital, I have often sat in ward meetings, where patients and nurses were discussing the administrative shortcomings of the institution. Sooner or later, everyone's eyes would be turned to me, as superintendent, obviously expecting me to be able to solve the problem. The problem was often not insuperable, and I would agree with everyone present that a good superintendent ought to be able to deal with it. But somehow I would prove unable as the universal fixer that everyone assumed I should be; and I would make excuses - which became less and less convincing even to me as I heard myself making them. But as I got more and more embarrassed, I would find to my astonishment that this demonstration of my incompetence as a superintendent had precisely the effect of enabling the group itself to become more responsible. My inability to find a bed in another ward for the disruptive patient they were complaining about allowed the group to find within themselves the resources for dealing helpfully with the disruptive member. Through my powerlessness to 'cure' this situation, they learned how to become more healthy. It is obvious enough really: you can't expect people to become responsible if you always take the responsibility yourself - if you treat them as irresponsible.

There remains something paradoxical about this situation, nevertheless - the power for good which seems to lie in powerlessness. I could, I suppose, have acted just as powerless if I had immured myself in my office, and not been present with the group in the ward in their discussion. But it is very doubtful whether in that case the group would have learned to be more responsible. Failure and weakness can be seen as evil and an enemy so long as they are external to the group; and of course there are enormous pressures from within the group's unconscious to extrude anything so uncomfortable, and to make a scapegoat of someone. It seems likely that my failure could only be of positive value so long as I was able to maintain a presence with them, resisting their unconscious pressure on me to accept a status as one apart from them, acting so as to convince them that I shared the 'we-identity' of the group in spite of my failure to live up to their expectations. I suppose all children have to learn that Daddy is not omnipotent; but they can't forgive him for this disillusionment, they can't be reconciled to him, if he isn't present with them to accept it.

What I hope emerges from this discussion is that failure and death can play a constructive and creative part in our lives so long as we can experience them in we-contexts. So long as we can move away from an egocentric view of life to a sociocentric view; for, in doing so, I believe we become better able to appreciate the Christocentric view.

"I am what survives - of *us*."

108 - On Losing one's Life - Failure and Death.

THE NATURE OF PREJUDICE

<u>Survival and Discrimination</u>

It is a matter of common prudence to assume that any aspect of our human nature which we now find deplorable probably arose because at some time past in our evolutionary history it had survival value. Before we decide to reject it, we do well to consider what virtue it may once have had, and may therefore, at some time in the future, have again.

In the Book of Ezra, it is written that Shecaniah son of Jehiel spoke up and said to Ezra: *'We have committed an offence against our God in marrying foreign wives, daughters of the foreign population. But in spite of this, there is still hope for Israel. Now, therefore, let us pledge ourselves to our God to dismiss all these women and their brood.'* Dictionary definitions of prejudice speak of opinions or judgements which injure someone by disregarding their rights. We have no record of what the foreign wives and children thought of their dismissal. Yet this, what to our eyes seems an appalling communal act of racial prejudice, was seen as a virtue; and indeed it contributed to Israel's sense of being set apart for great things, so that the early Christians, taking over the old tradition, could be addressed as *'a chosen race, a royal priesthood, a dedicated nation, and a people claimed by God for his own.'* (I Pet.2.9). We owe much of what is noblest in our Christian tradition to the 'disregard of other people's rights' which Israel displayed.

"It is not right to take the children's bread and throw it to the dogs" said Jesus to the Canaanite woman. But in this case Jesus made it clear that even those defined as non-human may nevertheless be regarded, if we so choose, as having human rights.

In the course of development, all of us have to recapitulate evolutionary history before we can emerge as fully human. It is biologically necessary for all the higher animals to learn to recognise other members of their own species, and to perceive other species as foreign to them, either predators or prey. It is a discrimination which is fundamental to the survival not only of the individual, who must eat but not be eaten, but also of the species, which requires the individual to find a mate and ensure that the species is replenished by reproduction.

So the human species, too, has to learn to discriminate between their own kind and others. And because this species alone has a well-developed capacity for self-consciousness, we humans are able to examine our situation from the inside, as well as objectively. We are able to spell out our categorisation of ourselves as human and of other organisms as not human. Since all of humankind is able to interbreed, there is no biological differentiation of the human species; but our capacity for discrimination allows us, if we wish, to distinguish particular groups of people as what Erik Erikson calls 'pseudospecies'. In some primitive languages, the same word is used to denote a member of one's own tribe, and a member of the human race. Foreigners are not categorised as human.

Individual and Social Identity

Perhaps the most fruitful way of thinking about our consciousness of ourselves as different from others is the concept of the sense of identity which each of us develops. I think all of us go through life with the question in the back of our minds, 'Whom do men say that I am?' Erikson says that one's sense of identity contains not only those elements of which we are immediately conscious, but that it includes unconscious elements too; and that it also includes our expressive behaviour, which is observable by others, and which results from our unconscious as well as our conscious sense of who we are. Because of this behavioural component, our self-awareness is constantly reviewed by those who see us in action; and their acceptance or rejection of the way we behave reacts immediately upon our sense of identity. So it is a social, as well as a personal construction. The question is not just 'Who am I?' but the more comprehensive one 'Whom do men say that I am?' When the child takes his first few steps, he achieves a new status as 'one who can walk'. Immediately, he probably experiences this only as a pleasurable extension of his ability to move around; the enhancement of his sense of identity comes from the recognition and approval which his new ability receives from his mother and the family.

As we continue growing through childhood, we find ourselves impelled to various kinds of behaviour - exploratory, aggressive, and sensual - which, while in some ways gratifying, are not recognised, or are positively frowned upon, by those around us. In these respects our sense of identity is not confirmed. If the impulse to this kind of behaviour is deeply felt and not allowed free expression, it is repressed and made unconscious. The self which I consciously recognise and affirm is that I am a good boy; I do not steal from the larder or smash the furniture in rage, or peep through the bedroom door when mummy and daddy are undressed. And if the impulses break through my repressive defences, mother will look sad and say 'that's not my Jimmy', or I am told I am 'beside myself', or 'not myself'. Maybe the forbidden impulses colour my dreams: there is a valuable convention that we are not to blame for what we dream. . . . In spite of the effectiveness of the mental defence mechanism of repression, these primitive impulses which we inherit from our animal ancestors remain active; indeed, they are part of the fount of spontaneity and vitality upon which our lives depend. But since we cannot keep our self-esteem if they are allowed freedom, and since denial of their existence doesn't always work, what we tend to do is to project them, throw them out - on to people or agencies external to ourselves. In infancy, when I bruise myself on the chairleg, I am liable to describe it as a 'baddy chair'. At a later age, I may populate the darkness of the night with hobgoblin or foul fiend; but by the time I am ten years old I am likely to find myself one of a group of my peers, maybe a gang at school, and now the most obvious way of dealing with the badness in myself is to project it on to another gang (or on to one member of the gang who is treated as a scapegoat by all, and who is excommunicated, and goes off to join another gang). Here we see the roots of prejudice as it presents itself as a social problem - the division between 'them' and 'us'. They are evil, we are good; they are dirty, we are clean. Dirt is the name we give to disorder, or to matter in which we can discern no order. They have destructive impulses against which we must protect ourselves. They are beasts, dogs, pigs - we alone are human.

Now let us look at these problems from a social rather than an individual aspect. I have already suggested that it is when the growing child moves away from mother's apron-strings and into peer-group situations that prejudice begins to show itself more clearly. Even before this, the fundamental categorisation of people into 'them' and 'us' will have been learnt as the small child recognises the basic distinction between adults, who can do things, and small children, who can't; and that other distinction which is written into our bodily structure, between male and female.

As children, between the ages of 7 and 12, we learn how to manipulate things and people. We learn various ways of seeing ourselves members of a particular 'in-group', of making our group or gang 'exclusive', of being loyal to our friends and of making outsiders (whether they are children or adults) aware that they are not wanted. At this stage of development such activities are - at least on the surface - relatively passion-free - the Freudians call it the 'latency period' - and children of this age can appear very cruel to one another, and to adults, in consequence.

With the coming of puberty and adolescence, the physical changes are accompanied by an upsurge of strong feelings again, which make this a period of instability and vulnerability for the individual's sense of identity. The attitudes we have developed through childhood are all called in question. There is a shaking of the foundations - a major identity crisis - before the adolescent finds for himself a new, adult, sense of who he is. Although adolescence is often an age of introspection, it is still true that the individual's sense of identity depends very much on what other people make of it: the question is still 'whom do men say that I am?' rather than 'who am I? ... At this stage, the groups with which we identify ourselves take on a new significance for us: having learned what it is to be loyal, we take some care in deciding what group of people we are going to be loyal to. Indeed, we may test ourselves out by trying one or more 'experimental identities' before finally settling into a particular one. . . .

Anxiety, Rights and Courtesy

Anxiety - the dread of non-being, of not knowing who you are - is the fuel which keeps the fire of prejudice burning. And this gives us a hint as to how we may lessen the harm it may do. We have to look carefully at the way our attitudes and behaviour may be interpreted by others - individuals and groups - as a threat to their sense of identity. If we can behave towards them in a way which confirms and acknowledges their sense of who they are, if we can return an encouraging answer to the unspoken question 'Whom do men say that I am, or that we are?', their self-confidence will increase, and they will be the readier to encounter and confront the human world around them; and will thus expose themselves to the possibility that those hitherto labelled as bad and non-human will begin to appear human, and not so bad, after all. And this adventurous letting go of the old 'keeping-your-self-to-yourself' attitude means that people can begin to learn from one another, not only to see the other man's point of view, but actually to accept it as part of one's own point of view as well. I think this is what 'integration' really means. When we read that Jesus said *'love your enemies,'* I suspect that it was some such process as this that he implied: don't turn your back on your enemy, or ignore him; if you can overcome your fear of confronting him, you may discover that he too is human, and he may cease to be an enemy. To ignore someone is, after all, the easiest way of threatening his sense of identity.

The primitive tribe, living perhaps in an isolated valley among the mountains, only recognises other members of the tribe as human. At some stage of its history, it may so far overcome its fear of natural enemies - drought or pestilence or earthquake or whatever - that some of its members may feel secure enough to venture forth from its familiar territory and meet up with strangers. Sooner or later there would inevitably be hostile encounters leading to feuds and perhaps war between tribes. But, over very long periods of history, the gradual enlightenment of their self-interest will lead the two tribes to develop structured channels of communication, and they will appoint specially protected ambassadors, who will in turn develop systems of etiquette and hospitality. So we find a slowly achieved set of customs, shared by both tribes, enabling the peace to be maintained between them even while both sides may feel hostile to one another. And so, eventually, throughout the tribes, or communities or nations which maintain diplomatic contact with one another, this immensely civilising achievement becomes generalised as the virtue of courtesy.

Thus we can return to the individual's problem of mastering prejudice: he can learn to show courtesy to other men, which still means, essentially, respecting their sense of personal or group identity; and subsequently he can offer them hospitality, which means, not thrusting one's preconceived ideas of what is good down the other man's throat, but laying oneself open to the other, risking an invasion by new customs, new ideas, learning new ways of what it means to be human.

Self-Acceptance, Variability and Openness

I do not think any of us are free from prejudice, and at our present stage of evolution I am not convinced that it would be good if we were. It can have survival value. But it seems clear that we do well to recognise our own prejudices. If we do this, we are in control of our tendency to project on to others attitudes of our own of which we are not proud. We have to learn to accept that there are some bad things in all of us; and we have to learn to live with our own badness rather than cast it out. Human history shows how in earlier societies social organisation needed the concept of the scapegoat as a symbolic way of expressing our inability to cope with our own evil. But this represents a stage in social evolution which we should hope to transcend. We should recognise that tomorrow's greater good is more likely to emerge from the reconciliation of today's good with today's evil, than from the elimination of today's evil.

Primitive social organisation sets a high value on conformity. The acceptable, respectable member of society is he who conforms to custom. But nature dictates that if a species is to survive, it must maintain a reservoir of variability among its members, so that changes in the environment do not kill them all off at once. While conformity may have short-term survival value when a community or group's existence is threatened, variety is the greater virtue in the long run. Conformity is regarded as a virtue by those who are prejudiced, variety by those who have mastered their prejudices.

It is important to keep an open mind. I am prepared to respect those who say that 'black is beautiful', and I am prepared to respect those who believe that Mr. Enoch

Powell is beautiful, though I may not agree with either of them. It seems to me to be important not to be too prejudiced against those who are prejudiced: which saves me from getting involved in demonstrations against those whose views I do not hold. Occasionally, I admit, I find myself compelled to draw a line between myself and the behaviour of others which I find unacceptable. But I try to draw it only faintly, and temporarily, in case my views change, or their behaviour changes, or the circumstances change, and make our disagreement irrelevant.

112-2 The Nature of Prejudice.

Chapter Two

MORALE

One of the most formative experiences in James' life was his active service as a field psychiatrist with the 36th. Division on the Arakan front in Burma (1944-45). He made original observations in the front line on the effects of a battalion's morale on soldiers' mental health. James followed his conclusions through into the way he treated battle casualties from stress, panic and mental breakdown. As a result he completely changed his medical style from the individual medication of sick individuals to strengthening a soldier's personal bonds with his comrades.

His clinical notes (1-1 and 1-2) reveal an unusual awareness of the way human solidarity supports our integrity, and strengthens our ability to cope with the stresses of combat: and how traditional medicine, by diagnosing problems to be solved in individuals, can actually alienate people from one another ('us' who are healthy: 'them' who are sick) and cut the life line of human solidarity. This could make all the difference between returning a man to duty with his comrades, or sending a casualty back to base hospital.

As we have seen in Chapter 1, this distinction (without separation) between the treatment of disease and the treatment of persons became fundamental to his style of social psychiatry thereafter. And the concept of morale became basic to his understanding of mental and community health in families, church congregations, institutions and the wider society.

M.W.

MEDICINE AND MORALE

Some years ago I wrote a number of essays discussing a distinction between the two ways in which we approach problems of medical treatment.[1] I called them the disease-attacking and the health-enhancing approaches. We rarely make explicit the distinction between our treatment of disease, which is an attacking procedure, and our treatment of the person who has the disease, which is a nurturing procedure. The attack on disease tends to be specific, using surgical or chemical methods which have potentially dangerous or uncomfortable side-effects and which thus need to be administered by an expert. Such methods also tend to be impersonal: during their administration the patient himself lies in the background of our awareness - a mere trolley on which the disease is carried. Most scientific medicine is of this kind.

By contrast, health-enhancing procedures tend to be non-specific, much safer (and can therefore be administered by non-experts), and are directed not at the disease but at the whole person who has the disease. Such measures are sometimes referred to as conservative: when I was a medical student and knew no better I tended to equate conservative measures with no treatment at all - because I was trained to think in terms of disease rather than in terms of sick persons. Measures of diet, bedrest, much physiotherapy, occupational therapy and rehabilitation come under this heading. Health-enhancing measures, in hospital at least, are usually delegated by doctors to the so-called ancillary professions. (Of course, there are marginal cases: is an injection of vitamins health-enhancing or disease-attacking?)

Tuberculosis offers a useful example. In 1946, F.W. Price's textbook of medicine advocates rest in bed, good food, plenty of fresh air, and carefully graduated exercise - measures which would be as good for the doctor as well as for the patient. Seven years later, the treatment prescribed for this disease consisted of three antibiotics, painful when given by injection, foul-tasting when given by mouth, and plagued by unpleasant side-effects. They are effective even while the sufferer continues to be poorly nourished, getting inadequate rest, and living in a slum, as has been shown in Madras.[2]

Nowadays he has to wait for some other disease before he is able to die. Surgical practice offers another example: an operation regarded as necessary to deal with the patient's disease may be post-poned if the sufferer is of poor nutritional status, and health-enhancing measures of a conservative nature used until he is strong enough for the operation.

In this paper I want to propose that the distinction between disease-attacking and health-enhancing procedures can also be applied in the social field, and is not confined to dealing with individuals. Social Medicine is the name currently given to epidemiology. Although it is intended to be preventive rather than curative, it also is based upon methods which are concerned with specific diseases and syndromes; it uses traditional analytic scientific methods, it is statistical and depends on random sampling, and thus excludes personal factors; and it is clearly a disease-attacking or disease-eradicating approach. Sometimes it is called community medicine, but this is a misnomer. It might reasonably be called population medicine, but this is not the same thing. A community is, at the very least, a number of people who relate to one another in significant and systematic ways. Epidemiologically speaking, a population is a number of people whose impingement upon one another is strictly random.

The field of what might truly be called community medicine seems to me to have been almost entirely ignored by theorists of medicine so far, except by the few psychiatrists who have begun to work out the implications of a therapeutic community approach to treatment,[3] and perhaps also some of the workers in the Tavistock Institute of Human Relations. But I am not yet sure that what they say to us, and the examples they are setting, are conceptually comprehensive enough to provide a model for what I am after, which is a social analogue for health-enhancing medicine, to match or complement the disease-attacking medicine of the epidemiologist.

I expect this new kind of true community medicine to share with epidemiology a preventive function. But I also anticipate that it will share the characteristics of health-enhancing medicine as it applies to the individual: that it will be relatively non-specific (and be as good for the practitioner as for the community served); that it will be safe, in the sense that its procedures will not need to be controlled by medical experts; and that it will be focussed on the health of the whole person and the whole community rather than on the depersonalised bits of the person or community which are at risk of disease or disorder.

The concept which most nearly seems to fit these requirements is that of morale.

. . .

References:
1. See for instance '88 'Two Approaches to Healing' (Guild of Health pamphlet no. 28); and '79 'Psychiatry and Religion', ed. M.A.H. Melinsky, in **Religion and Medicine,** (S.C.M.), London, 1970.
2. ed. M.King, **Medical Care in Developing Countries,** (O.U.P.), 1966.
3. Maxwell Jones, **Beyond the Therapeutic Community,** (Yale U.P.), 1968: and
    D.V.Martin, **Adventure in Psychiatry,** (Bruno Cassirer), Oxford, 1962.

153-1 Man, Medicine and Morale.

THE PASTORAL ROLE – A PSYCHIATRIST'S VIEW

. . . It is commonly recognised in a military formation, for instance, that high sickness rates are often an index of low morale, and that this can be true whether the diagnoses of individuals' illnesses are of infectious disease, such as malaria, venereal disease or the common cold; or of accidental injuries, or of emotional origin - psychosomatic conditions or neurosis. And it is well recognised by commanders that in the face of high sickness rates, there is an often preferable alternative to multiplying medical services, and that is to take steps to improve morale. These steps are not medical, nor focussed on the individual, but consist of measures to improve the quality of leadership, the programme of training and exercise, and the men's awareness of the purposes to which the formation is committed. Morale is a function of the shared sense of security of the men, and of their shared sense of purpose. These two variables are not entirely independent of one another, but both are indispensable. However much care is taken to build up the sense of security, morale will fall unless the men are informed by a common sense of purpose.

This discussion of the morale and health of a corporate body illuminates the proper context in which the individualised care of the single member begins to make theological and practical sense. Whatever individualised care he may receive, the single man will only be able to reach his best possible health, his optimum, inasmuch as he is a participating member of a community or social organism of which the morale is good. Without this context, the best that can be offered him is the mediocre, average condition which medical science so often takes as its norm - the mere absence of disease. And such a condition is of course essentially transient: robbed of his social context and sense of common purpose, it is unlikely that a man will stay free of disease for long. (Conversely, of course, morale in the community is likely to be adversely affected if there is frank neglect of the care of the individuals composing it.'). . . .

103 - The Pastoral Role – A Psychiatrist's View.

MEDICINE AND MORALE

. . . As psychiatrist to a division of troops in wartime, I was able to see all men thought by their units to be poor risks in battle, while they were still in training. My assessments were made on aditional psychiatric lines, and the distribution of the diagnoses I made showed no unexpected findings. Although the age, length of service, marital state, amount of battle experience and so on of the various men showed no interesting correlations, there was a marked variation in the total numbers of men referred by each of the seven battalions. Since arm-chair survey of my records gave no clue as to why this was so, I began to do some simple fieldwork, and visited each battalion to discuss the problem. It was then relatively easy to see that the number of men referred was clearly related to the morale of the various battalions. This was confirmed by the subsequent behaviour of the units in action. My career with this division culminated in my reporting to the general that the morale of one battalion was so low that I recommended he should sack the battalion commander; whereupon he - quite under-standably - sacked me instead. But I know that he had previously found my reports on the morale of his troops valuable, since he had published one of them as a directive over his own signature (naturally without acknowledgement).

Although the factors, which affect morale, are of great diversity, it is essentially a psychological concept. It can be assessed (evaluated rather than measured) along two dimensions: the shared sense of security of members of the community, and their shared sense of common purpose. Note that I speak of the *sense* of security and the *sense* of purpose. It is not the actual security which is critical for morale. My morale can remain high even if I am standing on a landmine, provided I don't know it is there. Conversely, I may be actually secure if I stand on a dummy mine, though my morale may be somewhat impaired if I don't know it is a dummy. Note also that I speak of the sense of security and purpose as being *shared*. It is possible, in a badly run authoritarian structure, for two subordinate units to be pointed towards the same objective, but unless each is informed of the other's aim they are likely to show destructive competition rather than co-operation the nearer they approach the goal.

The shared sense of security is affected by all sorts of material considerations, such as the adequacy of food, shelter, care for absent dependants, care for casualties, weapons or tools or equipment. But once the adequacy of these material things for the task in hand is assured, a superfluity of them becomes an embarrassment rather than a help to morale (an observation which may be of particular significance in an affluent society). There are more important needs to be met than the material. People need to be educated or trained in the use of their equipment for the tasks the community needs from them. Like material needs, provision of such education can be made with only minimal regard for personal considerations: it is still largely a technical matter. This kind of provision in the community at large would include such facilities as retraining within industry, acculturation classes for immigrants, pre-retirement courses, antenatal instruction and many other activities as well as the formal education system.

Even more important than these technical considerations is the essential requirement for a shared sense of security - that members of the community should know one another personally, well enough to trust one another. This requires at the minimum that they should *meet face to face, regularly, over a period of time, in relatively unstructured circumstances*. It is this requirement which, in urban western society in general, is much the most difficult to meet, and to which, therefore, health care professionals might well pay more attention than they do as a rule. So far as I know, at present it obtains in psychotherapeutic communities, in some few schools and homes for deprived or maladjusted children. It probably is met in some closed 'total' institutions such as convents, the army and expeditions of exploration. Perhaps it is to be found in some research laboratories. Most such communities contain small numbers, from say 20 to 90 in my experience; but there is good reason to suppose that it would be a help to morale in communities of up to some figure not much bigger than 500 souls.[1] When a community consists of more than a thousand, face-to-face knowledge by one person of nearly all the others becomes impossible, and a basic necessity for the raising of morale is lacking. This means that in communities of larger size, we need specifically to make opportunities for people to cluster on this sort of scale, not all the time, but regularly, over a period of time. Not every such group would take advantage of the facility, of course, but for good community morale all should have the opportunity. The alternative is one we are already faced with: of masses and mobs agglutinating in an unmanageable way, trying to satisfy their needs for morale-enhancement in a dangerously inappropriate medium.

Let me now say something about the shared sense of common purpose. It is the more important of the two dimensions of morale. When strong, it can compensate for weakness of the sense of security, but not vice versa. Rearguard actions, in battle or elsewhere, demand very high morale in circumstances where the perceived threat to security is at its greatest. Conversely, even among the most actually trusting of companions, morale will fall if the sense of purpose is lacking. This is of great significance to the man of religion, for all purely human purposes run the risk of being fulfilled, and - humanly speaking - nothing is so destructive of morale as actually to achieve your objective. It is in the highest degree rational for the Christian to set his sights on the kingdom of heaven - a kingdom which is not of this world.

We should note that when we speak of an objective we imply that the goal, the object in view, has necessarily to lie outside - at a distance from - the individual or group whose morale depends on it. The goal of health, or riches, or power will lead to the collapse of morale unless we can answer the further question, healthy (or rich or powerful) *for what*? I suggest that Britain's concentration on economic and welfare provision for its citizens in the last thirty years has failed to improve morale because we have had no convincing foreign policy: we have looked inward rather than outward and the result has been a sort of social hypochondriasis. Our health service has certainly made us no healthier judging by the statistics of sickness absence.

Empirically, it seems that the expression of a group's sense of purpose nearly always requires to be embodied in a person, a man or woman who symbolises, in his or her presence, behaviour and utterances the often unspoken aspirations of the generality of the group's members. During the 1939-45 war, the army went to enormous trouble to try to ensure that the ordinary soldier understood what the country was fighting for, what were our 'war aims'. In my experience the effort was very largely ineffective. Men fought or did their jobs well or badly depending on their relationship with the officers who were directing them. Scripture suggests that Jesus understood very well man's need for a person to symbolise the objective: *'I and the father are one'*; *'If you have seen me you have seen the father'*, *'Follow me'*. Indeed, this is one of the important meanings of the incarnation.

Leadership, so called, can be of two kinds, best indicated by the latin words 'rex' and 'dux'. Leadership in society seems to fluctuate between the two. Every now and then a charismatic leader attracts followers to him, as Jesus did; they no longer recognise the authority claimed by the preceding rulers and their mouthpieces: *"He speaks as one having authority, and not as the scribes"*. But then, if the new movement is successful the 'dux' of leadership becomes institutionalised and formalised into the 'rex' mode, loses its adventurousness and flexibility and settles down to new rigidities, ruling with power instead of leading by attractiveness - as happened to the post-Constantine church; and morale gradually falls until a new charismatic leader arises and there is a reformation or a renaissance - a rebirth.[2]

What does all this teach the seeker after health who has a concern for morale? Clearly there is much he can do to enhance men's sense of security whether as a professional or an amateur. But this in itself is not enough, and after a certain point it may be positively damaging. The healthy life is a journey, movement toward an objective. By all means help the traveller to cross the stream which bars his path; but if stepping stones will do it is a waste of time and resources to build a concrete bridge. Our present welfare and health provision is already beginning to price itself out of existence.

More important is the question of the sense of purpose, which we can now see to be largely a question of leadership. I would suggest that the man committed to the health of the community, Christian or otherwise, must first of all identify himself as a member of it. Certainly he will need to develop a capacity for detachment if he is to criticise it effectively; so what he must seek for, in Michael Wilson's phrase, is *involved* detachment, or critical involvement.[3] He must be particularly wary of any preconceived idea he may have that he is called to a leadership role within it. It is true that some of the world's greatest leaders, like Moses, have come to their positions from outside the communities they led; but this does not alter the fact that before they are accepted as leaders they must necessarily be identified with the communities they aim to serve. The good group leader is always a good group member first.

Having been accepted as a member of the community in good standing, his next responsibility is to discover who *are* the effective leaders of the community. I suppose it is generally easy to discern those who are fulfilling the 'rex' functions; though it is often difficult thereafter to decide whether they should be supported, or opposed, or whether they are too powerful to be opposed and one should bend one's efforts to protecting and insulating the community from them, while building up its strength to resist them. I was once tactless enough to define my task as superintendent of a mental hospital as protecting the people in it from the committee which was officially responsible for managing it. At the time when I said it, it was an accurate job description.

It is more difficult to discern the people who are performing the 'dux' functions at any one moment. They are the disturbers of the status quo, the radicals, the revolutionaries; sometimes the entertainers, the jesters, the Pied Pipers; sometimes - for a Christian often - they are the delinquents, the mentally sick, the dropouts who still wear spectacles and false teeth, denying society yet still living in it. All these diverse kinds of people do in fact lead society in one direction rather than another. They are leaders in this sense. They influence people. Of course you will not discover who they are by only hearing what people say about them, you will have to watch people's behaviour. Who do they 'go out of their way' to see, or to avoid? These are the people to look for, and look after. Their influence on the community's morale is critical. Remember that the line between acknowledged leader and scapegoat is one that is very thinly drawn. Both arise because men in groups project their own unexpressed feelings on to others - their unexpressed aspirations on to the leader, their unexpressed bad feelings on to scapegoats. And history, long past and recent, shows how easily the one can turn, suddenly and unpredictably, into the other.

The kind of involved detachment or critical involvement, which is needed by the man who cares about the morale of his community, is not easy to acquire. It is not uncommon for communities to be ruled by unsuitable people: psychopaths in office can actually make people ill as well as denying their communities opportunities for health-enhancement. Under such a ruler it is hard not to collude with other members of the community in making him a scapegoat - in blaming him not only for his own shortcomings but also for shortcomings of our own. One has to be aware of one's own prejudices. The field is one fraught with the need to make ethical decisions and judgements, a field characterised by the confusion and uncertainty implicit in participant observation rather than the detached precision and clarity and freedom from anxiety which we associate with the scientist or statistician. But it is a field which should not be ignored by those who recognise that the best of health for the individual person will only be obtainable in a healthy society.

I am not able here to consider the theological implications of this perspective on health in detail. In my earlier essays I tried to show how the healing ministry of Jesus becomes much more intelligible to twentieth century man if seen as a health-enhancing rather than disease-attacking endeavour. The concept of man implicit among the Jews of the first century is now recognised to have been fundamentally a corporate one; and although the scriptures do not use the word morale, I have found that an appreciation of this perspective adds new depths of significance to much that is written there. The French expression *'esprit de corps'* suggests that there are important links to be made between the concepts of morale and 'spirit'. But we must leave this for other occasions.

SUMMARY

I have tried to demonstrate the usefulness of distinguishing between two concepts of health care, one concerned with the attack on disease and the other with the enhancement of health; both in the field of care for the individual and in the field of care for the community. We tend to attack diseases as if we were mechanics, and nurture health as if we were gardeners. I have used the word morale to conceptualise an approach to community health. This word has militaristic connotations, which have made it unfashionable, so I would point out that in this essay I have not found a use for three concepts, which are often felt to be implied by the word. First, the idea that loyalty is something which a leader can demand as of right. From the perspective, which I adopt here, it is never useful to morale to demand loyalty: but its absence is an indication of the leader's failure and not that of those he purports to lead. Secondly, I want to do without the concept of externally imposed discipline. For good morale, self-discipline, voluntarily imposed, is the only kind of discipline worth striving for. Thirdly, I do not believe that the concept of power-based authority is of anything more than transient value to the building of morale. I believe, with R.A.Lambourne, that a man only has true authority when he is 'authorised' by other men to act in such a way as to alter their perceptions of themselves and their situation.[4] Official 'authority', which relies ultimately on the sanction of physical power and control, plays no part in raising morale. To discuss these three concepts would need an essay not on morale, but on its pathology.

References:

1. Antony Jay, **Corporation Man,** (Jonathan Cape), 1972, especially chapter 10.
2. The source of the material in this paragraph is in an unpublished paper by G. Stanley Windass.
3. J. Michael Wilson, **The Hospital: A Place of Truth,** (University of Birmingham), 1971.
4. R.A.Lambourne, 'Authority, Personal Knowledge and the Therapeutic Relationship' in <u>Contact</u>, no. 25 (S.P.A.) Edinburgh 1968.

153-1 Man, Medicine and Morale.

MENTAL HEALTH AND MENTAL ILLNESS

. . . I had at one time the good fortune to be a divisional psychiatrist in the Army, to a division which had two brigades, one of three and one of four battalions of troops. I joined the division while it was mobilising for active service, and my first task was to ingratiate myself with the regimental M.O.s and junior commanders (coy. commanders) and invite them to let me see any soldier about whose mental stability in action they had any qualms. When I saw these potential patients, I gave them a fairly straightforward psychiatric interview letting them talk about themselves until they ran down, then asking questions to fill in details of their present condition, and continuing with a rapid but comprehensive account of their previous history, designed to bring out their emotional reactions in the important areas of their experience from a developmental point of view: relationships with parents and siblings, at school and work, and in marriage and the army. On the basis of this I was usually able to make a provisional estimate of their stability in action and advise accordingly. I often asked their views about their present unit, officers and NCOs, feeding arrangements, etc., but the answers I got were always interpreted in the light of their previous personality reactions and in any case tended to be stereotyped and of little obvious value.

After some time I had seen enough patients for figures to become interesting, I found that some units had a far higher incidence of cases referred than others. Careful study of the history of the patients and of their battalions showed no obvious reason why this should be so. There were no convincing differences in age-range, battle experience, and so on. Enquiry now took an epidemiological turn; and I quickly discovered that the incidence of psychiatric disorder was closely paralleled by that of sickness absence in general, of the V.D. rate, and of minor delinquency. By this time the matter was of sufficient general interest to warrant my asking for interviews with battalion commanders, and from them I got almost immediate answers - consciously or unconsciously. Some of them would point out that they had recently had to sack a catering officer, or that all my cases occurred in one company and that the company commander had been sick; while others would demonstrate only too clearly that morale in their units was a reflection of their own morale. I then returned to my case notes to see whether I could have deduced low morale in the unit as being a relevant factor in the individual case, and was soon convinced that I could not: the individual's views on morale were, clearly enough, all his own.

Thus I had strong reason to suppose that failures in group morale, due often to failures in leadership, were a major aetiological factor in the individual's emotional instability or breakdown. And not only this. Since there was no evidence that the number of 'predisposed' individuals was greater in one unit than another, it seemed likely that good morale in a unit had a definite therapeutic effect in keeping the predisposed individual well. . . .

11 - Mental Health and Mental Illness.

GROUP MORALE

. . . In all acute battle neuroses, the causative factor is environmental rather than in personality deficiency (though, of course, the latter may play a part). This indicates the by now accepted principle, that treatment of the individual personality by psychotherapy, in the narrow meaning of the word, is of less importance than the treatment of the environment - represented by the physical organism, the condition in the battle area, and the psychological atmosphere of the rest centre.

Treatment of the physical organism is a matter of rest, food and drink and in the treatment of minor physical injuries or complaints.

The conditions in the battle area come very much under the eye of the psychiatrist in certain respects; and since these contain the predisposing and the precipitating factors of the psychological illness, they are of more than ordinary interest. When a dozen admissions occur in a day, all from the same unit, all with the story that they have not had an unbroken stretch of six hours sleep for 2 to 5 weeks, then if the story is confirmed, there is an opportunity for a little preventive psychiatry with the help of executive officers. I met a feeling among combatant officers that if a Coy. failed to take an objective, they should be put in to take it later, rather than another Coy., so as not to lessen their faith in themselves. An excellent reason, but it carries the *sine qua non* that the men should be adequately rested before the attack. Points like this may escape the attention of the C.O. in the rush of battle. Any common factor occurring among admissions should be discussed with executive officers. If in a Coy. attack all the cases occur in one platoon, the psychiatrist should find out whether the weight of enemy attack fell only on them; whether the platoon commander was jittery, whether the men were overtired beforehand. He can only decide these questions - and they may be of considerable value in future operations - in personal consultation with executive officers. And only the executive officer can decide to what extent these factors were preventable, and how they can be prevented or lessened in the future.

The psychiatrist of a Division in action will have a certain amount of therapeutic work in his rest centre, but his main importance to the Division lies in his collecting information on morale which he can get from his case notes. In order to put this information into perspective, he must know a little at least of the battle area, which means a great deal of moving about and a good deal of inquisitiveness. The psychiatrist needs a Jeep.

The third factor is the psychological atmosphere of the rest centre. At MDS level a rest centre can hardly be very elaborate or very comfortable. I doubt if it would be an advantage to have it any better equipped than the patients can make it themselves.

Germany, in a recent article in the Lancet, uses the term 'group-sense', defining it simply as an 'awareness of, and adherence to, group attitudes and values'. He says that a diminution of this group-sense is the chief cause of chronicity in war neurotics, and that the essence of treatment is to raise or maintain group-sense (which is perhaps a more restricted term than group morale). He also says that a normal day's work is the best occupational therapy for such cases. With these observations I emphatically agree. In everything but case-taking, the men occupying a forward rest centre should be treated as a group. I would go so far as to say that in a forward rest centre, the normal medical interest in the difficult or unusual symptom should be curbed. The physical examination should be reduced to the minimum after initial examination. This needs emphasising because an exhausted patient complains of various physical symptoms which are almost entirely functional, and, as a psychiatrist, one tends to expect functional somatic symptoms only in certain hypochondriacal types. Consequently one tends to take the complaints seriously in men of good personality. Any expression of interest in a physical symptom, or a particular individual, is an opening for the patient to allow his group-sense to deteriorate, an opening which the majority of patients are not slow to take, since their group-sense offers them only a return to arduous and unpleasant duty. Men are discouraged to talk about their battle experiences except in the presence of the psychiatrist, as the recent admissions tend to spread alarm and despondency among those about to return to duty. If there was an intelligent trained nursing orderly (preferably an MNO) on duty in the rest centre, this very real difficulty would be lessened. The men ask, at every visit of the psychiatrist, what news from the front is, and it increases confidence and gives the opportunity for a little very useful group therapy, if the psychiatrist can give a clear picture of what is happening, and listen to and discuss the men's comments, and to listen to and debunk inaccurate or undesirable rumours.

In general, men are kept asleep for two days, and are encouraged to get up on the third day. On the fourth day they are expected to be up and working all day. Finding work is not always easy, for it must be both useful and not too dull. But constant medical supervision is not necessary by then, and the men can be sent off to work anywhere in the area of the MDS. If they can get a swim or a bathe, so much the better. PT is not very practicable so far forward, with so few men in the centre for so short a time.

It is essential that morning and evening temperatures are taken throughout. Especially in this area men may develop malaria, and since for psychological reasons the complaint of headache is made little of, and the examination of the spleen is not desirable, there must be some check on physical condition. It is better if done by an orderly at a routine exam, and it will be safer if done by an MNO, rather than by the M.O., except of course initially (on admission).

Germany's article is concerned with the treatment of reactive anxiety, not of exhaustion. He says that a mild sense of guilt should be suggested to the patient early in treatment of anxious cases. I do not think such a measure is indicated in the exhaustion group, and in my experience it is always present in cases with anxiety. To infuse a sense of guilt would doubtless provoke *effort* to improve up to a mild group standard, but it would surely lessen the group-*sense,* by causing a mild sense of inferiority. Group-sense is maintained and boosted by overtly treating a man as being an effective member of the group not as being less efficient than the others. Attempts at improving insight by intro-spection are out of place in a forward area rear centre to my mind. A robust line of common sense is the keynote to therapy.

Men are discharged to duty. RMOs arrange for them to be kept out of actual combat for another seven days, with mild nightly sedatives if necessary. A certain amount of judgement is necessary about returning men to their units before they have stopped complaining of headaches, dizziness etc.. I feel that the week's light duty at the unit is continuation of treatment rather than mere convalescence. From the group point of view, it is better to disregard a complaint of headache, and have the man readmitted with malaria two or three days later. The atmosphere of the battalion maintains a man's group-sense better than any rest centre could hope to do. The RMOs, with whom I have the privilege of working, understand this well enough and are aware of the possibility - and unlikelihood - of the complaints having an organic cause. . . .

1-1 Psychiatric Report, Arakan Front, Burma.

. . . At its simplest group morale means that the individuals in a group are prepared, not necessarily consciously, to subordinate their individual aims and activities to those of the group. Particularly in war, individual desires and needs, considered in isolation, may be diametrically opposed to one another. This subordination can only be achieved if it fosters a greater sense of security among the individuals. Luckily, man is of a gregarious nature; and normally he does feel more secure when he is one of a crowd - provided he is in some respect similar to the other members. Group morale gives a foundation of common purpose upon which activity can be organised, and rendered thereby more effective than the mere sum of the individual activities - toward the same end - could ever be.

To feel secure in the company of one's fellows, and to have a common purpose with them, these are the basis of group morale. What circumstances, then, will tend to weaken it? Obviously, those which allow individual needs and desires to take precedence over those of the group. This is not a logical process, but emotional. Individual men are, though more rarely than is generally recognised, sometimes guided by reason. Men in a group may for practical purposes be said to be entirely guided by emotion. The art of man-management lies in thinking in terms of human emotion rather than human reason.

The reasons for individual demands taking precedence over those of the group may be surveyed from two directions.

1. *Individual demands are too insistent.*

(a) This may be because the individual is of abnormal mental make-up. This is the field of medical psychology, and problems in it come within the province of the psychiatrist. The leader is concerned with the group, and if any of his individuals are too different from the rest, he may reasonably try to remove them.

(b) Individual demands may become over-insistent temporarily (as opposed to the comparative permanency of the former group). This may result from either physical or mental over-stress: exhaustion, or normal worry of a personal nature - e.g. over domestic affairs. These kinds of difficulty affect normal healthy men and are a concern for the leader. The commonest fault of officers in this respect is failure to spot the trouble early; and failure to realise the importance of emotional compared with intellectual factors. Officers too often expect an adult, reasonable attitude in the men toward their private problems. Commonly, a sympathetic hearing, allowing a man to repeat himself, and a few uncritical words of comfort do more good than a short, snappy, intellectual analysis of the problem followed by 'logical' advice - however accurate the analysis and however logical the advice. As regards fatigue, it must be remembered that this is a 'whole' process, affecting a man both physically and mentally, particularly in war; and therefore mental and physical rest and nourishment must go hand in hand. It is important to demonstrate that even at times of stress, when the individual's need of rest overwhelms all group considerations, yet the rest is provided *by the group.* One of the most difficult problems of individual morale is raised by a man's admission to hospital - or, more generally, by his leaving the unit - when he is exhausted. An environment which gives succour and rest has a greater emotional attraction than one which is associated most vividly with overstrain; and if the group provides the former, after the latter, the succour will be remembered and associated with the group and group ties will be strengthened. Furthermore, the mutual succouring of men in a group is good for the fit as well as the exhausted and sick: it enhances the feeling of security and 'one-ness'.

2. *Group demands are not insistent enough.*

(a) A man who is normal enough in one environment may be quite 'out of it' in another. A single Glaswegian or Welshman in a Home Counties regiment may make a hopeless soldier, though in his own county regiment he might be thoroughly sound. This difficulty is frequently encountered among reinforcements. The magnitude of our army's manpower problems perhaps precludes any care in individual postings in this respect, but it is by no means insignificant from the point of view of morale.

A similar psychological difficulty occurs with regard to variations in intelligence. A dullard or a highly gifted man may feel 'out of it' in a platoon of 'average' men. Selection procedures go a long way to ease this problem, but it will always exist in some degree.

(b) Group demands may be too weak simply because of bad training or discipline, and will then affect the whole group. Here we see a lack of our second basic requirement - awareness of a threat to security. This is closely allied with the lack of a sense of purpose. Much has been made of the phrase 'keeping men in the picture'; and during actual battle, most leaders ensure that their men know what they are going to do. War calls for more initiative than it did in 1914 - 18. Opportunities will occur of which only a man who knows the objective as well as the proposed method of getting to it could take advantage. But training continues to appear pointless to many men in many of its aspects. I remember a man I was asked to see because he had thrown down his rifle while on parade. The man told me that he lost his head because the Sergeant-major had given the squad 'as you were' seventeen times in succession. It is obvious that the man would have been much more able to control himself had the Sergeant-major taken the trouble to explain beforehand that there was some point in the exercise - that self-control on parade is good training for self-control in the field. In training, reasons should always be given for orders. This practice breeds confidence and sense of purpose. Discipline is a natural result of, and belief in, a purpose. The old-fashioned type of repressive discipline only worked well when men had a belief in their purpose, or in their commander, symbolising their purposes in himself. . . .

2-2 The Psychological Basis of Morale.

LEADERSHIP

. . . I must admit that I have little enough to say to you about how morale should be studied in the world of Birmingham as we know it. First of all, for instance, there is the difficulty of defining the local community in an urban setting where the process of cultural disintegration has already proceeded probably beyond the limits of, for instance, Durkheim's most pessimistic imagination. But I did devote a good deal of thought to the general problem when I was in the army during the war, and possibly these reflections may start trains of thought which you will be able to follow up. Clearly, one must try to delineate a group of people who are in some sense a genuine community - who have in fact something in common, whether it be work, or play, or a sharing of common community services as in a neighbourhood unit. One must start from a community, that is to say, rather than from a crowd or a 'population', such as one finds in statistical tables in the Registrar-General's reports, or in a railway station waiting room, where no-one has any relation to anyone else. The next thing to look for is some kind of index or indices of morale. In the services, one can work out the incidence rates of delinquency and sickness, (in general - the number of men on sick parade; or more specifically, the number of cases of venereal disease, or of psychiatric illness). In civil life, when large enough numbers can be obtained, the rate of absenteeism from work is probably of some significance, depending on local circumstances. So would be the incidence of suicide, or attempted suicide. Others would be accident rates, and, again, the incidence of delinquency or broken marriages. You will find that when you have excluded the obvious reasons for a high figure in any one index (such as, for instance, an epidemic of mumps as a reason for

absenteeism from school), that variations in all the indices will run reasonably parallel.
. . .

. . . In the army, one could see very clearly how for most men their sense of purpose depended upon the quality of their leaders. Leadership is a quality which is only partly inborn. Much of it can be taught. Here is a list of leadership qualities which I made from my own observations:

1.   *Loyalty to a higher authority*. There was once an independent brigade group which had a very fine record of service under a particular commander, who was much beloved by his men. After some years, this brigade became part of a division and lost its independent status. It was notable how the morale and efficiency of this brigade fell away, because no-one had a feeling of loyalty to the divisional commander - at least not for some time. All the best commanders in the field openly acknowledge their allegiance to a higher authority, and the best of them, of course, are deeply religious.

2.   *Proper regard for the security of his followers*. This is taught to every officer in the army as 'man-management'. It is his continuing responsibility to see that his men are fed, clothed, armed and guarded. If he neglects this responsibility, morale will soon fall.

3.   *He has to make himself visible*. He has to walk around, seeing and being seen by, his men. Montgomery and Mountbatten in the last war made a great deal of this aspect of morale.

4.   *He must avoid an appearance of anxiety* - remember Kipling's poem *"If you can keep your head when all around you /Are losing theirs..."*

5.   *Keeping men in the picture.* Montgomery was an artist at this. It isn't always easy to do in wartime, and sometimes it doesn't matter because soldiers are trained in obedience. In civil life I am sure it matters a great deal - but I still think it is not easy. Mass media of communication, the civil equivalent of 'orders of the day', are highly suspect for this purpose, and to my mind nothing adequately replaces the personal contact between leader and led in this regard.

6.   *You must train your followers.* The sense of purpose soon flags if it is not brought forcibly to one's notice by having demands made upon one.

7.   Finally, I would mention as an important quality of leadership: *the ability to withstand embarassment.* The leader must be prepared to stick his nose into things and ask pointed questions which people would sooner not be asked.

It is 15 years since I was in the army. If these are the points which occur to me now it is because I have found them to be relevant to problems of morale which I have met since, in hospital. I don't know how relevant you will find them in the parish, but perhaps they will stimulate you into making your own lists. It is perhaps in the sense of purpose that the Christian has most to contribute. It is all too easy for well-meaning people to get side-tracked in their Christian vocation. They become concerned with marriage guidance, or care of the elderly, or juvenile delinquency - all estimable activities, of which there certainly aren't enough. But it will do us no harm to realise that these questions only become problems needing special attention because of a general failure of the community's morale; and that if we could instil a more significant sense of purpose into our respective neighbourhoods, then these problems would be less overwhelming, and much of them would be prevented from occurring at all. . . .

29 - Mental Health.

CHURCH LEADERSHIP

... What indeed could be more unexpected than that the prophetic search for better ways in which the leadership function could be exercised should arrive at the vision of the Suffering Servant?

It was our concern with the health of the community, and the individuals who are part of it, that led to our study of leadership. Leaders, be they in the kingly or prophetic tradition – are concerned to see that their people come to no harm. Their very reason for existence might be thought to be to minimise the suffering of their followers, at least in the long run. No doubt Israel's allegiance to God, even when it was only nominal, had kept its rulers aware that they were God's servants; and it need cause no surprise that they should see themselves as servants of their people also. No doubt again that in their best moments they were concerned with the suffering of their followers – and if they were not, the prophetic voice would be raised to remind them of it. But the notion of a suffering servant as leader must have seemed as paradoxical to them as it often does to us. A quiet, gentle servant (Is. 42 v 1-3) of no form or comeliness. You would not notice him in a crowd, or, if you did, your glance would quickly pass on. He has none of the qualities associated with human leadership, and none, either, of those popularly associated with a divine leader. The portrait is that of a man of whom one might say 'he's just the man who would fall ill' – *stricken and afflicted, despised and rejected (Is.53).*

Indeed, it is probable that the only meaning which this vision would have had for us would be that it was a poetic representation of the role of Israel as a nation suffering creatively among nations - had it not been for the way in which Jesus of Nazareth subsequently enabled us to see that the Suffering Servant can be not only a nation, but a single, unique person, among other individual people.

One of the major shortcomings of Israel's rulers had been their failure to deal adequately with those who suffered. Through most of recorded history, government has concerned itself with the 'greatest good of the greatest number', rather than the greatest good of all. The needs of an orderly society always seem to have required the ex-communication or rejection of the sick, the poor, the delinquent and the mad. Even our modern societies seek to isolate such social misfits by confining them in institutions - hospitals and prisons. In doing so, we hide from ourselves the realisation that it is *our* badness, *our* sickness which is being confined or rejected. We forget that we are the community, the social organism, and that the sickness of individuals is our sickness. If there is inflammation in my stomach, and its cells are diseased, it is *I* that am sick. So it is that the task of the Suffering Servant is to bring good tidings to the afflicted, to bind up the broken-hearted, to proclaim liberty to the captive - showing them that the community cares, not out of pity alone, but because if it is to be truly healthy - if its morale is to be raised to an optimal level - it must care for *all* its members. The suffering of Everyman can only be relieved by the suffering of the Unique Man. The suffering of Everyman is destructive, but the suffering of the Unique Man is creative.

The way in which Jesus exercised the ministry of the Suffering Servant, the care which he showed for the lost sheep, the sick, the outcast, is well recognised and needs no emphasis here. What is less well recognised by us today is the social context in which he lived. The Hebrew under-standing of the community was much nearer the concept of the social organism than we are familiar with today. For Jesus, and those to whom he spoke, this was perhaps so obvious as to require no explicit statement. But if we read the Gospels with this in mind, it may shed new light on his meaning. Of course, he didn't use the word "morale", but perhaps this is the implicit background of his teaching: mutual under-standing and support between all men in pursuit of a common goal. A readiness to act unselfishly - in pursuit of the common goal. The sense of purpose is overriding: *"If thine eye cause thee to stumble, cast it out". "Give to everyone that asketh thee, and of him that taketh away thy goods, ask them not again."* Nothing must stand in the way of the common purpose. *"Love your enemies"* - you are all soldiers in one army, share and share alike, and don't quarrel, but keep your eye on the objective. And what is the objective? Life – *"I come that they may have life, and have it abundantly"*. The aim of the good leader is to train his men that they act 'as one' in pursuit of the goal. So Jesus prays *"that they may all be one ... I in them and thou in me that they may be perfected into one"*. And, characteristically, Jesus enabled his disciples to identify him with the objective, so that when they were in doubt about the way ahead, they could simply obey his injunction *"Follow me"*.

If the life and teaching of Jesus makes real for us how leadership and health are necessarily related to servitude and suffering, all in the one human person, his death and resurrection bring us to a new understanding of his uniqueness. For if St. Paul can say *"In my flesh I complete what is lacking in Christ's afflictions for the sake of his body the church"* (Col.1 v 24), and if he can say that not only is the church Christ's body, but also that Christ is the head of the body (Col. l v l8), then we are forced to realise that we, who are members of the body, each of us partakes of the nature of the Unique Man, each of us is invested with the responsibility of his function of leadership, and each of us has the responsibility of making suffering - whether of ourselves or others - creative. The church, now conceived as a spiritual organism, turns away from any tendency towards localising or structuring its leadership or serving function. Perhaps this is one of the meanings of the phrase *"whose service is perfect freedom"*. **...**

72 - Church Leadership and Health.

Chapter Three

HEALTH?

In James' view health involves harmony of interpersonal relationships: it is a quality of life-together, and therefore is descriptive of a community, whether family, hospital ward, professional team or wider society. The nature of health is shaped by the values of different cultures, and influenced by practical choices. His view of health is inclusive of sick and handicapped people, and he regarded racial and religious differences as an enrichment of health. Beyond 'being healthy' is a further question: healthy for what? Which implies that a healthy group or society is bound together by a common purpose. Good morale and mental health are synonymous.

These values clash with the idealistic view of health in Western culture where health is regarded as perfect freedom from all defects and diseases in individuals - a fantasy of absolute purity.

M.W.

WHAT IS HEALTH?

'There is no way to health through the cure of illness.' That may sound a surprising statement to come from a doctor. But it is true. What clinical medicine aims to do is to restore someone to the state he was in before he fell ill. We doctors talk of the restoration of function, of rehabilitation - of getting a patient back to the point at which he became a patient. We wouldn't see it as part of our professional task to get a patient to be better - more healthy - than he was before he fell ill. I think most doctors would think that to be a kind of arrogance. If some of our patients do turn out to be better people than they were before, as some do, we can claim no professional credit.

Curing illness, or even preventing illness, does not make men healthy, except from a very short-term perspective. All it does is to help them to live on a bit longer so that the illnesses they ultimately suffer from will be different. What medicine does is to shift people from one 'at risk' category to another. We all have to undergo some disease or accident before we are allowed to die: the law insists that a 'cause of death' is entered on your death certificate.

But if we take a longer perspective, we can see that 'health is a *positive* quality of well-being '- fullness of life. It is not a matter of being well adjusted to a society that is itself not healthy. Plenty of people are healthy though crippled or diseased: they transcend their limitations. Indeed, for many of us it is the experience of illness that challenges us to a new and deeper understanding of the true nature of health. . . .

152-2 What is health?

. . . St Paul advised the Philippians to think on things that are pure and lovely and of good report. As a doctor I was trained, like most other health professionals, to focus my attention on what was ugly and impure and evil. It took many years for me to learn that there were ways of helping sufferers, not just by attacking the evils that beset them, but rather by discovering their strengths and fostering them. By this change of focus I found that quite often the evil disappeared of its own accord - or became an additional source of strength. By being helped to become stronger, the patient learned something of how to deal with his evil himself, instead of my teaching him to be dependent and passive while I eradicated the evil with some technical trick which he didn't understand. I began to learn how important it was not to put myself in blinkers by concentrating exclusively on the evil which a patient presented to me, but deliberately to pay wide-ranging attention to the context in which that evil was set. Thus if a patient said he had something wrong with his stomach, I would be slow to say 'let me look at *it* ' but would enquire further about him as a person. If he said that he felt bad, I would seek to learn about his family or work relationships, and became concerned with the group of which he was a member. By attending to context in this way, I often found it was healthier for the context to be changed than for the organ or body system or individual with which I was initially presented to be interfered with. If someone broke his leg, or developed a nervous breakdown, I found myself asking why did he fall ill *now*, rather than at some other time? Or, why did he get infected while all the other members of his family escaped? For the patient, the answers to such questions were usually much more meaningful explanations of the illness than technical medical answers would have been.

And so by looking at the social context of those whom one designated as sick, I began to see that health is not to be sought in separate individuals, but depends on healthy relationships between people. We are not healthy if we are badly adjusted to society. Nor are we healthy if we are well adjusted to a sick society. The health of society and the health of its component members are inextricably intertwined, and the community's health is an essential prerequisite for the individual's health. Health is corporate. My understanding of the Christian Gospel is that salvation does not come to a man as an isolated individual: we will all be saved together or we will be damned separately. So it is with health. It is neither virtuous nor expedient for a man to seek health for himself in disregard of the health of other people. Health is something we share, not something to be competed for. . . .

. . . Sometimes we talk of health - either of the individual or the community - as if it were our goal. But a goal is an objective, and to call it an objective means that it lies outside ourselves. If we aim at health, we need to ask the further question, what do we want to be healthy *for*? If we fail to do this, and make health our ultimate concern, we won't get health but hypochondriasis.

152-3 What is Health?

A HEALTHY SOCIETY?

The question mark in the title is important, because a healthy society is a visionary concept, a work of the imagination, far removed from current realities. I do not intend to describe my personal utopia: if I were to do so the result would be a static image which I would be ready to discard tomorrow. The vision I want to share with you is that of a dynamic and evolving society whose glory, if ever we glimpse it, is iridescent, changing, continually new and unpredictable. It seems to recede further into the future with each new discovery we make about the world we live in. It is constantly being altered and (we hope) corrected by fresh experience.

The vision of a healthy society is perhaps the one aim or goal that all men, everywhere and in all ages, have in common, however much they differ as to the path by which it may be approached, or disagree as to whether it can be realised in time or only in eternity. Since all life is movement, our activities gain their significance by leading us either more or less towards our vision, or more or less away from it. It gives us a compass-bearing, a sense of direction. It gives us a dimension along which we can evaluate our lives and actions. We try to give it form and plausibility by seeking to endow it with a harmony of optimum values rather than average ones: it is a vision of what ought to be obtainable, not of what we currently know to be obtainable. Although it is a creature of the imagination, it is a vision which each man wants to share with others, for only when it is shared is there hope of progress towards its realisation. Perhaps we should be glad that such a vision seems to recede as our experience grows, for nothing is so fatal to human endeavour as actually to reach one's ultimate objective. The zest for living depends upon all realizable goals being recognised as only provisional. Neither wealth nor health are more than dust or ashes unless you know what to do with them when you have them.

The healthy society will include everyone.

Until recently it was always possible to conceive of any society, small or large, as being an area of ordered existence surrounded by chaos. In such a context, a healthy society could be conceived as one from which disorderly elements could be extruded or exiled. The deviant who could not or would not abide by the rules could go into the wilderness or be transported to a penal colony or become a tramp. But our twentieth century electric and jet-propelled communications technology has now so enlarged the perceived boundaries of all societies that there is no wilderness left into which the deviant can be exiled. The wilderness of yesterday has become our neighbour's garden, and he will protest if we try to throw our rubbish over the hedge. We live in a global village. There is no future in any attempt we may make henceforth to regard our neighbours as non-human denizens of the wilderness. In future we have to consume our own smoke, to discover some way of dealing with deviant members of society to our mutual benefit.

We still tend to think of such problems as if they were matters of ethics, areas in which we feel it appropriate to make moral choices or decisions. But biological considerations may be more compelling than moral ones. From the immensely long span of evolutionary history we learn that any species of organism multiplies until it fills every ecological niche to which it can adapt. If it is a successful species, as ours is, these niches may vary quite considerably. Subsequently, through the slow but inevitable changes of the natural world, such niches may become so separated, in space or in kind, that the organisms in question can no longer move easily from one to another. The inhabitants of each niche then become, over generations, specialised: first in habit, so that fairly quickly their differing patterns of mating behaviour ensure that there will be no interbreeding between them (though mating would be physically possible for the few who are still able to visit from one niche to another); and then, more slowly, they specialise in structure, as mutation occurs and their specialisation becomes written into their genetic inheritance. Thus do new species arise. Darwin's finches in the Galapagos Islands, of which fourteen species are known all stemming from one South American ancestor, are perhaps the best known example.

Now the interesting thing is that - alone among the species known to us - mankind has avoided this biological trap, of becoming so well adapted to a specialised niche that he can no longer breed with his erstwhile fellows. And human curiosity and adaptability being what it is, it is inconceivable that he will ever be thus constrained by his environment in the future, at least on this planet. For better or worse, the whole of mankind will almost certainly henceforth always share a common gene pool, and thus remain one species. And if one applies relevant Darwinian principles analogously to cultural evolution, the conclusion seems even more certain; because each human society not only refreshes its genetic make-up by physical intercourse with members of other societies, but more importantly, it communicates with, and learns new ideas from, even those societies to which it is most hostile. Even when we build an iron-curtain we employ soldiers and agents to keep us informed about what happens on the other side. We are thus committed not only to a single shared gene pool, but to a single shared *idea* pool as well.

Thus we are biologically as well as ethically committed to recognising mankind as one society. There is no place outside society to which we can consign elements or members whom we choose to label deviant or disordered. Since this situation has never occurred before in evolutionary history, its consequences are unpredictable. I suppose it is possible that humanity may find a temporary escape by colonizing other planets, but the discovery of humanity as essentially one species, committed to coping with its own disorder as an internal problem, will henceforward be a fact of life to be reckoned with. It is not an easy idea. It is a fundamental fact of our experience that health depends upon the excretory apparatus functioning properly; but for the future the social organism, society, must learn to live with, and re-interpret the significance of, its own waste products.

Diversity or conformity?

Evolution shows us that a species only survives as long as there is sufficient variability among its members to withstand the changing environmental pressures which constitute the process of natural selection. The law is quite fundamental, and will apply as much to humankind in the future as it has to all other species in history. Since all natural environments are themselves evolving and changing, a species whose members all conformed to the same constitution would be doomed to extinction when change occurred. The generation and maintenance of a pool of variability is a biological imperative. Since we can now rely on the transmission of ideas through the generations as well as genes, our capacity for variation is multiplied enormously. It is safe to say that the human race has sufficient potential variation to be adequately armed against almost any imaginable environmental change on the planet; but there is a warning implied in the word 'potential'. Rene Dubos has said: *"The cultivation of diversity is essential, not only for the growth of society, but even for its survival."*[1] But it does have to be cultivated.

Perhaps because of our evolutionary history, we have a vestigial respect for conformity which is likely to be too strong for our future good. Among other species, to distinguish between members of the same species and those of other kinds had survival value. The distinction between 'us', who conform to our pattern, and 'them' who don't, is still common among human beings. But this would not obtain in the hypothetical world-wide society; for a moment's reflection will convince you that you would not regard yourself as healthy in a society which did not recognise and value you for those aspects of yourself which are unique and belong to you alone. Your differences from other people will have a greater significance for your sense of well-being than will your similarity to them.

For the time being we have to live with this inherited tendency to draw lines between ourselves and some of our fellows, and we must learn to keep it under control. Erik Erikson speaks of our tendency to distinguish *pseudo*species: our tribe, class, nation or religious association is seen as the only one - all others are lumped together as outsiders.[2] And to preserve this illusion of the oneness of our own special pseudospecies, we demand from one another a great deal of conformity to custom and law, and only tolerate diversity within narrow limits. In fact, out inherited nature is such that we actually need the cultural invention of the pseudospecies in order to develop a sense of identity. When you first meet a stranger, he identifies himself to you by saying what groups he is a member of: his place of origin, his occupation, and so on. Each of us needs a sense of individual identity to be healthy, but it is always a social as well as an individual creation. My affirmation of who I think I am has to be confirmed by my fellows if I am not to fall prey to crippling self-doubts or feelings of alienation. So my sense of identity is constantly developing and maturing as I grow up into wider and wider social environments.

Erikson shows that from infancy onwards there are times when we respond to stress by making a kind of 'total' restructuring of our experience, usually of a transitory nature. We can all recall childhood occasions when, following an angry encounter with someone, we said 'Alright; that settles it. I'll never speak to you again'. Thus for the moment we restructure our experience which 'till then would have had a healthily variegated patterning of light and shade, into a sharp distinction of black and white. At such a time the boundary of the sense of self becomes rigidly inclusive and exclusive, contrasting with its open and fluid nature at more normal times. Whereas in infancy such a temporary shift from 'wholeness' to 'totality' is usually individuo-centric, in adolescence this kind of experience tends to be group-centred, and is often associated with what Konrad Lorenz describes as 'militant enthusiasm' - for some cause which claims our allegiance and with which we identify ourselves. Adult groups in later life may show similar patterns, particularly when they feel threatened. Parallel features can be found in W.R.Bion's descriptions of the way groups unconsciously organise themselves for 'fight or flight.'[3]

The shift from wholeness to totality may therefore have survival value in that it sharpens our sense of identity when it is threatened. But, like bodily emergency defence mechanisms, it is only for emergency use. It is more primitive, less complex and differentiated than the best of our potential, and is less often evoked as we grow into maturity. It increases the value we set on conformity and the negative value we set on variety. Under stress, conformity gains approval: otherwise it is seen as a virtue mainly by those who cherish prejudice.

Technology with a human face

Modern technology needs a re-examination in the light of our vision. Unlike nature, it has no built-in self-adjusting mechanism. Nature is self-cleansing and has her own rhythms of seasonal change and balance. But mankind has unleashed a kind of technology which doesn't know where to stop. Its speed increases in an ungovernable way, creating pollution faster than nature can deal with it. Technologists work in terms of populations rather than societies. The characteristic of a population is that it is composed of a number of entities which are seen as equivalent to one another, and to be related in a random rather than a systematic fashion. In this sense a population is the antithesis of a society or community - especially a healthy one: for in the latter each component member is valued for his uniqueness and difference from others; and the healthy man relates to other people systematically rather than at random.

Too often the technologist of today thinks in terms of the mass: mass advertising, production, markets - and even mass education. By ignoring the uniqueness of the people he employs and the people he purports to serve, he depersonalizes and alienates them. Mass technology does not improve the standard of living of the very poor, nor does it make people more comfortable by relieving them of distressful labour. In the world as a whole, the rich get richer while the poor get poorer. The more so-called useful goods it produces the more useless people feel. The faster the speed of transport, the greater the traffic jams. Not so long ago the psychiatrist was known as an alienist. If alienation means insanity, then mass technology drives people mad. Its complexity is dealt with by the proliferation of specialists, each with his own private language which becomes less and less intelligible to the rest of us. Specialisation has become a disastrous caricature of the differentiation and variety which should characterise a healthy society. It leads to the fragmentation of endeavour, to the substitution of proximate and partial goals for the over-all goal of society's well-being. As E.F.Schumacher[4] says we need a technology which makes machines we can use and govern instead of machines which use and govern us. We need technology with a human face.

The excellence of a whole society depends on its components being 'just good enough'

In a truly healthy society, each man would see himself as partly responsible for the whole of it, rather than wholly responsible for a part of it. Each of us has his special interest, and seeks excellence in his chosen field. But excellence in one field can usually only be achieved at the expense of resources which are needed in neighbouring fields. A healthy society cannot be one which has unlimited resources available to it, for it will inevitably expand until their limits are in sight; and the healthier it is the sooner it will see them. Difficult though it may be, we must come to terms with the idea that the excellence of the part will nearly always have to be subordinated to the good of the whole. So a degree of individual frustration has to be built in to our vision of the healthy society: we must learn how to tolerate it rather than escape from it. But is this psychologically possible?

We have seen that a man's sense of personal identity matures as he grows up and moves into wider and wider social environments, in each of which other people recognise him anew and confirm his sense of who he is now. Self-interest constrains a man to identify himself with successively more comprehensive groups, even though his commitment to them is only partial. Enlightened self-interest impels me to act for the good of others beside myself. We begin to transcend egocentricity early in life, as we identify successively with our parents in infancy, our heroes in childhood, the social causes to which we commit ourselves in adolescence; and then with those with whom we fall in love and by whom we have children, and so our family and, in maturity the community in which we perceive ourselves as living. All such groups are in some sense supra-individual, outside and beyond our egos, though they include them too. We only regress to egocentricity when we are sick or anxious. At our healthiest, then, it is not inconceivable that we might hope to identify ourselves with the whole of society, and by this means transcend the frustrations which we feel as individuals.

Death will be something to look forward to

The healthy society will be one in which its component members will die. I think this unpalatable conclusion is inescapable. To ensure long-term adjustment to environmental change society will need continual replenishment of its reservoirs of variety, both genetically, by the recombination of patterns of genes, and culturally, by recombination of traditions and customs and ideas. This means that children must be born, which in turn means that others must die. . . .

. . . What I have tried to do in this essay is to affirm my belief that each of us has some kind of vision of a healthy society, even if it remains unuttered: all of our lives are lived in the faith or hope that our future state will be 'better' in some way than what we experience at present. I have tried to illustrate how a man's vision grows and develops as he modifies fantasy in the light of empirical experience; and conversely, how his vision provides him with a means of evaluating that experience. We mostly prefer to keep our fantasies private; but even a moderately healthy society will only be realized inasmuch as men are able to share a common vision. The healthy society is not a vision of society for other people: it must include everyone of us, those who are currently our enemies as well as our friends. Because we see it from inside, it is useless to seek to define its boundaries; and because it values our differences more highly than our similarities it does not call for quantification or measurement. It is a vision of what it might be like to be truly human. We all of us need such a vision if we are to grow towards maturity. We do well to nurture it, not in the hothouse atmosphere of privacy, but in openness of mind, exposed to the wind and rain of critical evaluation from others, sharing it with them as an affirmation of our hope in a common future.

References:
1.   B.Ward & R. Dubos, **Only One Earth,** (Penguin), 1972.
2.   E.H.Erikson, **Identity, Youth and Crisis,** (Faber), 1968.
3.   W.R.Bion, **Experiences in Groups,** (Tavistock Publications), 1961.
4.   E.F.Schumacher, **Small is Beautiful, (Blond & Briggs), 1973.**

113-4 A Healthy Society?

2.   . . . There is another reason why we have begun to feel dissatisfied with the caring procedures which take people out of the community. Traditionally, we have been able to have a vision of the healthy society as one from which all disease, disorder and discomfort have been eradicated. If things or people wouldn't fit in with our idea of what was good, we would arrange for them to go away - delinquents could go to penal colonies, tear-aways could join the army and be sent on foreign service. The mentally ill could be put away in isolated mental hospitals in the country. Evil spirits could be exorcised. But we are only now finding that there is no longer any space to tip our human or material rubbish. We are troubled by pollution problems: we are trying now to preserve our wildernesses. We are beginning to see that a healthy society is not one which gets rid of its evil, but one which can learn to live with it, to withstand, or 'stand with', it. We are thinking about recycling our waste products in the material sphere; and this is what we have to discover how to do in the social sphere, with people. So we no longer want to take people out of the community: we want to enable the community to live with them, even if it is rather uncomfortable. . . .

143 - Care in the Community

. . . I propose to discuss some aspects of what a *healthy society* might be, to give us a context in which we can consider the appropriateness of preventive policies. I do not mean a *medicated* society, like we have at present; nor a *sanitated* society, as we might have if some policy makers had their way - a society swept clean of all that the policy makers find offensive[1] - but one that is truly healthy. And by society I do not mean merely a population, which is a statistical aggregate of people who are assumed to be only randomly related to one another. A population is quite different from a community, which is made up of people who inter-relate with one another in complex and systematic ways. Because of their inter-relatedness, a true community cannot be very large - perhaps 500 - 1000 people. And a healthy society is really a community of communities - even though it may contain a minority of social isolates whom we find it hard to relate to and who find it hard to relate to us or their fellows. They, too, maintain a life-style which investigation shows to be not random, but highly systematised even if idiosyncratic.

Now here are some aspects of a healthy society which are often ignored by policy makers and planners:

1.   A healthy society does not occur in a vacuum: it can only survive in an environment. Since it is healthy, it is constantly exploring the limits of its environment, or enlarging it or altering it in some way - just like a healthy dog will do if you shut him up in a confined space. And because it is always pushing against its limits in this tentative, adventurous way, some of its most lively and vigorous members, those in their

prime, are at risk of becoming casualties. So we should not hope to do away with death, nor with physical and mental injury, disease or permanent crippling, striking down some of those who are the flower of their generation. If ever we were to eliminate such personal tragedies we would no longer have a healthy society but one which had lost its zest for life and adventure and was therefore sick.

2.   Because the healthy society constantly enlarges or alters its environment, environmental threats to survival are always changing. To defend itself against such selection pressure (whether we call it natural or artificial selection), our species, like any other, needs to contain within itself a reservoir of genetic and learned diversity or variability. So some of its members are going to be poorly adapted to the particular environment at any given moment. There will always be those whose genetic or acquired constitution renders them deviant or inadequate or biologically incompetent - in the environment current in their own time.

3.   If variability between individuals is necessary for society to remain adaptable, what about variability within each individual? Here, as in the species as a whole, we find that adaptability is inversely correlated with adaptedness. Our genetic coding writes for each of us an astonishingly open programme; but as, from intrauterine life onwards, the environment evokes this or that adaptive response, the rapid and irreversible learning or habituation, which follows steadily, diminishes our freedom of choice. We can only adapt to the environment at the cost of at least some of our adaptability. But - environments keep on changing, and the adaptation we achieve kills us in the end. Obsolescence is built in to the human structure even more firmly than it is built into our motor cars, even though it happens a little more slowly. . . .

. . . But we should try to preserve diversity of behaviour as well as of genes. Preventive policies should be so designed as not to constrict subsequent choices should people's attitudes or behaviour change. For instance, a housing policy which too readily assumes the myth of the nuclear family forecloses for several generations the possibility that many families might come to prefer to live in an extended, three- generation pattern. Houses don't fall down fast enough. Another example is that of maternity services. The Health Department's aim of encouraging all births to take place in hospital has resulted in very many family doctors, midwives, parents and grandmothers losing, and of course not passing on, their previous skill and experience in coping with home deliveries; so that any return to domiciliary midwifery, however desired and desirable, is likely to be marked by an increase in morbidity of infants and their mothers, which could have been avoided by a policy which respected diversity of behaviour and did not try to solve the problem by a 'single thrust' solution.[2]

Now I want to turn from biological considerations to some of the psychological characteristics of the healthy society. It would be one in which morale was high, both in its component communities and as a whole. High morale means that people have a sense of mutual trust, and of movement towards a better future, in common. Far too often, policy makers seem to assume that morale will be high when a community has access to plenty of material resources. This is much less than half a truth. Material security does not suffice to evoke a sense of security. So long as material resources are *just enough* for physiologically healthy survival, then morale depends on interpersonal factors such as affection and mutual respect which do not use up material resources, but, on the contrary, grow by being used: they are self-generating.[3] There is plenty of evidence, in our affluent society, that a superfluity of material provision, in the absence of mutual trust and a coherent vision for the future, lowers morale rather than raises it.

There are objective ways of estimating the morale of a community.[4] The incidence of absenteeism from place of work, of many kinds of sickness, of accidents at work or in traffic, of minor delinquency or vandalism, are all measurable. So is the incidence of excessive consumption of drugs or alcohol. In communities which have a definable purpose external to their own survival, such as industrial or military enterprises or expeditions of exploration, fluctuations in such incidence rates will alert those in charge to taking measures to improve morale by, for instance, improving the quality of leadership, or the clarity of the group's objectives, or communication channels, or the resolution of disaffection by careful attention to grievances. It is only in the civil community at large that such general measures of improving health or preventing illness are so widely ignored. All that the state's agencies seem able to do nowadays is to multiply medical or social service or punishment facilities at enormous expense to deal fragmentarily with the respective symptoms of social sickness, with the predictable result that more and more patients or clients or offenders present themselves to make use of the facilities provided. Grievances are not even recognised, let alone dealt with, until they have been translated, and usually mistranslated, into terms of money. . . .

. . . Policies designed to lessen the risks of violence are unlikely to be effective until we are persuaded to give up our unrealistic and unhealthy fantasies of a perpetually expanding material economy. In the meantime, I am personally very doubtful about the wisdom of any social policy in the caring field which costs extra money, unless the plans show in equal detail where the savings are to be made in other areas. It is time for us to discipline ourselves to seek new solutions to our difficulties within our present resources, instead of mortgaging those of future generations. . . .

Reference:
1. M. Wilson, **Health is for People,** (D.L.T.)London, 1975.
2. B.Ward & R. Dubos, **Only One earth,** (Penguin), 1972.
3. A.H.Maslow, **Motivation and Human Personality,** (Harper Row), 1970.
4. R.W.Revans, **Standards for Morale,** (O.U.P.), 1964.

200 - Issues of Prevention

A CHRISTIAN OUTLOOK ON MENTAL HEALTH

The idea that there may be a specifically Christian outlook on mental health carries with it the implication that there are others. I don't think anyone has ever produced an entirely satisfactory definition of health; and this perhaps is not unrelated to the fact that we all have different outlooks - different points of view - about it. The definition of physical health given by the leader of an expedition to Everest will probably be different from that given by a middle-aged mother of a family living in a slum district of an industrial city. And the definition of mental health given by an army commander on active service will not necessarily be exemplified by the behaviour and teaching of a Jewish carpenter of no fixed abode, who was hanged for antisocial behaviour some two thousand years ago.

I wonder if politicians have an outlook on mental health? In recent years our Government has given us two Acts - The National Health Service Act and recently the Mental Health Act - which are almost entirely concerned not with health at all, but with ill-health and its treatment. At best the outlook here seems to be defensive and conservative - to maintain what health we have without defining it in any but the most negative way as an absence of illness.

Medical men might be expected to do somewhat better; but they have, very largely, fallen victims to their own scientific training. If you ask a doctor to say if you are healthy or not, he will probably, at first, try to escape by the same route and with the same caution as the politician, and say he can find "no apparent disease". If you are not satisfied, and push him into doing some experimental work to discover more exactly whether a particular person is healthy or not, he would probably go about it like this. He would collect at random a number of people of the right sex and age, who lived under similar circumstances, and he would make sure that they had no apparent disease. He would then measure them in various ways - perhaps their height, chest expansion and weight, and the amount of haemoglobin in their blood, and the number of decayed teeth in their heads; and perhaps (if he were particularly concerned with mental health) he would measure their ability to do certain mental tests. For each measurement he would plot all his figures on a graph, like this:

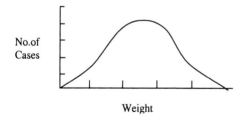

Weight

and would obtain a number of similar bow-shaped curves. By fitting an arrow to the middle of each bow, he could give you what he would call the 'normal' measurement for each variable, and he could thus give you an apparently reasonable specification for the healthy individual within the limits set by his choice of sample. His graphs would show what he would call the acceptable 'limits of normality' within which 'normal' variability might be expected. I want you to notice that when we use the expression 'normal measurement' we really mean nothing more than 'average'. For all the application of scientific method involved, we are not much further forward, because this kind of 'norm', which is really only a glorified average, has only a limited application to the particular population studied. If you had examined the heights and weights of schoolchildren aged 8, say in 1910, and had established the healthy 'norm' for that generation, you would probably find in 1962 that your 'norm' was no longer of any use, because children of age eight are nowadays both taller and heavier on average than they were then. A 'norm' ought to be a standard which we can measure things by, but a foot rule wouldn't be much good if it were a different length in different places and at different times, and this kind of measurement doesn't give us much help in a scientific definition of health. I don't know whether children of age 8 are any better off for being taller and heavier than they were in 1910, but what about the doctors' idea of the 'norm' when applied to intelligence? It is measured in just the way we have described, and so-called 'normal' intelligence is in reality nothing more than average intelligence.

But no-one who is concerned with the bringing up of children is likely to be satisfied with nothing more than average intelligence. Educationists and school medical officers spend much effort in trying to ensure that children are as intelligent as possible; far from being satisfied with the statistical 'norm' they are delighted when they find they can alter it upwards. And we could say the same about many other measurements besides intelligence. The definition of average health is only of limited value if everyone is aiming at something other than average health; and the medical outlook on health, therefore, has limitations, just as the politicians have.

Now let us consider the outlook on health which we can imagine the commander of an army to have. I use him as an example, but the leader of any group of men who have a definite job to do would have the same outlook - the leader of an expedition to the South Pole, of the manager of a mine, or any institution where people work together for a definite objective. Each of these would be very interested in the health of the employees, or troops. He would be worried by a high sickness rate, and take steps to have it reduced. He would introduce selection methods to weed out those who were unfit for the job. In fact, he would define health as being a state of physical and mental fitness *for the job that has to be done*. And here he takes a great leap forward in outlook from the politicians and the medical scientists, because he defines health in terms of an objective. He has a ready answer to the question "Healthy for what?" The Army commander has the responsibility for the health of his troops - not the doctors. The doctors are responsible for the soldiers who are ill, and they have a duty to advise the commander when he leads his men into situations which will be likely to cause casualties of any kind. But it is the commander who is responsible for health. In fact, the way that commanders think about their responsibility for health is to think in terms of morale. They would say that they don't care if the men are of low intelligence, or are undersized, or have varicose veins - provided they are contented, and provided they will do their job efficiently. And if they find that one unit is persistently showing more men on the sick list than another, they don't just send for more doctors - they sack the leader and put in a better one. They know that where you get a high sickness rate, you are likely to get a high delinquency rate, and a high rate of battle casualties, and inefficiency in general. They will say that morale is what matters, and that keeping up morale is the job of the leader. He does it in two ways. Firstly, by keeping the men as contented as possible. This means not only seeing that they get their meals, and their leave, and good billets, but also seeing that they are properly *trained*. (You don't feel contented if you know you are going to have to fight the next day with weapons you have never used before). And secondly, the leader has to instil into his men a sense of purpose. He has to make sure that the men know what their objectives are. Sometimes it is difficult to explain to soldiers just what the object of a particular campaign is, even though the leader knows himself. And in this case the men's objective has to be the leader himself: he says "Follow me", and if they trust him, they follow.

You may feel that for me to be talking about morale when I am supposed to be talking about mental health is something of a digression. But, you know, it isn't. In fact I suspect that morale and mental health are two expressions which almost mean the same thing. The army commander's interest in morale need not extend into the medical field of detailed diagnosis of the individual case. He is just as angry if one of his battalions suffers from a high rate of cholera, frost-bite, duodenal ulcers, or nervous breakdowns. He leaves it to his medical officers to sort that out. All he cares about is the actual number of men reported sick. . . .

. . . Now although I have made disparaging remarks about the politicians' and the doctors' outlook on mental health I don't mean that all politicians and doctors are in this respect un-Christian, and I have no doubt that, for instance, other members of my profession would give widely differing accounts of their outlook on this subject. So when I talk about the Christian outlook on mental health, I should make it clear that I speak, as a Christian should, from my conscience, and not necessarily as a representative of any established body of Christian opinion.

Was Jesus really interested in disease? The first thing the medical scientist has to learn is that he can't pursue the study of disease unless he becomes dispassionate and objective about it. But Jesus wasn't dispassionate, he was compassionate. I was taught as a medical student that there are three things needful for the sound scientific doctor - diagnosis, diagnosis and diagnosis. (Diagnosis, mark you of the disease, not the patient.) But I see no evidence in the Gospels that Jesus was ever interested in the diagnosis of the diseases that his patients suffered from. I suspect that he was only interested in healing, in getting rid of the disease. He never spoke, as doctors do today, of a 'beautiful case' of this or that, of a 'typical example' of a lesion. Disease is always the work of the devil and I don't think the Christian outlook on disease can be taken further than that. To bring in a personal note: I have often found, over the years, that I am reluctant to go to my clinic to see new patients. I thought for a long time that this was just an expression of my natural laziness, but was puzzled by the fact that, if it was laziness, it disappeared when I started to work. But I have recently begun to realize that one of my unconscious reasons for becoming a doctor in the first place was - because I don't like illness. I rejected this idea at first as it seemed a bit sanctimonious; but then I realised that it was no different from a man becoming a plumber because he doesn't like leaky pipes, - or a gardener, who can't stand the sight of weeds; and eventually I woke up to the probability that many doctors feel the same way. We don't like illness. Now St. Paul says *"whatsoever things are pure and lovely and of good report, think on these things"*. And I wonder whether we all wouldn't do better if we thought more about mental health and how to enhance it, and worried just a little less about mental illness and how to get rid of it. I think many Christians have an idea that their duty to love their neighbour is best illustrated in the parable of the Good Samaritan. Well, it is a good illustration, but it isn't the whole of Jesus' teaching. He didn't apparently draw a clear distinction between his healing and teaching ministry (he talks of releasing the captive, recovering of sight to the blind, and announcing the Good News to the poor - all in the same breath); and much of his teaching was in fact a fairly blistering attack on the established customs and social order of his day.

It is true that in the parable of the Good Samaritan he didn't happen to mention the inadequate policing of the Jerusalem to Jericho road, yet if we try to translate this story into twentieth century terms, to work for the better policing of such a road would certainly be part of our Christian duty.

Which is more Christian - or indeed more responsible - to give money to a famine relief organisation, or to bring pressure to bear on a government to invest capital in the underdeveloped countries where people starve? Clearly, the Christian has to look at problems from many points of view and not from one only. The scientist, in his dispassionate approach to a human problem, focuses attention on a single point of the individual before him. The size of the field which he studies under his microscope becomes smaller the greater the magnification which he uses. The Christian, being compassionate, looks at the whole man and not only at the sick or injured part of him, because health and wholeness have the same meaning. And when we pay attention to the whole man, we soon begin to realise that his wholeness is only to be found in his relationships with other people. If a human infant were brought up from birth by an animal of another species, like a wolf, he could never become a 'whole' person. He can only develop his healthy humanity in relationship with others.

The scientist doesn't like this approach. A clearly defined limit to the field of study is one of his basic requirements, and so traditionally the doctor likes to examine his patient in isolation, either behind closed doors or at least screened by his nurses from all those personal relationships which confuse and blur the boundaries of his field of operations.

The twentieth century psychiatrist is likely to find himself awkwardly placed halfway between the scientist and the Christian in this respect. The discoveries of Freud and his disciples have forced him to realise the importance for health of his patients' personal relationships, and he is finding that he must enlarge his field of study to include other people - the patient's family, or the small group he is most intimate with. But since he is trained to be scientific, he still tries to isolate his small group, or the family, which he now regards as his proper field of study - but with, I think, diminishing success. He may say, rather forlornly, that he "must draw the line somewhere", but I have a feeling that this is a sort of scientist's rearguard action. If we turn back to the gospels, we don't find any evidence that Jesus was keen on drawing lines of demarcation around particular human groups. One might have expected him, for instance, to indicate a high regard for the family, as a biological human group with a greater potential for health and wholeness than the isolated individual. But instead we find him saying: *"unless a man hate his father and his mother he cannot be my disciple"*. The word 'hate' in this context cannot simply mean the opposite of love, and I take it to imply that a mentally and spiritually healthy man should be no more dependent on his relationships with members of his family than on those with any other human being. Jesus' compassion was for the whole of humanity. As John Wren Lewis expresses it, his love was always inclusive rather than exclusive.

The realities of our human situation, however, seem to compel us to approach this Christian ideal of inclusiveness step by step; and in the first instance, when we are dealing with problems involving more than one person, we should think, not as our scientific doctor does, in terms of populations, but in terms of communities. You will recall his habit of collecting a random sample of individuals. He does his best to avoid any possibility of relationships being formed between them. In doing so he reduces their status to that of mere pieces of human mechanism. But this isn't how people really are; they talk to one another, form relationships, come to a common understanding about things; in fact, they live in communities.

Now I want to consider with you the Christian view of 'normality'. You remember that the medical scientist took as his norm what was really only a glorified average. Let me read you what Bishop Stephen Neill says about it:

> *"The word 'normal' has been so abused in common speech that it has become almost impossible any longer to use it in its correct sense. It is constantly used in the sense of "average". We do know fairly well what average humanity is; looking at our fellow human beings, we can perhaps echo the cynical remark of Macbeth to his hired murderers, "Ay, in the catalogue ye go for men". But this is not what 'normal' means. It is the adjective of the noun 'norm', and 'norm' means a standard, a criterion, that against which something else can be measured and judged. The norm of human nature should be human nature in its highest and fullest manifestation. . . . What we are looking for is human nature that, under favourable conditions, has attained to full and free development in every aspect of its being; and, since human nature is to be understood not statically but in terms of action, that has been able unhampered to act creatively over such a period as is required for the attainment of full human maturity. . . .*
> *. . . The Christian answer is plain and simple. Human nature has once been seen in its fulness - in Jesus of Nazareth. In Him is seen the answer to the profoundest questions that every man inevitably asks about himself. This is the way the machine ought to work. This is what it looks like when it is working properly. Here it is possible to see the kind of work which human nature was intended to accomplish."[1]*

It strikes me that *this* concept of the norm is exactly what we need in the mental health field. It gives us not only a standard against which we can measure the mental health of human beings, but also it gives us an objective towards which we can work in our efforts to improve it. In fact, it brings back into our picture the sense of positive purpose which I regard as so vital to a true concept of mental health, which was so clearly lacking in the conservative, defensive and cautious outlook which we ascribed to the politician and scientist.

The viewpoint of the soldier, or man of action, seems to me to be much more closely allied to that of the Christian precisely because he is prepared to state his objective. He knows what he wants to be healthy for. His trouble is, of course, that he is likely to achieve his objective in time. He runs a risk of winning his war, and when that happens the morale of his men is likely to fall to pieces. The Christian's objective, however he defines it, is something which cannot be achieved in the dimension of time as we know it, but only in eternity - whether we think of this as infinitely distant time, or as a different dimension which embraces the present as well.

Jesus is not recorded as having used the word 'morale', but I suggest that this is in fact what he was talking about for much of his recorded ministry; mutual understanding and support between all men in pursuit of a common goal. A readiness to act unselfishly - in pursuit of the common goal. The sense of purpose is the over-riding thing: *"If thine eye cause thee to stumble, cast it out". "Give to everyone that asketh thee, and of him that taketh away thy goods, ask them not again".* Nothing must stand in the way of the common purpose. *"Love your enemies"* - you are all soldiers in one army, share and share alike, and don't quarrel, but keep your eye on the objective. The aim of the good commander is so to train his men that they act 'as one' in pursuit of their objective. So Jesus prays *"that they may all be one... I in them and them in me that they may be perfected into one".* And, characteristically, Jesus enabled his disciples to identify him with the objective, so that if they were in doubt about the way ahead, they could simply obey his injunction *"Follow me"*.

Attention to the morale of the group does not mean neglect of the individual's problems. Jesus' care for the individual has always been apparent, and so is that of all the best leaders. In fact, the individual's illness is likely to be ascertained earlier, and more competently dealt with, in communities where morale is good. One of the horrifying symptoms of the poor morale of our society is the fact that old ladies can die of starvation and neglect, alone in their houses, even in large cities where all the apparatus of the welfare state and modern medical science is immediately accessible. These services rely on - of all people - the *milkman* to tell them when old people living alone are needing help. But some of them don't need to buy milk every day.

Doctors are always saying to the friends and relatives of patients "Why didn't you call me in sooner?" The chances of a full recovery are diminished because treatment wasn't started soon enough. Where morale is good, those who fall sick come to notice sooner. Good morale means that there are effective relationships between members of the community; and the best definition of a human relationship that I know is that it is a *continuing channel of communication* between people.

I cannot over-emphasize that the most important aspect of the Christian outlook on mental health as I see it is this one of the sense of purpose. Every day in the mental hospital where I work we are faced with the problem of the old lady suffering from so-called 'senile dementia'. Old age has become a major social problem, and people say "what can we do for the elderly?". A question which is just as important - perhaps more so - for mental health is to ask "what can the elderly do for the community?" The failure of the old person's sense of purpose, their feeling of uselessness, is often the major cause of their breaking down, and if, as can sometimes happen, the sense of purpose can be restored, a remarkable improvement in their health - physically and mentally - will occur. I do not for a moment suggest that it is an easy matter to restore a sense of purpose to someone who has lost it, or for that matter to find an aim in life for someone who never had one. Every Christian will have developed his own, and the more convinced he is of his own way ahead, the more convincing will he be to those who are in contact with him, and the more effective he will be as an agent of healing. Note that I say the "way ahead". There is nothing static about mental health. It is always either improving or falling back.

Sometimes people who see the senile patients in our hospital say "Why not put them to sleep? They have nothing to live for. They are a burden to themselves and everyone else". I don't know a really convincing, practical, worldly answer to this question. For the world's purposes the elderly sick are no doubt a liability. I imagine they always have been, in view of the fact that Moses was put to the trouble of stating as one of the natural laws of the healthy community that every man should *"honour his father and his mother"*. But the world's purposes are capable of being improved. For all my tilting at the scientific outlook I am well aware that scientific method is another of God's gifts, and that it has brought about an immense increase in our medical knowledge and is still doing so; and it may well be that new discoveries will be made that will prevent the mental deterioration which is so common in old age. In fact, the present failure of some of us to see any point in the lives of the elderly sick, as with the severely subnormal child, is a reflection of our own ignorance and nothing more. We seldom want to take the responsibility for things we are ignorant about, but in the eyes of God as well as in the eyes of man 'ignorance of the law is no excuse', and I think that the Christian's outlook on mental health must include an acceptance - a suffering - of some measure of guilt for our failure to maintain it. Those who talk of euthanasia are running away from a problem which they might do well to face with patience and accept as a challenge.

You may be surprised that I have used the word love so little in this lecture, in view of its title. So often the word is used in a sloppy and sentimental sense, even by those who are not addicts of modern 'pop' songs, that it seems to be a cloak for woolly thinking. As people say, love is blind. But I don't think Christian love should be blind. Before two young people settle down in marriage to discover what love really means, we say they have to come to an understanding, and it is as a contribution to our understanding, that this lecture is offered. Nevertheless, if our concern with the matter is not rested and grounded in love, then all that I have said will be as sounding brass or a clanging cymbal.

Reference:
1.   S. Neill, **A Genuinely Human Existence,** (Constable), 1969.

33 - The Christian Outlook on Mental Health

A THERAPEUTIC COMMUNITY APPROACH

... There is no standard institution, or type of institution, which I could describe for you as being truly therapeutic. For me, the therapeutic community is a concept, a way of thinking about the task of enabling people to become more healthy. In my eyes it is a vision, an orientation towards a goal, a direction to travel in. It gives me a criterion by which I can evaluate the various communities and institutions I encounter - all of which fall pathetically short of what I would like to see. In fact, I prefer to think in terms of a therapeutic community *approach* to the problems we encounter in community homes or hospitals, rather than in terms of a particular category of institution.

What are some of the characteristics of such an approach? You will recall that the original psychoanalysts made use of three tools, all of which were at the time totally novel. Firstly, there was what was called *free association.* The patient was invited to say whatever came into his head, however irrelevant or outrageous it might seem to be. Think what a scandalous innovation this must have seemed to doctors at that time, who expected the patient to live up to this label and be entirely passive, doing and saying nothing of his own initiative, and only obeying the doctor's instructions or answering his questions.

The second tool of the analyst was his recognition of *unconscious mental mechanisms,* such as repression, displacement and projection - the way the mind works when we are not paying attention to it - all the tricks and twists which it uses to mould the raw material of experience into something it finds manageable. I don't need to emphasise the novelty of this idea - that active and purposeful (if irrational) work was being done by the mind even when a man was behaving 'absent-mindedly' - for instance when he was dreaming. Who is the dreamer who dreams my dreams? Am I responsible for him? Will I be answerable for him on the day of judgement? The challenge to a man's sense of personal responsibility, and personal identity, which Freud faced us with is one which we are still loth to face up to.

And thirdly, the psychoanalyst made use of what he called the analysis of the *transference,* the study of the way in which a client's relationship with his therapist was coloured by (or distorted by) his relationships with other people in his past such as his parents; his tendency to transfer to the therapist attitudes and feelings which properly belonged to others. The novelty here lay in the implication that the therapist, traditionally regarded as a detached observer of his patient. was now seen as a participant in the process he was examining. It is this more than anything which has made the 'pure' scientist so reluctant to accord scientific status to psychoanalysis and its derivatives.

These were the three main tools which the early analysts developed. What was not widely realised at first was that in acknowledging the importance of the transference, they were seriously undermining the rationale of the centuries-old medical custom of dealing with the single patient in a private place, consulting room or whatever, in isolation from his social context. For if, as they knew the client-therapist relationship was so much affected by the client's past relationships would this not also be true of his other current relationships - with his wife or his superior at work, and so on? Gradually therefore therapists began to use psychiatric social workers, to study the client's current relationships in the world outside the consulting room, and then, when the psychotherapist became an acceptable worker in hospital, he began to use group therapy, since a group of patients who were living together in a ward could itself constitute a sample of the client's current relationships. And in time, the logic of the situation led on to the idea of the therapeutic community, in which all the members, staff of all grades and all the patients, were seen as providing an interweaving pattern of relationships all of which were potentially relevant to the working out of the client's problem.

I have used this historical approach in order to point out that the three basic tools of the psychoanalyst are still the basic tools of the therapeutic community practitioner, suitably developed. Free association has been extended into the *creation of a permissive atmosphere,* in which people can not only say what comes into their heads, but (within limits) can even do what they feel like doing - they can 'act out', as we say. Since the word 'permissive' has been so debased by popular misrepresentation, I hasten to say that a truly permissive atmosphere only exists when there is someone present to do the permitting, and who is therefore able also to deny permission if he chooses. Permissiveness is not to be equated with anarchy - even though at times it may look not dissimilar.

The recognition of *unconscious mechanisms,* the second tool of the analyst, is no longer only concerned with intrapsychic psychopathology, but is enriched by recognition of the cultural determinants of behaviour of which we are so often unconscious - what's done and not done in a particular society or group. The analysis of social structure, the work of the sociologist and the anthropologist, has been added to the analysis of psychopathology.

And thirdly, analysis of the *transference* has been broadened to include study of all the interpersonal relationships which clients make with one another and with staff of all different degrees of therapeutic ability and experience.

Each shift of perspective, from the one-to-one situation to group therapy, and thence to the therapeutic community, has revealed new insights which are not only relevant to the situation in which they emerge but can be used retrospectively to enlarge our understanding of the preceding stages. With group therapy, for instance, emerged the realisation that even disturbed people, if they are truly members of a group, *"collectively constitute the very norm from which, individually, they deviate"*. . . . *"The group, as it proceeds, finds more and more common ground, and less and less contradiction between individuality and community. The sound part of individuality (of character) is firmly rooted in the group and wholly approved by it."*[1] This insight is reinforced in the therapeutic community, where it becomes even plainer that the forces which foster the health of the individual reside within the community even though each individual within it - staff and patients alike - shows symptoms of sub-optimal health in greater or lesser degree. Refracted back to the one-to-one situation, we can see how this insight shows up as illusory the traditional medical man's assumption that the client is sick and the therapist healthy. In fact, both are partly sick and partly healthy; and the therapeutic relationship is to be seen as a *joint* effort to transcend the separate badness of each of the two, rather than as an attempt by the healthy one to relieve the other of his load of evil. In the perspective of the therapeutic community, we are all in it together, therapist and client alike, all helping to remove the beams and motes from one another's eyes.

Foulkes says that as a group progresses, it finds *"less and less contradiction between individuality and community"*. This insight too is strengthened in the therapeutic community, which, at its best, is about as far from a conformist society as we can hope to get. It enables us to see, retrospectively, how inadequate was the early analyst's belief that the super-ego, representing the demands of society as expressed in the moral values of the parents, was always to be seen as the enemy of the individual's ego. Certainly, the suffering individual often sees society as his enemy, as denying him his individuality, and justifiably so. But this does not justify the therapist in entering into a collusive and alienating agreement with him. It demands of the therapist a recognition that he needs to maintain a therapeutic relationship with society as well as with the individual. In the truly therapeutic community, the therapist sees the community as his patient, and it is only in this context that his concern for the individual finds its proper expression. This is not such a paradox as it sounds when we recognise that an individual is not truly healthy if he is well-adjusted to an unhealthy society.

In the two-person situation, the therapist could choose his own moment to intervene and interpret what the client was expressing or seemed to be expressing. In the small group, the therapist found that he had to get used to allowing other members to speak before him, sometimes taking the words out of his mouth, or even making the same point as he wanted to with greater force or clarity than he could have; and on the other hand, often saying things which he would have preferred to have left unsaid. So in the group, the therapist (who never had any doubts about his power to control the interview with one person) found himself much less in control. In the community, the larger group situation, the therapist finds himself even more powerless to control the course of events. But here is the remarkable thing: he begins to see that it is precisely when the group makes him feel most powerless and useless, when he is no longer able or willing to act as the strong, god-like father-figure on whom everyone depends, that the group itself begins to discover its own resources for being strong and dependable.

So it is that, in a therapeutic community, those who hold official or profession-al authority seem to lean over backwards in their efforts to avoid using it - and run the risk of being branded as administratively incompetent by those who don't understand why they act in this way. Here lies the reason why some social psychiatrists (like myself) are becoming increasingly nervous of the one-to-one situation as an appropriate medium for psychotherapy or counselling: because in that situation it is so very difficult for the problem of the therapist's authority to be constructively analysed or turned to therapeutic account. From the social perspective, the one-to-one situation - which is as familiar in pastoral and spiritual counselling as it is in medicine - begins to look increasingly like one person, the powerful and authoritative one, manipulating another who is too weak to resist, in a way that is essentially a denial of the other's humanity and potential for healthy independence. Now, when I find myself engaged in an encounter with only one other person, I try to see myself as involved in a two-person *group.* I remind myself that biologically speaking, the group of only two suggests either a mother-infant situation or a courting situation. So one can anticipate transference manifestations appropriate to one or other of these, whether they are relevant to the client's problem or not. I console myself with the thought that biologically, neither of them last for more than a few months without the intrusion or emergence of a 'third person'. A therapeutic situation in which there is no third person involved is always dangerous, and needs to be kept as brief as possible.

So far, what I have said may help you to understand some of the more peculiar features of therapeutic communities: their lack of a clear cut authority structure, the difficulty one often has in deciding who are staff members and who are not, the general untidiness and vagueness of the institution. Here is another feature which may strike: most such communities seem very unconvincing in the way they select, or fail to select, particular diagnostic categories for particular kinds of treatment. It is common to hear criticisms that there are some patients or clients in the establishment for whom the kind of treatment offered seems quite unsuitable. I often used to feel this myself. So I want to suggest that this whole therapeutic community approach (and retrospectively I would say that this applies to so-called individual psychotherapy too) is really not primarily concerned with making a detailed diagnosis of the person's *illness* (or maladjustment or delinquency) and then trying to get rid of it or inhibit it; but is aimed at finding out what kind of a *person* it is who has this difficulty, and then trying to foster his capacity for healthy living - which means healthy-living-in-community. This distinction is one which many people find hard to grasp. Doctors and indeed our whole western society has allowed itself to become indoctrinated with the idea that, faced with a difficult situation, the right procedure is to delineate and define the 'problem' and then to solve it. We have failed to develop the correlative idea that a difficult situation is often one which may solve itself if only we make or keep ourselves (and one another) strong enough to live through it and, hopefully, learn from it. In dealing with human problems, the latter alternative is often preferable. Life itself - growing up, having babies, growing old - involves many difficulties. But though adolescence, maternity and senescence may be difficult, it isn't necessarily wise to label them as problems to be solved. If we can strengthen people who are going to face critical periods in their lives, they may not only live through them but gain in maturity and wisdom as a result.

The therapeutic community approach, then, is not a specific way of treating any particular disorder or group of disorders. What it does is to offer anyone, whatever his disorder, whether he thinks he is ill or healthy, a chance to learn from others a little more than he knew already of the facts of life, of what it is to be truly human, of what it might be to be truly healthy. And it is my belief that this learning happens to nearly everyone who lives in a therapeutic community, a little to some, a lot to others; unwelcomed by some, welcomed by others, and that this quite generalised, nonspecific learning is strengthening, and helps some to bear their illness or disorder better, while others find it no longer matters to them - that they no longer regard themselves as ill.

There is one other feature of the good therapeutic community to which I must draw your attention. The effective therapist - indeed the effective member of such a community - is one who pays attention primarily to the good of the whole community, the whole group; and only in that context will he pay secondary attention to particular bits of it - subgroups or individuals. This idea conflicts with the traditional tendency of doctors (and the rest of us) to be fascinated and obsessed just by the bit of evil in front of our eyes. Evil - the serpent - has always had this capacity for fascination. But it narrows our span of attention, so that we fail to see what is happening all around us. The devil rejoices when he can fragment wholes by persuading us to look at partial bits in isolation from their proper contexts. In a truly therapeutic community, each man would feel himself to be partly responsible for the whole of it, instead of feeling wholly responsible for just one bit of it, as is the case in most of our institutions. This is one reason why it is extremely difficult to keep a community even reasonably therapeutic when it gets too large. A maximum of about ninety people can meet for an hour in free discussion and feel they are part of one community, if they have a large enough room to meet in. About 500 can grow to recognise one another and to hear what one man says if he shouts loudly enough and provided they stay together for long enough. Above this number, personal recognition and the mutual fostering of healthy personality growth rapidly becomes less and less possible, humanly speaking.

Against this background, can we pick out some points which may be relevant to your task as chaplains? I think the first thing to say is that you will only be able to understand what is happening in a therapeutic community, and only be of service to it and to the people in it, if you are a member of it in good standing. This doesn't mean that you have to be there full-time, but I think it does mean that you have to be present fairly regularly at meetings when the whole community is present. (In practice, unless there are regular meetings when everyone, staff and clients, can be present and free to speak then there is not what I would call a therapeutic community.) Wherever you sit or whoever you know among those present, you need to constantly remind yourself that, as chaplain, your allegiance is to all the people in the community as a whole, rather than to any particular group - for instance staff or clients. It is only when you have established this as the context in which you function that you can afford to establish relationships with individuals or sub-groups without running the risk of splitting the community.

Next, I think you will only be of help to the community if you can see yourself as someone who needs the help of others in order to become more healthy, just as other members do. It is essentially a learning situation for you and them, rather than a situation in which you are qualified to teach while they are not. We doctors and parsons are both prone to believe that we have something to give others and are prone to discount the possibility that it may be the other person who has something to give us - that at a particular moment we need him more than he needs us. It is a difficult lesson to learn because - apart from our professional pride - people are continually appealing to us for individual help. This may flatter our vanity but it is the oldest devil's trick in the world to split a whole into fragments: the child in every man always tends to 'play one off against the other' in his dealings with those who appear to have some authority over him.

Perhaps the best help you can be to those who consult you individually is always to question - at least silently, but often aloud - why the problem couldn't be dealt with by the group or community of which they are members. This carries two implications if asked aloud: (a) that their peer group would probably answer their request more adequately than you could; and (b) that you would only feel justified in dealing with it if you felt that your intervention had been sanctioned by the whole group. I suppose you will be least likely to think of this when you are asked a religious or spiritual question - but it is still a good thing to remember.

And now to my final point. Inasmuch as in most caring communities there is a tendency for staff to stay longer than patients or clients, it is probably the staff to whom you should pay the closer attention. Any contribution you may make to improving their morale will make them more helpful to clients. But if you spend time with clients and ignore staff morale, they may, inadvertently or otherwise, find themselves working at cross-purposes to you. This bears upon the problem of leadership. In this kind of community, the function of leadership should not be exercised by any one person ex officio. Official authority - symbolised by staff uniforms or dog collars - is nothing but a stumbling block. It gives both the one who wields it and those who acknowledge it an opportunity to evade the realities of truly personal encounter with one another, uncomfortable as these often are. What *should* happen is that leadership authority - authorisation - is spontaneously accorded by the community to whoever at the moment seems to attract it to move in a convincing direction; and that authorisation is withdrawn, equally spontaneously, the moment the leader's attractiveness wanes. But human nature being what it is, it is not surprising that professionals tend to be thrust into leadership situations frequently, just as adults in a family are by children. Certainly parents and professionals have a responsibility for refusing to accept the role at times, so that others may learn to accept responsibility. But nevertheless the morale of the professional and the adult is critical for the health of the whole just because children, or clients or patients do 'look to them for a lead'. So if you want to help the children or clients or patients in an institution, *take care of the staff.*

Reference:
1.   S.H.Foulkes, **Introduction to Group Analytic Psychotherapy**, (Heinemann), 1948, pp29 and 30.

139-4 Therapeutic Communities

HEALTH IN COMMUNITY

Barbara Ward and Rene Dubos, (1972) in their book so delightfully subtitled *"The Care and Maintenance of a Small Planet",* draw attention to the dangers of seeking what they term 'single thrust' solutions to complex ecological problems; and I will not be so rash as to suggest that the therapeutic community (if we can agree about what that term means) is *the* prescription for Health Service sickness (if we could ever agree about what sort of an entity the Health Service is and what sort of sicknesses it suffers from). To take the last point first: the health service, however we define it, has arisen as a *reaction* to certain kinds of discomfort felt by the body politic. In fact, a health service - or at least the kind of health service we have - is itself a *symptom* of social disease rather than the cure for it. And as we know, it is dangerous to treat symptoms if in doing so you make diagnosis more difficult. Maybe, in any case, it is time for the health service we have at present to die. Much of it arose as a reaction to the presence in the community of acute disease such as infection, which killed off many people before middle age. Much of it arose as a reaction against disease caused by material or physical deprivation resulting from poverty. Much of it was based on the assumption that medical paternalism would find the answer to the major health problems of society as it was at the time when the service was founded. Nowadays, thirty years later, acute killing diseases of the young, and poverty, are no longer major problems in this country; while medical paternalism is of only historic and nostalgic significance - just about as much of a nuisance and problem as redundant churches are. Dr Finlay's Casebook takes its place alongside the Forsyte Saga: entertaining but largely irrelevant to the problems of today. So perhaps we should let the health service structure which we have now disappear, like the baby's milk teeth. It has outgrown its usefulness. And let a more mature service emerge to replace it, equipped with some strength to bite on the different and harder problems we now have to tackle.

Whether the therapeutic community is a concept of value to such a new, emerging health service is something for us to explore.

First we must clarify what I think is a fundamental confusion. *In my view the therapeutic community is not a way of treating disease.* By contrast surgery, for instance, does treat diseases: the surgeon can cure someone without even knowing his name. But the therapeutic community is a way of treating suffering *people*. Treating disease is an inhibiting or attacking activity; treating people is a nurturing, fostering, caring activity. There is no evidence that the therapeutic community is an effective way of treating disease, and (unlike surgery or other disease-attacking procedures) recovery rates from illness are a mistaken way of trying to assess its value - unless you can prove that it actually makes people more ill. What the therapeutic community sets out to do is to enable people to be better: better people, more fully human people, than they were before. Sometimes this will mean that they cease to complain of their symptoms, sometimes they won't; sometimes they will respond with enthusiasm to the challenge such an approach offers them, sometimes they will resist it. But whether they like it or not, if they don't run away, they will almost certainly learn something about themselves and about what it means to be human, and will be wiser, if not happier, as a result. I do not know of any statistically valid method of measuring how human or how wise a person is. We can't prove that it would be a good model for any part of a health service in an objective way: we have to make value judgements about whether to encourage this kind of approach or not.

The kind of therapeutic community of which I know most is that developed by psychiatrists. But it isn't the only kind. Kindred approaches have been made in the educational field by non-medical people of whom A. Aichhom, A.S.Neil, Geo Lyward, David Wills are representative names.[1] Such school communities are not dependent on psychiatrists either for inspiration or for the development of their social structure: like other people, they only consult psychiatrists when they can't avoid doing so. But there are common factors. Both believe in the idea that responsibility for what happens in the institution is shared by all members, staff and clients alike. This is expressed and explored in regular, face-to-face meetings of the whole community, where everyone, of whatever apparent status is able to say what he thinks or feels and is listened to seriously. Face-to-face contact imposes a limit to the size of the community in both cases. In practice, this limit seems to be about 90 people but most communities are smaller. This may result from the fact that both kinds of institution try to meet the needs of people who have difficulty in communicating with one another - either emotionally ill people, or deprived children. It can be argued that up to about 500 people can meet regularly face-to-face and recognise one another as persons, and thus foster one another's health and humanness, but perhaps it is only reasonably healthy people who can cope with this number. It is certainly almost impossible to avoid doing damage to person-hood in institutions of more than 500.

Another factor common to both is that there is a wide status distance between the members: between highly paid psychiatrists and others in the one situation, and between mature adults and children in the other. It is an interesting paradox that it is in places where the status distance is so pronounced that the attempt to establish shared responsibility should have been made. Theoretically, one might expect it to be easier to share responsibility when status distance was minimal. Perhaps this happens in fact, but if so such communities do not recognise themselves as therapeutic: perhaps they see themselves as just healthy. (This raises the possibility that a healthy community might be a better model for the health service than a therapeutic community, if only we could find one.)

As I have indicated, in the therapeutic community it is the suffering person who is at the focus of attention rather than the disability from which he suffers. The kind of specialisation we have at present, in medicine, is almost entirely designed to suit the convenience of the disease-attackers rather than the sufferers; and in such a community specialisation of this kind is a hindrance more than a help. This means that staff members who have special or professional training find themselves afflicted by a blurring of their specialist roles and often indeed by a degree of identity confusion. This is no bad thing because it makes it easier for staff to see themselves as not so very much healthier than their patients, thus lessening the status-distance problem.

All the members are recognised to have a potential therapeutic value for one another. This contrasts with most hospitals, for instance, in which staff are regarded as the purveyors of health, and quite distinct from patients who are sick. So (apart from the identity confusion problem) staff have to recognise that they, as well as the patients, are partly well and partly ill, and that they can learn about health from one another. The therapeutic community has been well described as a 'living-learning arena', for all its members.

Since the community staff make no claim to be the exclusive purveyors of health, they deny themselves any paternalistic or ex officio right to authority. The basis on which authority can be exercised effectively is when the community by consensus authorises one or another person to act. This means that authority is sapiential rather than official, and its location is always problematic, since the consensus varies from day to day.

Implicit in what I have been saying are two basic assumptions which underlie the therapeutic community approach. They are, first, that the free-est possible communication between members makes for the health of all of them - so they spend a great deal of time in trying to elucidate covert or unexpressed disagreements or hostilities between members; and second, they believe that the health of the whole community is fundamental to the health of each member of it - you aren't healthy if you are badly adjusted to your community: you aren't healthy either if you are well adjusted to an unhealthy community - so they spend much time in discouraging any tendency for the community to split into factions or sub-groups.

I am trying to describe the therapeutic community concept in terms which may make it useful as a yardstick to evaluate other kinds of health service social structure. I haven't dwelt on its shortcomings, though several of them will be clear enough. It is not a good approach where specialised disease-attacking is required; and its lack of clarity of role-definition might be dangerous in an operating theatre, for instance. It demands a capacity for learning, for putting professional and other prejudices and established beliefs at risk of being changed, which scare many people who haven't experienced this kind of challenge. It does not, and I believe can not, produce statistical evidence of its value.

Now let us look at its somewhat peculiar way of managing its objectives. The objective towards which the therapeutic community is directed is the health of the individual in his social context; and as we have seen, this implies working towards the health of the whole community. Now this objective is infinitely distant, both in time and in the number of people concerned. In practice it is unattainable.

But it means that whenever nearer, attainable objectives are set up, they are seen as provisional, means rather than ends, and can be superceded by slightly more distant goals before they are reached. Faced with a problem in reaching a proximate goal, the therapeutic community is more concerned to understand it than to solve it - and one thing which justifies faith in this approach is the frequency with which this attempt to understand a situation is followed, unpredictably and 'miraculously' by disappearance of the problem. It seems that the method removes problems by changing perspective on them rather than by solving them in a linear, cause-and-effect way. Clearly the method is not likely to be successful in stopping bleeding from a gastric ulcer or a cut throat. But it does suggest that, in all health service settings, one should always judge one's activities from several different perspectives - for example, by considering their significance not only in the short term, but also in the middle term and in the long term. Suffering in other people always raises anxiety in those who try to care for them; and this means that the carers feel compelled to take immediate action, too often without regard for long-term consequences. The specialised attack on disease requires the operator to wear blinkers - to 'keep his mind on the job'. But the specialist, and the rest of us, must learn to take off our blinkers whenever we have a spare moment, and think about the long-term meaning of what we are doing. Authoritarian or paternalistic leadership is valuable in emergency and short-term activities, no doubt. It is when we look at the long-term significance of what we are doing to people that it is such a disadvantage.

Many of the implications of the therapeutic community idea for future health service planning (or daydreaming) will have already occurred to you and I will only (have time to) make one or two observations. Such methods seem to me to be of value in all situations where one is dealing with people who are capable of being agents in their own recovery, rather than wholly 'patients'. This last word implies passivity and complete dependence on others, and strictly applies only to the acutely ill, the comatose and the anaesthetised. As soon as a patient in hospital is fit to put on his dressing gown and get out of bed for more than a few minutes, he could benefit from a therapeutic community regime. All staff organisations other than those needed for operating theatres or intensive care procedures could benefit from the concept, and so could all the bureaucratic back-up organisations. In all these situations, the need to promote the human-ness of the participants is fundamental. This implies that there should be a limit to their size: hospitals should be no larger than 250 to 500 places, and - an even more difficult requirement to meet at present - there should be facilities for all the staff and all patients who are not in bed to meet regularly face-to-face. This should include night staff, which makes it more difficult still. Economies of scale should never take priority over the needs of health promotion. I suspect, though of course I can't produce evidence, that existing hospitals of more than 500 beds do more damage to the health of patients and staff by depersonalising them, than they do good by the eradication of disease. (Unless they are only half-full!)

While it is justifiable in certain diagnostic and disease-treatment facilities to give priority in design to the convenience of the specialists who will work in them, this does not apply to hospitals as a whole, which should be primarily designed to provide the kind of spaces needed for staff and patients to live and learn together.

Of course, a health service has to think in terms of millions of people. Even if we use the therapeutic community model for some of the grass-roots organisations which deal directly with sick people, some organisational situations must necessarily take account of large numbers. When dealing with any organisation involving more than 1000 people, we must take trouble to diminish the harm it will inevitably do by depersonalising those involved. This means that every one must be given a chance to make his voice heard, as well as having a job specification or role-specification. And we must keep the executive channels distinct from the information-collecting channels in large organisations. 'Whenever power and information flow in the same channel, information becomes distorted'. At present, we have sophisticated and fairly well understood executive channels, but expect them to deal with the two-way communication traffic. So far, the only distinct information-collecting body is the newly created CHC. Compare this with the central nervous system, where not only are sensory and motor pathways kept quite distinct, but the sensory paths are much more complex than the motor paths, not less. No one likes the idea of authoritarian hierarchies: the CNS has two hierarchies, but neither is authoritarian. There is no elite among nerve cells, each of them being functionally equivalent to every other one. The CNS is not relevant in these respects as a model for therapeutic communities as these are always small. But it is noteworthy that such communities do ensure that each member has a chance to make his voice heard - even if sometimes their executive efficiency is less good than in more traditional organisations.

Finally, let me pose the question, what do we want to be healthy *for?* If there were a national emergency such as the threat of attack from outside the country, I have little doubt that almost all the statistics of health would show a dramatic improvement. Perhaps the nation's foreign policy - or lack of it - has more to do with the national health than we realise. But when, as now, we have no clear-cut idea of what we want to be healthy for, we seem to fall into idolatry, and see health as an end in itself, instead of as a means of living more fully and more adventurously. So we seek for a comfortable security of health, and multiply protective measures to preserve the status quo - wanting more doctors, more nurses, more social workers, more hospital buildings, more regulations. But you needn't erect a concrete bridge to cross a stream if a stepping stone will do; and if as a nation we felt we were actually going somewhere, if we could find a purpose worth being healthy for, we would be healthier with far less material expenditure.

The therapeutic community aims to make people better than they were before. It is not merely concerned with *re*habilitation or *re*socialisation - words which indicate a mere getting your patient back to the point at which he became a patient. Although they might not express it in such language, I believe most of its practitioners are concerned to help the emergence of *newness of life* - that unpredictable, adventurous vitality which for most of us, in our complacency, is only a latent potential - unrecognised and unexpressed.

In this sense the therapeutic community concept is dangerous, potentially explosive and revolutionary, like pre-Constantine Christianity. I don't know where or when it will be embodied, when it will fall on good soil, when the vision will be effectively uttered (outered) in practice, but the seeds are being scattered.

Meantime, at the national level, perhaps we should concern ourselves with foreign policy - what do we want to be healthy for? How can our country be of service to the rest of the world? And let the dead bury their dead as far as a national health service is concerned. And at the local level, let us look afresh at all our caring institutions to see how they enhance our humanity and adventurousness, instead of trying to provide for those who suffer nothing better than a stultifying and depersonalising cocoon of security.

Reference:
1.   P. Righton , see Journal of the Association of Workers for Maladjusted Children, 3.1, Spring 1975.
139-5 - Is the Therapeutic Community the Prescription for Health Service Sickness?

COMMUNICATION
The following article arose in response to the 'Thoughts on the Possibility of Community'
by Brian Carpendale.[5]

Those familiar with Teilhard's thought will know his ideas about the parts played by cerebralisation and socialisation as life ascends the evolutionary tree. In *The Future of Man* Teilhard lets his imagination soar:

> *"This idea of the planetary totalisation of human consciousness ... may at first sight seem fantastic: but does it not exactly correspond to the facts? ... However mad it may seem, the fact remains that great modern biologists ... are beginning to talk of mankind, and to predict its future, as though they were dealing (all things being equal) with a brain of brains."[1]*

This suggests that we should take a careful look at the central nervous system (brain and spinal cord) of the higher mammals to see what advice nature can offer us about the evolution of human social organisms, or communities. A community consists of individuals each of whom not only lives, but also *communicates.* So the nervous system may in some ways be a more useful model for community than the body as a whole - of which many component cells do not have an essentially communicating function.

A nerve cell (neuron) consists of a cell body with long fibres extending from it. All neurons perform essentially the same action, the transmission of impulses from one end of the cell to the other. The impulses are of the same sort in all neurons. It is not the separate neurons, but their arrangements and connections that determine different outcomes. Each neuron has its cell body in or very near the spinal cord or brain, and of its fibres (one usually longer and less branched than the other) one extends up or into the spinal cord or brain and the other down or outward to the rest of the body.

All neurons are so arranged that they function either as elements of the sensory system or the motor system of the CNS. Although in the laboratory a stimulus applied anywhere along the fibres of a neuron will cause an impulse to spread in both directions, the anatomical arrangement is such that in practice each fibre is stimulated at one end, and the impulse travels in one direction only. The motor system, consisting entirely of 'efferent' nerves, contains pathways from brain to periphery which consist of only two neurons. Though complex, it is relatively simple and distinct in structure compared with the sensory system, which consists only of 'afferent' nerves bringing messages from periphery to the centre. The sensory pathways consist of at least three neurons between periphery and brain, and the 'exchanges', nuclei where one cell contacts another, are quite differently arranged.[2]

The fact that the motor system, the 'final common path' for outgoing messages to muscles and other organs, has stayed relatively distinct and simple during vertebrate evolution suggests that the increasing size and complexity of the brain has been necessary to cope with increasingly complex *information-processing* (especially from distance-receptors dealing with smell, sight and sound) rather than motor activity. So perhaps we may allow ourselves to simplify terminology and to regard the brain as predominantly part of the sensory, rather than the motor system. (At the community level, this is analogous to saying that Parliament as a whole is part of the community's information-processing system; and that it is only the government (Premier and cabinet) which is part of the executive - and which would exist in some form even if there were no Parliament).

(Although afferent and efferent pathways are structurally distinct, they communicate at all levels. The simple 'reflex arc', in theory consisting of one afferent and one efferent neuron, is in the healthy organism always under higher control through communicating loops of neurons. Reflex activity may appear relatively autonomous, but its activity is always predictable and never innovative.)

In applying this model to the study of human community, we must recognise that, unlike nerve cells, each human individual is capable of both sensory and motor functions, and to be fully human must be enabled to exercise both. But I suggest that *it is important to distinguish which of the two an individual is exercising in any particular social context.* In industrial organisation, the executive system has historically had priority of attention. We have been more concerned with *how* to do things than we have been with *why* we do them, or whether they are worth doing, or worth doing now as opposed to later. But we are discovering, in all sorts of fields, that an executive system, however efficient in itself, is likely to have crude, inappropriate or even dangerous results if it is not serviced by a more sophisticated information-collecting and information-processing system than is usual at present. Currently, environmental pollution problems come to mind as an example. We have hardly begun to realise that the moods attitudes and opinions of workers however irrational they seem, are facts, information, which need to be taken into account just as much as production figures or faulty machines do. But industry is beginning to learn the importance, not only of feedback of information from the executive system or production line, but of what Wilfred Brown[3] describes as the 'representative' and 'legislative' systems, in which information from external sources such as shareholders and customers, as well as internal sources such as employees' attitudes and production line feedback can be processed. A similar shift of preoccupation from the executive system to the information-collecting and processing system ('intelligence') is indicated in the military field by Frank Kitson.[4]

In the individual person we can recognise more easily the distinction between 'knowing how' and 'knowing why' we do things. Learning 'how' to do things is characteristic particularly of the growing child between the ages of say six and fourteen years. Thereafter progress towards maturity depends increasingly on learning when, why and whether to do the things one knows how to do, so that in maturity we expect to find a decrease in impulsive activity and an increase in reflective thought. But such recognition has not yet become common in our thinking about social organisms or communities. In most organisations, whether in industry or government bureaucracies or elsewhere, few people recognise the importance of Dr. Carpendale's observation that *'whenever power and information flow in the same channel; the information becomes distorted.'*[5] An organisation which uses only the executive system as a means of collecting and processing information is like an organism depending only on proprioceptive sensations - feedback from muscles and internal organs - and making no use of sight, sound or smell, which tell it what is happening outside itself. In terms of our model, such organisations are indeed 'without brains'.

The social analogue of the individual's role in the motor system is, of course, his job. Our society, at least, pays very sophisticated attention to problems of employment and to be unemployed is widely assumed to be one of the worst things that can happen to a man, causing loss of self respect and alienation. By contrast the social analogue of the average man's role in the sensory system is simple, trivial and primitive. It is - a vote, which he can exercise once a year or less and for which society provides a processing system which is similarly simple and primitive. Otherwise, a man's opinion on anything other than the occupational field which he inhabits is regarded as unimportant. Even among intellectuals and academics, it is thought to be unmannerly to express opinions about any field of study except one's own. In fact, as everyone knows but few take seriously, 'the onlooker sees most of the game'; and an enormous amount of the information needed to keep any social organism healthy lies in the opinions and judgements which men hold about what goes on in their neighbours' gardens, rather than their own. Ignorance does not disqualify a man from holding an opinion; it does qualify him to ask naive, fresh and thus potentially important questions. Nowadays it is probably just as dehumanising or alienating for a man to feel that he cannot 'make his voice heard' as it has been in the past for him to be lacking a job.

Our use of such an obviously hierarchical model as the CNS may disturb those who feel that there is an inevitable link between hierarchical social organisation and authoritarian or totalitarian government. Such a link is not inevitable. Teilhard pointed out that the failure of such 'collectivised' social experiments as nations have tried so far should not discourage us: *"it is not the principle that is at fault but the clumsy and incomplete way in which it has been applied."* [6] What we are suggesting here is that a healthy community needs two hierarchies, not one. The deplorable aspect of authoritarian regimes lies not primarily in their executive hierarchies, but in their failure to develop and foster the sophistication of quite distinct information-processing hierarchies.

They tend to control and inhibit the flow of information and the free expression and discussion of opinion, and it is by this that they stand to be condemned. The disastrous features of their executive behaviour are consequent upon this.

People who take impulsive action upon their initial unreflective or specialised perception of a problem are always a threat to community. This is obviously true of revolutionaries, taking the law into their own hands. It is still true, but less obviously, of autocratic or paternalistic managers of an enterprise, who so often act on the basis of inadequate or poorly processed information.

There is a great need in our society for more exchange and sifting of opinion and information at all levels. In particular, cross-disciplinary discussion groups with no commitment to action as a group are valuable as a means of sharing and clarifying information, attitudes and opinions. Those who decry the setting up of more formal bodies such as community councils, consumer councils or community health councils on the grounds that they are 'without teeth' are misguided.

In a healthy social organism there are only two kinds of social action which can safely be initiated at levels other than the highest. They are (a) automatic responses concerned with routine 'service' functions of the organism which are strictly predictable in their effect. (Such behaviour is analogous to the reflex operations of the nervous system); (b) action designed to collect or process information, without interfering with the organism's output (motor) system. Such action may be innovative and unpredictable to the organism as a whole; and it should not be entitled to, or expect, more than provisional recognition or acceptance until it has been thoroughly processed by the information system as a whole, and translated into whole-organism policy. This kind of *apparent* social output (e.g. in research projects, and many kinds of compassionate social action), innovative but starting at the grass roots, might well be categorised as part of the social input system.

When an innovative group asserts its *right* to determine action on the basis of its idiosyncratic information, and in opposition to current establishment policy, it is effectively claiming independence of the social organism as a whole, and ought - analogously to a newborn baby - to see itself as a separate organism, striving to reduce its parasitic dependence on the parent organism. If it does not do this it is analogous to a cancer. Groups who claim the right to disregard the law - whether they are dockers fighting an Industrial Relations Act or city councillors refusing to implement a Housing Finance Act, should be careful to claim that their actions are intended to be persuasive of the body politic rather than rejecting of it, unless they see themselves explicitly as outlaws or revolutionaries.

So far, we have been discussing the social structure of the community as if we were detached from it. Indeed, this is how we often feel. Ever since Freud, psychotherapists have tended to speak as if society were necessarily hostile to individuality, as if it prevented a man becoming truly himself, truly human. Of course, this is less than half the truth. In some respects, society may inhibit a man's self-development; in all others, society is precisely the context - the only context - in which the individual can become truly human.

The model we have been experimenting with is only relevant for communities composed of many individuals. I do not know what was the cell population of the simplest CNS which discovered the distinction between motor and sensory function to be necessary (the functional distinction would precede the structural by many generations) - but in human communities the size of population seems to be from 500 to 1000. Five hundred men seems to be the optimum size of an infantry battalion in an army; it is the best size for a hospital,[7] and the same seems to hold good for industrial enterprises. Up to this sort of size, face-to-face mutual recognition of all members is possible. A regimental sergeant-major may be intelligibly audible to 1000 men, but only if he has an exceptional voice. Evidence has been found for the existence of communities-of-acquaintance, without visible boundaries, varying in size from 1100 in rural France and 900 in Paris, to 500 among Australian aborigines and 200 among negroes in Chicago.[8]

Once communities get larger than this, people can only deal with one another by categorising (and thus depersonalising) them in some way, so that 'old Joe in the heavy machine shop' gets listed as a 'hand' or a 'worker' or an 'employee', while young George who brings the milk becomes just 'the milkman'. Organisations begin to be troubled by communications difficulties and have to start routinising and institutionalising procedures which in smaller groups 'just happen'. Such are the beginnings of that considerable element of alienation, misunderstanding and conflict which is due purely to the factor of community size.[9] . . .

References:
1. P. Teilhard de Chardin, **The Future of Man**, (Collins) 1964, pp.115-6.
2. G.G. Simpson, C. S. Pittendrigh and L. H. Tiffany, **Life: an Introduction to Biology**, (London), 1957.
3. W. Brown, **Exploration in Management**, (London), 1965.
4. F. Kitson, **Low Intensity Operations**, (Faber), London, 1971.
5. B.Carpendale, *'Thoughts on the Possibility of Community'*, The Teilhard Review, X, (1), p.2 (1975).
6. P. Teilhard de Chardin, **op.cit.** p. 119.
7. *Hospital Trends and Developments 1940-1946,* (Commonwealth Fund), p.536.
8. A.Jay, **Corporation Man**, (Jonathon Cape), 1972, pp 112-113.
9. R.W.Revans, **Standards for Morale: Cause and Effect in Hospitals**, (OUP), 1964.

157-2 A Brain of Brains.

HEALTHY DEATH

. . . There are several reasons why I have been concerned with the topic. One is that because I am a psychiatrist I know that the healthy man is the man who looks frightening things in the face; and doesn't decide whether to fight or run away until he *has* looked them in the face. And since very many of us are afraid of death, whether we admit it or not, it is as well for us to examine it as thoroughly as possible before we decide on how we should prepare ourselves to meet it.

Another reason is, that as a doctor, I am conscious of the fact that I was never trained to deal with this particular fact of life. I learned about how to help people through the various other crises of development - through birth, puberty, pregnancy, and through the so-called change of life; but I was never taught how to help people through this last crisis of all. You may think this is quite understandable. A doctor's job is to save life, preserve it and perhaps enhance it. If he allowed himself to accept too readily that death was the inevitable outcome of all his efforts, he might not try so hard to get people well, and he would be more likely to bring an air of gloom or pessimism into the sick room. Perhaps this is a risk. But the trouble is that people in general - particularly the anxious relatives of those who are sick - tend to take doctors very seriously. And if doctors adopt the attitude, for whatever reason, that death is something to be fought against, evaded, not even to be thought about or spoken of - then it is inevitable that people in general will tend to follow their example.

Let me illustrate this. Many doctors still believe that it is unwise to tell a patient that he has a disease from which he is likely to die, such as cancer. Not only will they evade telling the patient, which may be wise; but they will tell the truth to the relatives, or the patient's clergyman - and then instruct them to evade telling the patient too. Now, withholding the truth, the bald unpalatable and perhaps frightening fact, until a suitable moment comes to tell it, may often be a good thing to do; and perhaps the suitable moment never comes. But if it is right to tell a relative or a priest that a patient is likely to die, then perhaps the decision whether to pass this information on to the patient should lie with the relative or priest, and no longer with the doctor.

A woman I know had her baby in a maternity ward where there were five other mothers. In the joy of their new babies they formed a happy and friendly group. Tragically, one of the young mothers suddenly died from a pulmonary embolism. Naturally, the other mothers all asked questions about it - how would the baby get on, what would the husband do, and so on. But the nursing staff acting on instructions from the doctors refused to allow any discussion of it. Death was a subject that was taboo.

I am told that in a newly built hospital in the North a tunnel has been made from the main ward block to the mortuary - so that no-one's susceptibilities will be offended by seeing a dead body leaving the premises.

Now these kinds of evasion of the reality of death are rather typical of the attitude of my profession (particularly those of us who work in hospitals). Nurses tend to follow our example, and so, to some degree, do the public at large. But it isn't a realistic attitude. All through human history the death of the individual has been recognised and faced up to as a real experience in rituals of burial or burning. A funeral, traditionally, was a solemn and public occasion, when the members of a community stopped what they were doing and gave themselves time to reflect on the inevitable fact of death, time to get adjusted to it, time to realise, to make real for themselves, John Donne's thought that "*any man's death diminishes me because I am involved in mankind*". It still is in rural districts and less industrialised places, but with the coming of the motor car, and the hurry and bustle of modern city life, the funeral is losing importance as a public or community occasion and the tendency is growing to allow it to become a private affair for near relatives only. Someone has said that our attitude to death is becoming like the Victorian attitude to sex - it is necessary and inescapable, but so long as the decencies are observed, the less said about it the better. . . .

. . . But listen to this instance of Dr. Lambourne's [1]:

> *"A sick child is cured after a long illness, but the strain set the parents at each other's throats, with the result that the wife went home to mother and the parents are now permanently separated. In a similar case the death of the sick child resulted in bringing the parents into a much closer relationship. Which of these is to be considered the best cure? At first sight the choice may seem easy. But follow the events of years and it may become difficult, as the broken home produces its psychopathology, perhaps alcoholism or suicide."*

To pray for the child's recovery in the first case might well be inconsistent with God's ultimate purposes for this family. We can't possibly know. No doubt God will get his own way in the end, whatever we pray for - but I think we must assume that our prayers are better prayers when they are directly in line with his will than otherwise.

This example, altering the focus of attention from the sick child to the family of which he is a part, brings me to one of the major points I want to make to you. Are we right, when we think about someone's death, to focus primarily on the individual?

Most of you, if not all of you who are members of the Guild of Health will be aware that both theologians and doctors have in recent years been rediscovering that health is something that does not belong to the individual in isolation. The individual, we are becoming more aware, can only be as healthy as the community of which he is or has been a member. We can only be fully human in relationship with other human beings - so we are interdependent on one another. Health means wholeness, and wholeness cannot reside in one member of the community while others are less whole. So we share our health; and we share our lack of it; and perhaps none of us are more surely sick unto death than those of us who try to keep healthy at the expense of our those around us.

Now since a proper understanding of health and life requires us to see the individual as part of the community; and since, as we have said, death is one of the most inescapable facts of life, perhaps it is time that we began to look at death in a wider context than that of the isolated individual too. . . .

. . . I want to emphasise the point, that whether we look at the physical organism or the social organism, the death of the individual component unit is an essential necessity to the continuing life of the whole. In social organisms where there is a high degree of mutual trust and understanding, and a strong sense of purpose - like Scott's expedition to the South Pole, or in an army in time of war - the individual person does not find it difficult to value the success of the whole body above his own personal survival. Not every soldier who willingly goes forward into danger is exceptionally heroic, or has a firm belief in personal immortality. But these kinds of truly healthy social organisms are rare - perhaps rarer than they should be - at our present stage of social evolution; and most of us, when we reflect on death, tend to look at it from an egocentric, not to say selfish, viewpoint, rather than a sociocentric one.

Perhaps the death of Captain Oates, walking away into the Antarctic wilderness, or the death of the soldier in battle - deaths which we tend to regard as heroic, as I said, are the nearest we have got so far to what I am looking for - examples of really healthy death. At least they show clearly how death can 'make sense' when it is self-less, when it is willingly faced because the individual is more concerned with the survival of the whole social organism of which he is a part, than with himself alone. . . .

Reference:
1   R.A.Lambourne, **Community, Church and Healing**, (Darton, Longman & Todd), 1963.

63 - Healthy Death

Chapter Four

SKILLED CARE

Trained as a doctor, James quickly found that the distinction between treating a disease (skill) and treating a patient (care) influenced his professional style of medical practice. Both approaches are needed, but he found his traditional medical training focussed on disease to the neglect of persons and their wider relationships in family and society. So his practice of skilled care embraced wider and wider social contexts towards the promotion of health and personal values. He recognised the individual and social need for a profound change of attitude (*metanoia)* in moving from treatment of disease to promotion of health: and that this involved a new balance between both scientific outlook and personal insight, between non-personal and personal skills. His insight and experience in this field was valuable to a wide range of other professions - nurses, social workers, counsellors and clergy - as well as his own.

M.W.

SKILLED TREATMENT AND PERSONAL CARE

Doctors have an obsession with the problem of 'combating disease' in their teaching hospitals and subsequently.

They have not developed any adequate balancing concept of 'getting the patient better' (a moral word). Their concepts of recovery, rehabilitation, health are limited to the negative: "n.a.d." (no apparent disease) or at best to a restoration of *status quo ante*. This kind of philosophy of health is not easily related to that implied in the New Testament, and its shortcomings are exemplified by the mission hospital in overseas countries, which, starting off to express a New Testament gospel of healing in practical terms, are now finding out that the real gospel they have been preaching is one of 'scientism' - whose values are secular.

Hospitals are in fact places where this dilemma is to be seen at its sharpest, because while nowadays all hospitals explicitly believe that their *raison d'etre* is to combat disease (they don't admit healthy people), in fact what comes in through the door is not primarily a disease, but a person - a patient who wants to get better, or be made whole. In fact, the patient presents us with moral, religious or at least philosophic questions which we are not conceptually equipped to deal with. Gerde Cohen gathers together the evidence that 'the patient does not count'.

Mental Hospitals in particular provide a suitable place for the problem to be studied. When the care of lunatics came out of its dark age of witchburning and Hogarthian amusement arcades, the renewed respect for the patient as person found expression in so called 'moral treatment' according the patient as much freedom to be himself, and responsibility for being himself, as the community could afford. This empirical compassionate approach accorded well with Christianity, but not well with the scientists' impersonal, detached and dispassionate approach to the 'fight against' disease. The latter was fashionable and very successful in many fields, and so led to the eclipse of the former.

Post-Freudian psychiatry has now reached a point where "*the principles of moral treatment are being restated in terms which are, one hopes, more intelligible to scientific man, even if he is still doubtful about them as science*". Freud[1] always insisted that he was a scientist, but by his discovery of what he called the transference, he introduced into the foreground or focus of our thinking the notion that the personal relationship between people had a therapeutic significance - a notion which had always been there, but had previously been in the background - the sort of woolly generalisation to which people paid lip service and no more.

We have now had, in psychiatric practice, a fair amount of experience of what happens when you focus attention on personal relationships as an important therapeutic possibility, and I think the time has come to try to see how these two approaches - the detached scientific focus on disease, and the perhaps less scientific and certainly more subjective focus on the patient in his relationships with others - can be fitted together. Practically, there is a great deal of conceptual confusion, We talk of the treatment of the patient and the treatment of the disease, as if it was one and the same thing. But it certainly is not logical to do so. To treat a person means to help them in some way. To treat a disease is to destroy or inhibit it in some way - a totally different thing. Another symptom of our conceptual confusion lies in our use of the word "normal". The scientific doctor's norm is usually an 'average' - the middle of a 'curve of normal distribution'. But this isn't what our patients want from us. They want to be 'better'. They want to function at their optimum rather than their average. The clinical psychologist who establishes a 'norm' of intelligence at IQ. 100 would be profoundly dissatisfied if his children could not produce higher IQs than this. What is the norm of human nature? Bishop Stephen Neill [2] asks the question, and would I think get support from others beside Christians for his answer that it must be *"human nature at its highest and fullest manifestation"*, though perhaps only Christians would go the further step with him to identify the 'norm' of human nature with Jesus of Nazareth.

To return to our two approaches.

Disease.

Traditionally, the doctor focuses on the patient's disease and, in his role as scientist, behaves towards the patient himself as an impersonal disease-vehicle - a 'case'. He goes to some lengths to *define the problem* - to diagnose the disease, and in so doing to draw a line round his sphere of study. The scientist likes to work in what he calls a 'closed system'. The privacy of the consulting room, the screens round the bed in hospital, the ritual isolation of the operating theatre, are some of the ways in which doctors try to express their 'scientificness' in this respect.

The attack on disease uses the *analytic* method. The doctor is taught to divide the human body into various functional 'systems' (cardiovascular, respiratory, nervous, digestive) and he examines each of them. Then having had a general look, he directs more minute attention to whatever part he is interested in. So with the microscope, he first uses a low power lens on a wide field, then a higher power on a smaller field: and gets to know 'more and more about less and less'. This is a highly successful aspect of scientific method, and leads to specialisation. The scientist studies *parts* and not wholes.

In order to systematise and quantify the results of his studies, he finds it necessary to look for *regularities, repetitions* and *similarities.* In this process of counting and categorising it is inevitable that he ignores the minor differences of phenomena which make each one unique. And his use of statistics makes it inevitable that he uses *averages* as norms. He is interested in what *is*, because this refines his diagnosis.

In the end, his scientific, analytic, quantified examination has taught him a great deal about the *mechanisms* of the body and what can go wrong with them, and has enabled him to make statistical predictions about the future progress of the disease. And he is more or less able to advise treatment so long as it is directed toward putting the mechanism right. So long as he has the patient 'under control' - in one or other of his 'closed systems', dependent on him, obedient to him, under sedatives or anaesthetics or hypnosis - he can not only advise the best course of action but can actually *do* it - and with some vestigial awareness of his presumption he still describes this as medical or surgical 'interference'. The *direct* result of almost all his analytic, diagnostic or therapeutic endeavours as we have described them is a *diminution of the capacity for life in some part of the patient's body.* The surgical wound is divisive, and the anaesthetic paralyses. The door of the consulting room or operating theatre shuts the patient off from his job, his home, his friends - from all that makes life worth living. Indirectly, of course, these diminishments are minor and well justified by the removal of major hindrances to the patient's life - at least that is the hope.

Finally, we must note that, when using this method of approach, the doctor is very careful to be dispassionate and detached. He rigorously excludes himself, as observer, from the field of study. The symbol of this detachment is the surgeon's mask.

Now I leave it to your judgement as to whether this is a fair account of the scientific method taught to medical undergraduates. I know that the bedside manner is never completely excluded, except in the operating theatre or laboratory, but, as far as teaching is concerned, it is regarded as the polish on the furniture, or the oil in the engine, rather than an essential part of the structure.

Patient as Person.

Now let us look at what happens when the doctor or psychiatrist chooses to take the patient seriously as a person, and not as a mere disease-vehicle. He often does *have* this choice: Michael Balint[3] has written a book about the process of mutual decision by patient and doctor as to what is the area in which the trouble lies. When the patient first sees the doctor, the doctor says "what is the matter with *you*?" But then the danger arises: if the patient says "Its my stomach doctor" the doctor may, if he's in a hurry, accept that the patient is a 'gastric case' and will thereafter focus attention on *it* - the stomach, and let the patient as a person become the mere background for the investigation of a part of himself. Or he may, on the other hand, continue the dialogue with the person in front of him, until it becomes clear that the real area of trouble lies between the patient and his wife, or mother-in-law, or someone - and that the stomach upset is a mere symptom of this.

We can see already that it is much more difficult now for the doctor to draw a definite line round his field of concern. The wife or mother-in-law may not be his patients, and any influence he can bring to bear on the total situation can only be indirect and partial. In fact, we can see that by taking the patient's relationships with other people into account, the field of study gets wider and wider - Freud started with the patient only, but then found himself inside the field of study as well as the patient. Subsequently we have had to introduce social workers and relatives: in hospital settings we have had to bring in other patients as well as nurses and others - so that we have moved from individual to group therapy, and from there (after some little argument about the merits of 'closed' versus 'open' groups) to the therapeutic community concept - culminating, when the institution was too large for face-to-face contact between all members, in 'administrative therapy' or 'therapeutic administration'. Still largely in the future lies the realisation that *all* communities, not only those whose explicit function is a medical or therapeutic one - are a legitimate area for attention from those who are concerned with the health of the individual. So that the social psychiatrist will have to move into industry, no doubt with fear and trembling. (The Tavistock Institute of Human Relations is already exploring this avenue). In using this approach, then, the therapist finds himself learning less and less about more and more: the tendency is *against* specialisation and specialised technique.

Next, we can notice that whereas the scientific approach uses a divisive and analytic kind of medical interference with the individual, the approach to the person respects his integrity and personal identity. It allows him to retain and value those aspects of himself which are *unique,* which he does not share with others. This has the result, (with which the scientific doctor has not yet come to terms) that the only interesting kind of medical record in this field is an anecdotal one. In the field of social psychiatry, the more rigorously one uses statistical methods, the more banal and trivial are one's conclusions.

In this approach, we are concerned with the *whole* of a person, not with a part of him. It is the whole man who relates to other men, not only his mind or body - nor his super-ego or unconscious or what have you.

Finally, with this kind of approach the doctor leaves the patient free to choose how he will live his life. He denies himself the right to remove a symptom by interfering, with drugs or other techniques. He merely hopes that by showing the patient the possibility of other ways of behaving than the one which constitutes the reason for his seeking help, the patient will become able to choose a more appropriate or effective one. This hope is, I think, precisely that which justifies the surgeon's incision in an operation - the implicit hope that the wound will heal.

Essentially, I submit, this second approach is a compassionate one rather than a dispassionate one. Essentially, the doctor has to allow himself - indeed, has to strive, to put himself in the patient's shoes, to become involved, to share the patient's feelings and attitudes. Certainly, having done so, he still has to be able to stand back again and see the situation objectively: but he has to be compassionate before he can understand. He has to allow himself to develop a relationship, and then be able to stand outside himself and see the relationship dispassionately. It is this necessity for prior involvement that makes this approach unacceptable to the scientist.

Some of the results of this kind of conceptual analysis are surprising. One of them is that analytic psychotherapy no longer appears to be primarily a technique with which to combat disease, but rather a method of building up a patient's capacity for healthy living, and leaving the 'disease' or disability to disappear of its own accord - or at least to become unimportant to the patient. I have always felt that this was true even before I had worked out an explanation for it: but I am sure it would be resisted by many psychotherapists whose technical competence exceeds my own. It implies that the core of analytic psychotherapy lies in the establishment of a fruitful, creative relationship between patient and therapist, rather than in any uncovering of buried traumatic experiences in the patient's unconscious: these latter are merely indications of the patient's improvement rather than the cause of it.

Another result is that it leads to a re-evaluation of the therapeutic task of the nurse, occupational therapist, physiotherapist or caseworker. It would seem that these roles, far from being mere ancillary workers aiding the scientific doctor's attack on disease, are complimentary to his role precisely in this respect, that their efforts are directed toward health enhancement rather than the attack on disease. And to the extent that this is true, it would indicate that the better they are at the job the *less* specialised they will become. Thus caseworkers are beginning to re-appraise the degree of specialisation which they have currently achieved, and are rather anxiously looking at the boundaries of 'agency function' which they have erected to maintain their professional identities. All of this argument does not, of course, imply that nurses or physiotherapists or case workers have not, or should not have, developed specialised techniques of their own: but it gives these a secondary rather than a primary importance.

Another result of this train of thought is that it leads one to take another look at the size of institutions such as hospitals which try to cater for people. If it is the opportunity of making good personal relationships which lies at the basis of all attempts to increase health, then it seems likely that an institution will be at its most effective - its most therapeutic - when there is the maximal opportunity for face-to-face contact and communication between those who are temporarily (patients) or permanently (staff) members of it. This is almost certainly much smaller than the hospitals we have at present or plan to have in the foreseeable future.

The need for free communication also has implications for the architecture of hospitals, which are becoming relatively widely acknowledged; and for their social structure too. The status, differences and hierarchies of doctors and nurses act too often as barriers to communication. They have a value in defending staff from anxiety, but they are ultimately a neurotic defence. Once you can label a person with a particular status, you feel entitled to manipulate him in a way which denies him reality as a person.

Having said all this, let me return to the original problem of relating secular concepts of healing to those in the New Testament. I think it will be plain that the search for wholeness, which is always a corporate community concept, is a continuum arising out of man's elementary biological need to establish relationships with others in order to maintain health and life itself. In this context, there is no primary emphasis on the differential diagnosis of disease. It is valuable to know the situation as it *is* - an average state of half health - but only in order to be able to move away from what *is* to what *ought to be* - an optimum. And the direction in which we ought to move becomes of primary concern. We must *first* seek the Kingdom of God.

References:
1. S.Freud, **The Psychopathology of Everyday Life,** (Hogarth Press), 1901.
2. S. Neill, **A Genuinely Human Existence,** (Constable), 1969.
3. M. Balint, **The Doctor, His Patient and the Illness,** (Pitman Medical), 2nd. Edition, 1964.

57-2 Two Ways of Treatment in Mental Hospitals.

HOSPITALS OR HOMES?

. . . In our mental hospitals - despite the succession of scandals we read about in the press - there are some people who have learned, often through bitter enough experience, how to care for a man in trouble.

Their expertise lies in their capacity for patience, for not appearing to be shocked by what they see and hear, for allowing difficult people to be difficult - and human, rather than insisting on their being docile and dehumanised. It does not lie in their confidence that they can cure disease, but in their refusal to be panicked by disordered behaviour, their readiness to go on suffering it. These skills may not sound dramatic, but they are much less common than we like to think - especially, perhaps, among doctors and nurses. The psychiatric doctor and nurse learn to live with difficult people; and they include colleagues, and patients' relatives and visitors, as well as those who are actually labelled as patients.

The task of the psychiatric therapist is to discern, and nurture, the humanity of those around him, hidden as it so often is on the one hand by the disordered behaviour of the sick, and on the other by the defensive tricks of status, professional role, and neurotic custom and rule in which institutional staff are imbedded. And since the therapist himself is imprisoned in this unhealthy social structure, his task of discerning the humanity of others is compounded by his struggle to remain human himself.

But the last twenty-five years have shown some gains. Over the country as a whole, the most difficult colleague of all, the autocratic superintendent, and the depersonalising social structure which he represented have begun to fade away. Doors have been opened. The system of underground channels of communication - the grapevine - is becoming recognised and explicit. Roles and status-differences, previously clearly defined, are becoming confused and trivialised as the humanity which they hid becomes clearer; and they can no longer be so easily used by staff to evade the responsibility for making decisions.

Mental hospitals have become uncomfortable places to work in. The staff find that a great deal of their skill and energy goes into solving problems which arise from the social structure of the institution itself, as it presses upon the freedom which patients need in order to 'get better'. They find that disordered behaviour by patients is often the result of unrecognised disagreements between those who are dealing with them. They see increasingly that the admission of a particular patient is often the presenting symptom of a more important social disease in the patient's family, which they are not expected to heal.

If the social structure of the mental hospital is dehumanising because of its bad old autocratic traditions and unwieldy size, it is also affected for the worse when planners model their perception of what it should be on the large general hospital. This, too, is intrinsically damaging to human personality, and for the same reasons of autocratic social structure and overlarge size. '*The more the psychiatric hospital imitates the general hospital, as it at present exists, the less successful it will be in creating the atmosphere it needs.*[1] That was written nineteen years ago, but it is even more true now.

Would not psychiatric skills be better deployed in the patient's home setting? We can give injections or pills wherever we are. We can talk with people in any room, anywhere. A hospital is an unnatural social setting, '*an organisation run by doctors in the interests of their own technical efficiency*'[2] - but dehumanising and intimidating for patients. Some American investigators did a controlled study of what they called '*Family Crisis Therapy.*'[3] Instead of admitting the acutely disturbed patient immediately to hospital, the team focussed attention on his family, and treated all of them (including the patient) on an outpatient basis. One-fifth of the patients were subsequently admitted for short periods, but the number of days in hospital they needed was only a fraction of those needed by the control group. The economic cost was only one-sixth of that for the control group.

Generally speaking, those who stay in hospital more than six months need 'residential care' more than constant nursing. In one hospital, of eight hundred in residence, more than five hundred (mainly elderly) had been there for more than six months. But nurse and doctor training is directed toward the care of the 'acute' patient, so that those who work in long-stay wards tend to feel professionally frustrated. Nurse training is not primarily designed to fit people for the responsibility of residential care, which is a profession in its own right, and I look forward to the day when nurses who undertake the care of long-term patients can take a further qualification in residential care. Their professional morale would thus be better based than at present. . . .

References:
1. **The Community Mental Hospital,** (WHO Technical Report), 1953.
2. T. F. Main, **The Hospital as a Therapeutic Institution**,(Bull. Men.Clin.), 1946, 10, 66.
3. D.G. Langsley et al, **Treatment of Families in Crisis,** (Grune & Stratton), 1968.
117-2 What is Going to Replace Our Mental Hospitals?

MACHINE MINDERS

The medical profession is in a muddle. The well-publicised arguments about the pay of junior doctors and private beds, however important, are symptomatic of a deeper conflict, between the kind of technological medicine we practise and the community's needs for health care. In such a time of uncertainty it may be inevitable that most attention is focused on the solution of short-term problems but it is always wise to moderate short-term impulse with disciplined speculation about possible and probable outcomes of a crisis in the medium and long-term. This paper takes a speculative look at one possible medium-term outcome of the current crisis. It is not an attempt to offer a solution for an immediate problem.

An important reason for our present malaise is the medical profession's growing dependence upon complex and relatively immobile machinery. Despite what is often said, it is quite uncertain that the NHS as a whole is being threatened: the threat is to only one part of the service, namely the *hospitals.* Now although we have allowed the hospitals to become the most expensive parts of the service and therefore the most important in terms of economics, it would be perfectly possible to have an effective national health service in which they played a much smaller part - as a second line of defence needed only when primary health care, offered by general practitioners, had failed. If we were to put more of our resources into primary health care services, the threatened collapse of many of our hospitals, though inconvenient, might not be such a disaster as we imagine.

The focus of our discontent

However, it is clear that for the moment it is in hospitals that our discontents are mainly focused, and this calls for a closer look at the value-system which underlies our attitudes and behaviour in them. Since all doctors are trained in teaching hospitals, even those who subsequently work in the community are infected by this value system, at least for some years and it also tends to affect patients and their relatives at times when their resistance is lowered by the anxiety which accompanies illness. Michael Wilson,[1] has made explicit six very questionable unconscious assumptions on which the value system current in hospitals is based:- that the cure of disease is more important than the care of patients; that staff assume power over patients; that individuals are separate from one another; that the provision of health is a task for experts; that every problem has a solution; and that death is the worst thing that can happen to a man. To these I would add a seventh, that medical men need to have personal control of a quantity of immovable clinical machinery.

The value of technological aids to diagnosis and treatment of disease is not in doubt. But their use exacts a price in more important terms than economic. In pre-technological times the prime function of the medical man was to make decisions which, whether expressed in words or actions, were usually made on the basis of grossly inadequate objective information, and the men who made them did so in a psychological atmosphere of freedom. The decisions were largely subjective and intuitive, but since they were so often matters of life and death they were taken seriously. Consequently the doctor tended to be held in high esteem, typically being perceived as a man of courage and disciplined imagination.

However, with the advent of radiological and pathological laboratory aids, of intravenous therapy and continuous monitoring techniques, a great deal of ignorance and uncertainty about various *part*-functions of the human machinery have been removed. Either decisions are made by the machine, or else the information needed to determine the outcome of a course of action is so complete that no decision is necessary. Thus the doctor finds himself robbed of the very aspects of his role upon which his self-esteem used to be based.

Forgetting wholeness

Unhappily doctors, like other human beings, like to feel that they are 'in control'. The feeling is not unreasonable so long as they are dealing with part-functions: we can indeed control the circulatory system or stomach or brain of another person with drugs or surgery, at least to an appreciable extent; and it is with part-functions that hospitals and clinical machinery are concerned. But this has meant that many hospital doctors have failed to recognise the important area of 'whole-person' medicine in which the traditional decision-making role is still paramount - unhampered by machinery. However, this is an area in which the doctor is no longer automatically in control: whole-person medicine is an encounter between two human beings, and must be modelled on a dance or a duel rather than on the mechanic dealing with a machine.

Either not recognising this area for their decision-making skill, or being unwilling to face the challenge to medical authority and control which it implies, many doctors retreat towards the place where the decisions about part-functions are in fact being made: they become, directly or indirectly, machine-minders. Marshall McLuhan has spelt out the dilemma in his inimitable way in his essay 'The Gadget Lover: Narcissus as Narcosis.'[2] Men grow to be like their machines; they lose or narcotise part of their humanity. 'Any invention or technology is an extension *or self-amputation* of our physical bodies' (my italics). And, of course, machine-minders in our industrial society traditionally expect to be paid an hourly rate, with special attention to overtime.

Machines are paramount

The problem is made very much worse by the immobility of the machinery. When a person falls ill, to avoid the risk of further damage or distress the caregiver should be careful to adapt to the sick person's situation at least until a diagnosis is made. *Primum non nocere.* Instead, the immobility of the machine is allowed to determine the immobility of the doctor-machine-minder; and it is the patient who now has to move towards and adapt to the caring agency. (The reluctance of family doctors to pay home visits is one of the more damaging results of this infection spreading extra-murally.) And once the patient arrives at hospital, the doctor promptly immobilises him too - entangled in tubes in a bed, or anaesthetised in an operating theatre. If in time the machinery can be miniaturised and made portable (and hopefully less expensive) then no doubt it will come to occupy the place once taken by the stethoscope, and become a sort of badge of office. But it will not then interpose the frightening barrier between the sick person and the supposedly caring person which it so often does in hospitals at present.

Even before this kind of development, it might still be possible to encourage all hospital doctors, 'junior' as well as 'senior', to become more mobile; to move into the community and see their potential patients at home, dressed and upright and independent, instead of in a strange place, naked, recumbent and dependent. So if the current controversies were to result in a flight of doctors from hospitals into the community (for not all of them will find work overseas), perhaps this would be not a disaster but a great improvement: they would find work as family doctors for most of their time, and do the hospital work they fancied only as a part-time sessional activity.

How not to dehumanise doctors

Hospitals might then revert to being places where people are cared for when they are sick, and would be managed as they used to be, by members of the nursing profession whose proper task this is, supported on the one hand by lay secretaries or house governors and on the other by such technicians as are necessary to maintain the machinery which still remains immovable - but which is regarded *by the nurses* as necessary for the proper functioning of the establishment.

Hospitals will make their full contribution to the nation's health only when doctors become as reluctant to spend time in hospitals as patients are, and reappear as masters of such machines as they use instead of their servants. It is as important to stop medical practice from dehumanising doctors as to stop it dehumanising patients.

References:

1. J. Michael Wilson, **Health is for People,** (Darton, Longman and Todd), London, 1975.
2. Marshall McLuhan, **Understanding Media: The Extensions of Man,** (Routledge and Kegan Paul), London, 1964.

164-3 The Medical Machine-Minder.

PATIENTS

. . . Doctors use the word 'patient' for those we try to help. The word means someone who is passive. It is appropriate for someone who is anaesthetised, and sometimes for those who are consciously submitting to diagnostic procedures. It is much less often appropriate for people to whom we offer advice or prescriptions. Many so-called patients - perhaps most - decide for themselves whether they will act on the advice, or take their tablets as ordered. They are not really patients - they are *agents;* and to expect them to continue to behave passively and obediently is unrealistic and confusing. . . .

79 - Psychiatry and Religion.

HEALING

I want you to accept for the purposes of this talk that if I use the word 'healing' it is only to be understood intransitively: wounds heal, persons become whole. But no-one ever 'healed a disease' or 'healed a person'. If I happen to use such a phrase, it is just a form of shorthand, meaning that someone helped another, or stood by another, while healing took place. Doctors don't heal people; they sometimes remove hindrances to healing, but otherwise their function is supportive, while healing occurs. Doctors don't heal people anymore than midwives make babies. So I talk about *health care* rather than healing. . . .

130-1 Strategy and Tactics of Health Care.

THERAPEUTIC COMMUNITY

1. A community with the immediate aim of full participation of all its members in its daily life, and the eventual aim of the re-socialisation of the neurotic individual for life in ordinary society.
2. A community in which a conscious effort is made to employ all the staff and patient potential in an overall treatment programme, according to the capacities and training of each individual member.

The assumption underlying these definitions is that the experts (the staff, the trained caring people), have no monopoly of the capacity to bring healing; and that this is to be found in everyone, so-called sick and so-called healthy alike. This means that in a therapeutic community the experts ought to be deliberately seeking, not so much for the badness in the sick so that it can be eradicated (as in ordinary medicine), but for the good in them so that it can help the rest.

Principle One

A therapeutic community is one which concentrates on fostering the healthy aspects of its members' functioning, rather than on inhibiting or eradicating the unhealthy aspects.

From this it follows that any member who *does* concentrate on eradicating the bad from individuals (which is what doctors tend to do) is likely to be criticised by the whole community i.e. is regarded as unhealthy himself.

Principle Two

The staff member has to learn to see himself as being just as potentially unhealthy as the clients.

Thus 'treatment' is directed at everybody - not in the sense of eradicating evil from 'patients', but in the sense of educating, nurturing, learning. A therapeutic community is a living-learning arena.

This means a near-total flattening of imposed or structured hierarchy and authority: leadership *function* is exercised by one or another person being temporarily and provisionally 'authorised' by the rest to speak or act for them at a given moment - and the authority is withdrawn the moment it is felt to be no longer relevant, and if the erstwhile leader attempts to persist he is seen as bad.

Principle Three

Anyone who wants to remain helpful to the members of the group has perforce to pay attention to the *whole group*, and to individual members only in the context of the whole group, i.e. to the whole and not to the part. . . .

20 - Therapeutic Community.

PERSONAL VALUES

Underlying the greater part of hospital practice in the NHS are certain implicit and often unrecognised assumptions. Here are four of them:

Basic Assumptions

(1)   That the cure of disease should take priority over the care and comfort
       of sick people;

(2)   That medical qualifications in dealing with disease (by attacking or
       inhibiting it) confer an equal expertise in the measures needed for
       fostering or nurturing health;

(3)   That the sick are best treated in an environment primarily designed to
       promote the technical efficiency of health care professionals; and

(4)   That sickness is located within an individual's body, his personal relationships
       with other people being of secondary or derivative importance.

Assumptions like these, accepted unthinkingly and without qualification, account for two features of hospitals which are widely criticised: their impersonality (the impression they give that 'patients do not count'), and the near-sacred respect they seem to demand for medical authority. It is in long-stay hospitals and especially psychiatric institutions that values of this kind are seen to be most questionable. The 'therapeutic community' approach as used at John Conolly Hospital and elsewhere tries to keep assumptions such as these explicit, so that they are open to question and criticism and do not adversely affect the patients to whom care and treatment is offered.

It is probably inevitable that an institution which thus challenges the assumptions of traditional practice will meet with misunderstanding and hostility. Its commitment to personal values above those of institutional order, and to consensual rather than authoritarian patterns of decision-making often raise fears of anarchy and undisciplined libertarianism. It is greatly to the credit of the Birmingham RHB that it supported the foundation of the JCH in 1963-64, and of the authorities who have maintained it in being for 15 years despite the attacks which are periodically made on it.

The Size Factor

If JCH were to be closed, patients needing admission from its present catchment area would have to go elsewhere and this would doubtless be to a larger hospital - probably Rubery Hill Hospital. It is therefore important to re-assert that the present size of JCH is about right, and that larger units such as RHH are too big and should not be made bigger. Large institutional size is a major cause of depersonalization (for both patients and staff). It was precisely because RHH was so large that in 1963 I avoided accepting responsibility for the use of the new building in the grounds of RHH which subsequently became JCH. There was a steady reduction of the number of beds at RHH throughout my tenure of office and I understand this has wisely been continued through the 70s. It would be a great mistake to reverse the process now.

It is unfortunate that the status and (except for medicals) the salaries of profes-sional staff are so largely linked to the number of beds for which officers have responsi-bility. It provides an ever-present temptation to empire-building (by taking over smaller units) even among those who are aware of the bad effect this has on the quality of health care and administration. So-called economies of scale, however valuable they may be in industrial manipulations of inanimate material, need very careful scrutiny whenever they affect the autonomy of human beings. Where such arguments are deployed to justify the closure of small units in the health service, we should beware lest the result is a service which is less humanly *effective* even if it seems bureaucratically or technologically more *efficient*.

As superintendent of a traditional mental hospital, I was only able to see my task, at best, as trying to diminish the harm the institution was doing to the people in it, both staff and patients.[1] There is no doubt in my mind that units such as JCH, of a size in which face-to-face communication between all its patients and all its staff is possible, and having the greatest practicable autonomy in the choice of medical and nursing staff who determine its 'therapeutic atmosphere', offer the most hopeful pattern for in-patient psychiatric care for the future, despite the anxieties which they may raise in traditionally trained minds.

Reference:
1.   J.Mathers, 'Custodial or Residential Care for the Long Stay Patient?', <u>Lancet</u>, April 22, 1972, pp. 894-5.

222 - Letter to the Secretary, Save the John Conolly (Hospital) Committee.

HOSPITAL VILLAGE

. . . The Oxford Regional Hospital Board is building a new hospital for the mentally subnormal in Northamptonshire. They want the patients to be able to live as normal a life as possible. So they are embarking on an imaginative adventure, and building a hospital *village*. There will be places (not just 'beds') for 500 men, women and children. The village will have separate groups of single-storey buildings for sleeping quarters, with small dormitories and single rooms. There will be shops, a cafe and clubroom, and a children's playground, as well as a chapel, a library and workshops. In fact, the village is designed for a hospital *community* instead of the 'hospital population' on which so much previous planning has been based. The main responsibility for the plan lies with Mr. W.J. Jobson, the Oxford Board's architect, and Dr. J.O.F. Davies, the Senior Administrative Medical Officer, with the help of Mr. Guy Webster.

Anyone who has experienced the difficulty of trying to find their way round the barrack-like buildings of many of our existing long-stay institutions will welcome this kind of approach to hospital architecture, but it means more than this. It means that those responsible have made a real effort of imaginative sympathy in trying to visualise this hospital *from the viewpoint of the patients* before they start building; and since the mentally subnormal can't speak for themselves on the matter, this must be regarded as a most praiseworthy act of faith.

Our older psychiatric hospitals were built on lines which suggested a prison or a workhouse. The whole structure was designed to make 'observation' easy and to make escape difficult. The watchword was 'security': you began with the assumption that patients couldn't be trusted, and it often took years for a recovered patient to prove otherwise.

Nowadays we are beginning to realise that patients can only begin to behave responsibly if you act as if you *expect* them to behave responsibly. But so long as hospitals are built and organised in 'wards', there will always be a tendency to regard the nurses as 'warders' - however vigorously we push such an unwelcome thought into the hidden recesses of our unconscious minds. . . .

43 - A Plan for a Hospital Community.

THE DOCTOR'S ROLE IN SOCIETY AND ITS FUTURE

The main reason why society at large is prepared to pay salaries to us as doctors is so that we may offer its members comfort and relief when they experience sickness or disease. Our profession exists primarily to serve persons, and only in a secondary way to serve the art or science of medicine, which tends to be more concerned with the objective facts of disease than with the experience which may or may not result from it. From society's viewpoint, the practice of medicine is a method of making manageable people's experience of pain and disease, not an end in itself.

Nevertheless, the study of medicine and disease is fascinating and seductive, and in my more pessimistic moments I see a risk of the profession getting more and more involved in the game of discovering (not to say inventing) new diseases and new ways of dealing with them while drawing further and further away from the real concerns of those unfortunate people who suffer from them. To use a phrase of Dr Tom Main's,[1] the modern hospital tends to be *"an organisation run by doctors in the interests of their own technical efficiency".* The way we plan hospitals, and the way we behave in them, is so widely criticised for being impersonal that when Kenneth Robinson was Minister of Health he said that the failure to pay attention to the human factor was a "challenge to voluntary organisations". He evidently felt the problem was beyond the competence of the professionals to solve. This is a rather shameful indictment of hospital doctors.

The pre-eminence of the hospital in the organisation and training of our profession is unfortunate. The doctor or student in hospital does not see his patient in his natural setting. He only sees him for relatively short periods when he is ill, when he is divorced from most of the elements of his normal social context which give him significance as a person - his status in his family, at work and recreation. Out-patient clinics located in or near the hospital suffer from similar disadvantages in only slightly lesser degree. This is because the specialist claims that he needs to have easy access to technical apparatus; but to the extent that he thus allows himself to be tied to his machinery, he becomes the servant of the machine rather than of his patient.

Because the general practitioner is still trained mainly in hospital and indoctrinated by hospital specialists at an impressionable stage of his career, he too is initially handicapped by a greater concern for the facts of disease than for the experience of persons. But to the extent that he is able to move around in the community, seeing his potential patients in their clothes, walking erect in the street as well as lying supine in bed, affirming their independence of him while they feel well, as well as their dependence on him when they feel ill, he has a chance to redress the imbalance of his training. With experience, he comes to respect the healthiness and adaptability of his patients, and tends to reinterpret his task as that of sustaining their sense of wellbeing. He learns to exercise judgement and control over his impulses to investigate the facts of their medical condition whenever there is a risk that such investigation will prove to be a disturbing experience. He will not, for instance, do a rectal examination as readily as his teachers may have exhorted him to do. It is a pity that this exercise of judgement should expose him to the risk of being thought professionally incompetent by hospital specialists, and even more of a pity that he should be so brainwashed by his medical school training as to take such criticism seriously. If a general practitioner's professional judgement is questioned during legal proceedings, it is a pity that the expert testimony called to support or oppose his actions is likely to be that of specialist consultants.

In the thirties, doctors at the Peckham Health Centre[2] established that the general practitioner lived in a community of whom only 16% of men and 4% of women were without disorder of some kind. But 63% of men and 75% of women had an experience of wellbeing in spite of their having diagnosable disorder, and only 21% of each sex were 'dis-eased' by their disorder. The figures will no doubt have changed with refinements of diagnosis, but the three categories still exist. Is it really in the interest of the community, or of the individual, to increase the proportion of those who feel themselves to be diseased now, in the tenuous hope of increasing the small proportion who are free from disorder at some time in the future? By reducing the quantity of disorder (in the individual or the community) doctors may make a contribution to the quantity of life. But if this is done by converting people who have a sense of wellbeing into people with a sense of being diseased, then the quality of life is impaired now, and we are inevitably increasing the volume of demand on geriatric services in the future. Both these results seem highly undesirable.

My vision for the future of our profession, therefore, includes the hope that we will learn to balance our interest in the facts of disease with a greater interest in the wellbeing of the persons who suffer from them. At present we still confuse the problem by talking of the 'treatment of disease' and 'treatment of the patient', as if these expressions were equivalent in meaning. Clearly they are not. Treatment of disease implies an attack on an enemy, while treatment of a patient means - or should mean - the sustaining or succouring of a person to whom one has an obligation.

I think we will all learn more about persons if we move out of our hospitals and into the community as much as we can. Doctors should be as reluctant to stay in hospitals as their patients are. Whenever possible - far more often than is usual at present - the first consultation between family doctor and specialist should take place either in the patient's home or in the general practitioner's surgery. Specialists should be appointed to a population area or a community rather than to a hospital; and the hospital should be regarded as a technical facility, provided for them when needed, rather than as the specialist's home base - a territory which he feels impelled to defend and enlarge and make more comfortable for himself. I am well aware of the difficulties and disadvantages this will have for specialists; but they would be more than outweighed by the gain to the wellbeing of patients. It is a question of whose interests we are going to put first.

* * * * *

The second problem I want to consider is the tension between our ideas about medical control and medical advice. The public interest is not well served by doctors' pretensions to omnipotence in matters of health. The doctor's belief that he is the right man to be in command whenever such affairs are to be dealt with seems to have its foundation in the mixture of fear and respect which people have for him when they are ill - when their morale is at its lowest and their judgement most disturbed. Just because my sick patient, in his state of infantile regression, treats me as if I were God it does not mean that I have to accept such a role. In the days when prolongation of life seemed to be the highest good, the doctor's pronouncements gained extra power from the implied threat that 'if you do not follow my advice you will die the sooner'. But in these days the prospect of medicated survival into querulous or hypochondriacal senility is steadily becoming a worse threat than death for many of us, and the increasing incidence of suicidal attempts shows that many people have at least an ambivalent attitude to any emphasis on the quantity, as contrasted with the quality, of life.

Within the hospital setting, the assumption that the doctor is the right man to be in control seems to date only from the surgical revolution and the invention of the operating theatre. Before the discovery of aseptic technique, doctors visiting patients in hospital were accorded no greater status than when they visited patients at home. But the mysteries of the operating theatre, and perhaps more recently the intensive care unit, seem such as to necessitate the almost military assumption of authority by the medical man, expecting and receiving immediate and unquestioning obedience from nurses and technicians involved in the operations. In the theatre or intensive care unit, as also in the post-mortem room, it is certainly justifiable to talk of an 'organisation run by doctors in the interests of their own technical efficiency'. But this is because the patient is unconscious and anaesthetised, or nearly dead - or quite dead. The justification for the doctor being in control depends, in fact, on the person being so sick as to have no, or minimal, awareness of his surroundings. Whenever the sick person's feelings have to be taken into account, whenever he is capable of accepting or rejecting any offer of medical interference, the doctor is not really in control even if he imagines he is; or, if he really is, then he is at grave risk of depersonalising his patient - of treating him as a thing rather than as a person.

> *A nurse told me about a woman doctor, dying of cancer in her thirties, who explicitly said to her that she wished to die without having her mind clouded by the narcotizing injection which (she knew) it was her surgeon's practice to give in similar cases. The nurse told the surgeon; but he nevertheless ordered that the patient should have the injection - given into the intravenous drip tube in such a way that she would not know that she was getting it.*

In most medical situations, the sick person is partly passive (a patient) and partly active and capable of decision (an agent). When you prescribe some medicine it is the 'patient' who decides whether he will take it or not. When you give instructions to a nurse or relative about what measures to take after you leave the house or ward, it is the nurse or relative who decides whether, and when, to follow your instructions. What we call instructions are really only advice. As the proverb says, *'you can take a horse to water but you cannot make him drink'.*

One of the most important parts of the art of medicine - badly neglected in the schools - is that of learning how to persuade, cajole or even trick people into doing what you think you know is good for them without doing violence to their feelings - which is to say without frightening them, or making them angry or embarrassed. As a psychiatrist, I am perhaps especially aware of this problem: psychiatrically ill people so rarely take advice that we learn not to waste time offering it. We spend the best part of our working lives (not necessarily the longest part) patiently trying to manoeuvre the client, or to educate him, into taking what we think are the appropriate steps as a result of his own free decision.

The senior grade in the hospital service is called 'consultant'. But when you consult someone about your affairs it does not mean that you necessarily put him in control of them. The senior administrative medical body in a hospital was until recently called a medical advisory committee - an expression which does not imply control either. By far the larger part of most doctors' work is in fact advisory, to patients, fellow pro-fessionals or administrative authorities. We should recognise that those who consult us always have a right to decide whether to accept or reject our advice. If we think they make a wrong decision, we should certainly strive to put our case more convincingly, but we should avoid getting into a competitive struggle or power battle with them to see who is the stronger.

We have a responsibility to advise the community that smoking is harmful. But I doubt if we have a *professional* right to lobby the government to control it, even if we have such a right as citizens. We have very little right to claim control over the design of hospital wards - certainly less right than nurses and patients who will live and work in them. We were certainly not right to claim control over social workers, as many of us tried to do when the Seebohm report was being discussed. And we are not justified in trying to control the flow of information between a patient and his relatives. When we find that a patient has a mortal illness, we may be right in not telling him, and we may be justified in telling his relatives; but we are certainly not justified in telling the relatives that *they* must not tell the patient. This common practice is an unwarrantable interference with people's personal lives at a time when they are most vulnerable, and would occur less often if doctors were clearer in their minds about when they should exercise control and when they should offer advice.

A leader in the BMJ in 1968, discussing the administrative structure of the NHS said: *"Doctors should not be relegated to a role of specialist advisers in a health service run by laymen".* Since doctors so often explode in irritability whenever the question of medical administration crops up, they are obviously unwilling as well as unsuitably trained to run the service, and they don't pay the piper any more than other tax payers. The service must inevitably be run by laymen, and why in heaven's name should we not act as specialist advisers to them? It either implies we are doubtful about the rightness of the advice we offer, or that we doubt our ability to make our advice convincing. Both implications may be true - but neither would support our claim to control the service.

* * * * *

The third area in which I think the present behaviour of the profession is moving in a dangerous direction is going to be the most difficult to alter. It is the balance between our capacity as specialists and our capacity as generalists. It is a fundamental law of biological evolution that 'specialisation paralyses; ultra-specialisation kills'. Each organism tends to adapt to the particular environmental niche in which it finds itself. But having done so, if it fails to maintain breeding contact with its erstwhile fellows in other niches, then its specialisation, first of habit and then of genetic structure, puts an end to its capacity for further adaptive advance and dooms it, sooner or later depending on the rapidity of environmental change, to extinction. The emergence of man as the species at the growing tip of the evolutionary tree has depended precisely upon his ancestors' avoidance of this biological trap of specialisation. There is every reason to suppose that this law applies just as rigorously in the field of cultural evolution, and I am concerned about its implications for modern medicine. We have made such enormous gains through our process of specialisation. Can we possibly contemplate a reversal of the trend? And in any case, since no one man can nowadays be competent in more than a small part of the whole field, are we not forced to accept a trend toward earlier and earlier specialisation?

Well, there are biological models for this kind of development, in the insect world, among ants, termites and bees. But they give me no great joy. I find it useful in thinking about this perplexing problem to distinguish between specialisation and differentiation; because the latter word carries an implication that although the differentiated part may have special functions, it still maintains a vital connection with a less differentiated whole; whereas the word specialisation too often carries the implication of fragmentation of a whole into isolated bits, whose autonomous behaviour (at least in the medical field) leads to destructive competition as often as it leads to co-operation - as anyone who attends a hospital medical advisory committee meeting to discuss the next year's budget will testify. It may well be that if the practice of medicine is to remain adaptable to a changing world, it will have to forgo some degree of excellence in its separate parts or specialties. As a species, man cannot fly as gracefully as a bird nor swim as gracefully as a fish, but his infinitely greater adaptability is compensation enough.

Here are some of the practical questions I am raising. Is it wise to allow doctors to specialise young and stay in one specialty all their working lives? Shouldn't we all have to spend at least five years in general practice before we are forty and at least one year in five thereafter? Should we continue to accept the trend by which any doctor other than a consultant anaesthetist is discouraged from taking responsibility for giving an anaesthetic, or by which a psychiatrist is expected to see every patient who takes an overdose of tablets? Or that only a specially qualified doctor should attend a woman in labour? Are we right to perpetuate a system in which the only remaining true generalist - the family doctor - is accorded a lower status by the profession than the consultant in some esoteric specialty?

I don't know the answers to these questions. But I put it to you that all of us, whatever our special interests, should see ourselves as *partly* responsible for the *whole* of the community's health; and that it is dangerous for any of us, or any group of us, to see ourselves as wholly responsible for only a part of it.

* * * * *

To conclude: I have discussed three aspects of the current medical scene which seem problematic: our tendency to attend to diseases rather than patients; to control rather than advise; and to specialise rather than to maintain flexibility. In each case I think we tend to take the easier choice of the two. If we are going to redress the balance in these respects, we are going to have to discipline ourselves to live with a greater degree of uncertainty, and often with a greater sense of powerlessness or impotence than is comfortable. Specialisation gives a sense of security: you can avoid admitting your ignorance more easily by saying 'this problem is not in my field' than by baldly admitting 'I don't know'. It is only the general practitioner who learns to say 'I don't know' without embarrassment. But if you can follow up the kind of suggestions I have been making, I think you will find they lead to greater job satisfaction for the doctor, as well as to a better service to the patient and to the community.

References:
1. T.F.Main, **The Hospital as a Therapeutic Institution,** (Bull. Men. Clin.), 1946, pp.10, 66.
2. L.H.Crocker & I.H.Pearse, **The Peckham Experiment,** (Sir Halley Stewart Trust Publication, Allen & Unwin), 1943.

119 - The Doctor's Role in Society and its Future.

NOTES ON A MODEL FOR SOCIAL THEORY

Introduction

Theories may be constructed with a view either to *understanding* or to controlling the phenomena studied. In the physical sciences it does not make any practical difference which is the prime motive, because the understanding of physical phenomena is detached, dispassionate - a 'knowing about' things; and the observer remains free of the control he seeks over the phenomena. But in the social sciences, a theory may be allowed to develop rather differently depending upon whether the motive is the understanding of one's fellowmen, or control of them. In this case, understanding can mean not only 'knowing about' other men in a detached way, but also actually 'knowing' other men - sharing their experience with fellow-feeling, involvement, imaginative sympathy. Understanding here carries a connotation of identifying oneself with the other; and the notion of controlling the other (while remaining free oneself) is therefore a concept of a different order.

The distinction between the two kinds of theory can be exemplified by the mental hospital psychiatrist, whose employers may expect him to control the behaviour of his patients; but who may only be interested in understanding them, and aiming to liberate them to be more fully human. His employers' measure of his 'success' may depend upon the fact that the response of his patients to his efforts to understand them is to change their behaviour in a direction which is generally regarded as more 'controlled' (i.e. self-controlled). Perhaps self-control is more likely to result from the effort of a caring-person to understand, than from the effort of a caring person to control.

The approach taken in this paper differs from that of e.g. cybernetics in that it is concerned with *understanding* the behaviour and experience of people. It is not aimed at the control of their behaviour.

The Model

Theorists in the social sciences often use organic models in their thinking, either explicitly or implicitly. Even allowing for the risks involved in taking such models too seriously, it is remarkable how little use they seem to make of a very important aspect of biological organisation, namely, the clear distinction that exists between the sensory (afferent) and motor (efferent) parts of the mammalian central nervous system; a distinction which is hardly blurred at all by the intimate interconnections and interaction between the two.

The individual nerve cell (neurone) never functions in both systems, but only in one or the other. Considered separately, the motor system is relatively simple in organisation, each pathway from centre to periphery consisting of only two neurones; while the sensory system is as a whole much more complex, each pathway from periphery to centre containing three neurones, quite differently arranged. The simple reflex arc, consisting of one afferent and one efferent neurone, functions automatically, but is constantly being moderated from higher levels in the healthy organism. It is only in states of disease that reflexes at lower levels operate autonomously; and this autonomy is always predictable and never innovative.

Although social organisms or communities are composed of human individuals who unlike nerve cells, are capable of both 'sensory' and 'motor' functions, I suggest that it is important to distinguish which of the two an individual is exercising in any particular social context. In industrial organisation, the executive (motor) system has historically had priority of attention. We have been more concerned with *how* to do things than we have been with *why* we do them, or whether they are worth doing, or worth doing now as opposed to later. But we are discovering, in all fields, that an executive system, however efficient in itself, is likely to have crude, inappropriate or even dangerous results if it is not serviced by a more sophisticated information-collecting and information-processing system than is usual at present. Currently, problems of pollution of the environment come to mind as an example. Industry is beginning to learn the importance, not only of feedback of information from the executive system or production line, but of what Wilfred Brown[1] describes as the 'representative' and 'legislative' systems; in which all kinds of information, from external sources such as shareholders and customers, as well as internal sources such as employees' attitudes and production line feedback can be processed. A similar shift of preoccupation from the executive system to the information-collecting and processing system ('intelligence?') is indicated in the military field by Frank Kitson.[2]

In the individual person, of course, we recognise more easily the distinction between 'knowing how' and 'knowing why' we do things. Learning *how* to do things is characteristic particularly of the growing child between the ages of say 6 and 14 years. Thereafter, progress towards maturity depends increasingly on learning when, why and whether to do the things one knows how to do; so that in maturity we expect to find a decrease in impulsive activity and an increase in reflective thought. But such recognition has not yet become commonplace in our thinking about social organisms, groups or communities.

Although most individuals in a democracy have what we may call a 'social input' role (e.g. a vote) as well as a 'social output' role (e.g. a job), there are few of us who can be in the critical 'governing' social positions which would justify us in translating our perceptions of a situation into action directly. For most of us, in most situations, our social input responsibilities are only quite distantly related to our social output responsibility. Nowadays it is probably just as dehumanising or alienating for a man to feel that he cannot 'make his voice heard' as it has been in the past for him to be lacking a job.

Implications

Here are some implications of this line of thought:

1.   People who take impulsive action upon their initial unreflective or specialised perception of a problem situation are socially dangerous. This is obviously true of revolutionaries, taking the law into their own hands. It is still true, but less obviously, of autocratic or paternalistic managers of an enterprise, who nearly always act on the basis of inadequate social input.

2.   Those who decry the setting up of community councils, consumer councils or community health councils on the grounds that such bodies are 'without teeth' are misguided. There is a great need in our society for more exchange and sifting of opinion and information at all levels. In particular, cross-disciplinary discussion groups with no commitment to action (as a group) are valuable as a means of sharing, sifting and clarifying information, attitudes and opinions.

3.   In a healthy social organism there are only two kinds of social action which can safely be initiated at levels other than the highest. They are:

(a) automatic responses concerned with routine 'service' functions of the organism which are strictly predictable in their social effect. (Such behaviour is analogous to the reflex operations of the autonomic nervous system).

(b) action designed to collect or process information, without interfering with the social output system. Such action may be innovative and unpredictable to the organism as a whole; and it should not be entitled to, or expect, more than provisional recognition or acceptance until it has been thoroughly processed by the input system as a whole, and translated into whole-organism policy. This kind of *apparent* social output (e.g. in research projects, and many kinds of compassionate social action), innovative but starting at the grass roots, should perhaps be more properly categorised as part of the social input system. (There is an analogous difficulty for instance in classifying the motor activity of the small muscles of the eye. Although these muscles necessarily have a motor innervation, their activity is clearly part of the sensory function of the organism rather than part of its motor function).

4.   When an innovative group asserts its *right* to determine action on the basis of its idiosyncratic information, and in opposition to the establishment's policy, it is effectively claiming independence of the social organism as a whole; and ought therefore to be

prepared to accept a total responsibility for itself as a separate community. Groups who claim the right to disregard the law, whether they are militant dockers fighting the Industrial Relations Act or City Councils refusing to implement the Housing Finance Act, should be careful to claim that their proposed actions are intended to be persuasive of the body politic rather than rejecting of it. Otherwise they may be regarded as outlaws or revolutionaries, which is probably not how they see themselves.

5.   At first glance some of these propositions may seem to smack of authoritarianism, but if we are clear about the distinction between the social input and social output systems, we can recognise that some authoritarian features are probably inevitable as far as the output (executive) system is concerned (at least in large organisations). The deplorable aspect of most authoritarian regimes lies not primarily in their executive systems, but in their failure to develop and foster the sophistication of social input systems. They tend to control and inhibit the flow of information and free expression and discussion of opinion, and it is by this that they stand to be condemned. The disastrous features of their executive systems are a secondary manifestation resulting from this.

6.   A leading article in the TIMES (28 July 1972) asserted that 'information is as essential to democracy as representation'. It said that 'no press is only less dangerous to democracy than no Parliament'. The notions of representation and Parliament are here set over against the notion of information (and the press); but I am suggesting that in actuality representation and Parliament are themselves only a means of obtaining and processing information, and that they - together with other sources of information - ought to be set over against the Government and Executive. The power of the representative (in and out of Parliament) is the power to influence opinion and decision by virtue of his access to well-processed information and his ability to communicate it persuasively; it is to be distinguished from executive power, which is in the last analysis a means of manipulation backed up by physical force.

7.   In the absence of an adequate social input system, social action tends to be either impulsive, or perseverative and repetitive. The state health service of a country so afflicted would tend to respond to pressure by doing more of what it has always done (increase medical staff, spend more on hospital building, for instance), instead of re-examining by research and reflection the real - possibly new - health needs of the community it means to serve. It might then discover, for instance, that it would be more helpful to reduce the number of expensive hospitals, and to teach doctors to supervise less skilled (and less expensively trained) auxiliaries who could do most of the clinical work in the field.

8.   The foregoing socio-political considerations offer no pointers toward the appropriate *size* of social organism for which the CNS provides a useful model. The model is certainly only applicable to a collective of some sort, but it does not help in deciding whether it should be applied at a national, regional or local level for instance. It can be applied to any sort of human collective provided it is judged appropriate (on other grounds) to regard that collective as autonomous. Thus it carries no implication of a 'one-party state' or other monolithic social organisation: it can be useful in considering the social behaviour of people in quite small communities - inasmuch as they operate autonomously or with delegated authority. But there is probably a lower limit of size of

a community below which the model is of no relevance. So long as people can recognise one another *as persons*, they do not need to relate to one another in terms of distinguishable functional roles. This is clearly true of the family or primary group. There is probably a critical limit of between 500 and 1,000 population above which conceptual differentiation of the kind suggested by the model begins to be of value. A variety of evidence for this figure is collected by Anthony Jay in his chapter on *'The Corporation Tribe?'*[3] A difficulty is that for some purposes a numerical count of the population in a community does not take into account a significant number of other individuals who have ties with it. For example, the works council at a factory explicitly represents a number of workers; but covertly, some of its deliberations are likely to be much affected by the opinions of the workers' wives and children - who may easily double the real size of the constituency represented. It will for instance have great influence on questions involving the mobility or redeployment of workers - particularly since those who are not formally consulted are likely to respond to proposals in an impulsive or perseverative way simply because they have inadequate information-input to enable them to make rational decisions.

9.   Much social science research has been preoccupied with the problem of leadership within social organisms or organisations. It is worth while noting that in terms of our model there is no evidence of any one neurone or set of neurones performing a distinguishable leadership role. The 'direction' of behaviour (by nerve impulses passing down the final common [motor] path) is the resultant of equipotential nerve impulses being collected through afferent neurones and being processed through central circuits in the brain - in a fundamentally *quantitative* manner. The leadership function is thus exercised by the activity of all the sensory neurones which are stimulated. There is no evidence of a cybernetic elite in the CNS. This is not to dispute that in social situations a minority of individuals prove capable of assuming leadership functions: but the absence of a biological analogue for this kind of differentiation strengthens the arguments of those who maintain that leadership is a function of social situations rather than a functional characteristic of particular individuals.

10.   This provokes the thought that strategy and policy making in social affairs, usually regarded as the work of an elite, might benefit from having a much wider social base; and that instruction in how policy is - or should be - determined should be widely available as a part of general education. It is customary in our society for a man's occupation (motor function) to be conceived as if it determined the limits of the field within which he is entitled to 'speak with authority'. The academic, asked for an opinion on a topic in which he is not expert, will courteously reply 'this is not my field'. We might re-interpret this custom uncharitably as indicating that a man's occupation blinds him to perspectives other than that required for his specialty - a tendency which Marshall McLuhan has pointed out in his essay *'The Gadget Lover: Narcissus as Narcosis?'*[4] In other words, the structure of a man's perception tends to be task-related. It is precisely this kind of psychological determinism which (if mankind is to discover how to make large-scale social organisms not only viable but palatable) man can teach himself to transcend. Just because the individual has a 'tendency' or 'compulsion' to limit his perspective in this way does not mean that he cannot learn how to free himself from it. In fact, some men of maturity

have always been able to overcome such a limitation. And so have some children, as the legend of the Emperor's New Clothes reminds us.

Conclusion

What I have been exploring in this paper is a possible kind of *conceptual* change - a change in the social input system. I am *not* proposing any change in the social output system. But the hypothesis would suggest that if we can improve our social input system, the operations of the output system (= behaviour, executive activity) - whatever its basic structure - will become more precise, more elegant and more adaptive than they often are at present.

References:

1.   W.Brown, **Exploration in Management,** (London), 1965.
2.   F.Kitson, **Low Intensity Operations,** (Faber) , London, 1971.
3.   A.Jay, **Corporation Man,** (Jonathan Cape), 1972.
4.   M.McLuhan, **Understanding Media: The Extensions of Man**, (Routledge and Kegan Paul), 1964.
                    124-5 Notes on a Model for Social Theory.

THE ACCREDITATION OF COUNSELLORS

The context in which the problems of accreditation for counselling and psychotherapy fall to be considered contains a number of implicit assumptions. Counsellors and psychotherapists, of all people, should be aware of the dangers and difficulties which unconscious or unconsidered assumptions can lead us into; and this paper is aimed to encourage discussion of some of them. Such assumptions are not necessarily wrong in themselves, but need to be brought into conscious awareness so that their appropriateness to a particular situation can be assessed. For instance, the assumption that pastoral counselling is to be categorised as one kind of counselling profession, rather than as one kind of pastoral activity, cannot be safely taken for granted. This has been cogently argued by R.A.Lambourne.[1] Another assumption, which seems entirely appropriate in the present context, is that if counselling is to be seen as a distinct profession, then it is proper to categorise it as one of the caring professions.

Taking this as my starting point, therefore, I propose to examine some of the conceptual tools which are common to the caring professions when they face the questions of accrediting new recruits to their ranks.

Each caring profession requires a different mixture of similar skills which can be seen to lie along a continuum. At one extreme lie skills which are directed at the treatment of definable, specific problems, where in a short span of time it is possible to see whether the technique used has solved the problem or not. Such skills can be taught and learned with a minimum of alteration or involvement of the personality of the pupil, and tend with practice to become routine, automatic activities needing little attention to the personal relationship between caregiver and client. Many surgical skills are of this kind: as a surgeon has said, "we can cure a person these days without even knowing his name". We will call such skills *non-personal*.

At the other extreme lie certain skills which are needed for dealing with caregiver/client encounters where the problematic situation is poorly defined, or defined differently by the people involved; where therefore there is no certainty, even in the short term, as to what would be the 'right' outcome of the application of skill; and where the caregiver has to share anxiety with his client without being seduced into premature action which momentarily relieves the anxiety but leaves the problematic situation unresolved. Such situations occur for instance in marriage guidance, or in considering with anxious parents the possible admission of a handicapped child to institutional care. The skills needed here can be learnt, usually only at the cost of some modification of the caregiver's attitudes and prejudices; but they cannot be taught by didactic instruction; and the personal relationship between caregiver and client is all-important in their exercise. They can be called *personal* skills.

Professionals in most if not all the caring fields have to be equipped with non-personal and personal skills extending over the whole range; but it is only in relation to the personal skills that doubts arise about the value of accreditation. Unhappily, we seem to structure training and accreditation processes to take account of the non-personal skills rather than the personal ones - not because they are more important, but because they are easier to instil and to validate. Certainly, for a surgeon, say, non-personal skills are indeed important. But by what criteria can we judge that a technically competent candidate for a surgical qualification is possessed of an adequate competence in personal skill?

Thinking about accreditation processes involves the use of a constellation of concepts which are interdependent. They include

        (a) the explicit recognition of skills;
        (b) teaching skills, and training people in them;
        (c) specialising in particular skills;
        (d) setting standards of competence in them;
        (e) seeking excellence in them, and
        (f) supervising students.

I will comment on each of these; but must first make some remarks about caring skill in general.

There is obviously a human need for people to acquire skill, and for them to learn new skills. This constellation of concepts does present one pathway by which certain skills may be learnt, and often it represents an efficient way of doing so. But perhaps other pathways are possible, and for some skills they might be preferable even if they were apparently less efficient. We need skills in order to deal with experiences of frustration or discomfort - whether such experiences are generated by internal factors of physiology or psychology (such as are responsible for growth) or by external factors in our material or social environments. Some skills, such as walking or sphincter control, come naturally; others, such as talking, have to be learned from skilled others. These can be *learned* by watching, listening and imitating: they do not necessarily have to be *taught*, though teaching may help.

People faced with problematic situations which are new to them are often unaware of the nature of the problem. They do not know which skill might help them or who is the appropriate expert. They are more likely to approach an unskilled person who 'speaks their language' and whom they are ready to trust. Such an 'informal caregiver' may be able - and will certainly try - to *define* the problem. In doing so he may enable the sufferer to *objectify* it, to conceive it as something distinguishable from his self or personality, to put it at a distance from himself. He is then ready if necessary to consult someone he thinks is expert in dealing with that kind of problem.

In other cases the informal caregiver may be as unable to define the problem as the sufferer is. Although this may be a blow to his self-esteem, it does not mean that he is useless. A trouble shared is a trouble halved; and provided the caregiver is willing to *stay with* the man in trouble, he may give valuable support to him while the problematic situation persists. In such a case the giving of care is not a matter of solving an objective problem, but of sharing in a problematic experience which has not been defined or objectified. Such care is a matter of *com*passionate involvement rather than *dis*passionate objectivity. The outcome of such a shared caring encounter is that both parties may learn some skill, not in problem-solving, but in living with discomfort or anxiety until it disappears. As a result, both are likely to be more competent, more fully human, than they were before; but to the extent that they failed to define or objectify the problem they are not qualified to *teach* anybody anything of a problem-solving nature - though of course, others may *learn* from their example.

Of course such a description of informal care-giving is idealised. More often in real life the informal care-giver - the amateur - who cannot define the problem, quickly learns, and teaches, the wrong sort of skills - directed at the evasion of discomfort and anxiety rather than staying with it and learning from it. Nonetheless such a description of a possible amateur approach to human problems may give us a standpoint from which we can usefully criticise the 'professional' constellation of concepts.

(a) Explicit recognition of skill

The acquisition of skill is always of value, particularly if it is employed with discrimination, and calls for no criticism here. It is the *explicit* recognition of a man's skill by others to which I am drawing attention. The child who learns to walk acquires a useful skill which he enjoys using. But *"he also acts under the immediate awareness of the new status and stature of 'one who can walk' with whatever connotation this happens to have"* in his particular cultural setting.[2] Erikson goes on to say that the child is not fooled by the empty praise of his parents saying "what a clever boy". What really strengthens him is the *"whole-hearted and consistent recognition of real accomplishment"* - which comes from his parents saying things like *"go into the kitchen"* or *"fetch that object from over there"* or *"close the door when you go out"*. Such communications contain an *implicit* rather than explicit recognition of his new-found skill in walking.

At a more sophisticated level the same truth holds. When an expert is exercising his routine skills he may momentarily be 'fooled by empty praise' when a lay bystander says how clever he is; but his true satisfaction comes from the unthinking acceptance of his skill by fellow-experts who rely on him to do his part so that they can do theirs. The implicit recognition of skill by fellow-workers with whom one stands shoulder to shoulder is of greater value than the explicit recognition given by those over against whom one stands face to face. Paper qualifications of course are an explicit recognition.

They mean little compared with the opinion expressed by an experienced man of skill about the apprentice or pupil who has worked with him - and people may be highly skilled without having a paper qualification. However necessary it may be, therefore, the *explicit* recognition of skill is not always an unmixed blessing and we do well to take thought before drawing the attention of others to a skill which we appreciate.

(b) Teaching and Training

Teaching conveys information and is of value to a pupil who wants to learn. But a teacher inevitably directs attention to the elements of a situation which *he* thinks significant, and in doing so he distracts attention from other elements - which may be more significant in actual situations than they appear in the classroom. The teaching process narrows the pupil's span of attention: by putting certain elements in the foreground it leaves the background relatively unconsidered. Such a procedure is justified when the subject matter is something that can be properly understood in isolation from its context. Otherwise it is dangerously limited. Teaching can tell us how something works; but it is context which gives it meaning. So teaching is useful in the lower reaches of physical science, for instance, and in dealing with part-functions or part-systems in the biological and possibly psychological fields. But when we want to learn about wholes - about whole human beings or whole communities - situations in which the background or environment has to be understood as well as the organism in the foreground, since each interacts with the other, the didactic instructional method is inadequate. In human studies, as in aesthetic appreciation, we have to think in terms of *education* rather than teaching, of drawing out instead of putting in, of mutual discussion between peers, even when some have greater experience than others.

Like teaching, training is a word with the connotation of narrowing and limiting the field of experience rather than broadening it. Both processes are aimed at intensity of experience in a limited field. Both tend to specialisation. If our aim is to foster the emergence of well-balanced, fully human people, teaching and training have limitations of which we must beware.

In our society, those who are explicitly recognised as teachers or trainers (or, indeed, educators) all pass through a sort of quasi-academic, quasi-middle class indoctrination process. Of course this is not deliberately planned and is indeed often contrary to the intentions of the educators. None the less it is a fact. From whatever variety of social class backgrounds they come, students are for one or more years exposed to a particular set of values which their teachers have learned from those who taught them; and they unconsciously absorb this value system even if they consciously resist it. Basil Bernstein[3] shows how all formal educational processes from school onwards depend upon the adoption by students of what he calls an 'elaborated' language code employed by their teachers, while many children and uneducated adults communicate only in terms of a 'restricted' code. Thus formal training tends unconsciously to increase the psychological distance between the trained caregiver and the untrained client - a distance initially established by the objectifying process which led to the definition of the problem area for which the skill is required. Robert Dingwall[4] points to the fact that systems of knowledge tend to be 'absolutised' by those who share them. In the caring fields this means that both students and their tutors unconsciously tend to assume that the expert knows best, and certainly better than clients; whereas in fact clients may often 'know' better than those they consult, but in terms of their own culture and knowledge system rather than that of the experts. Communication is easiest when caregiver and client share the same cultural and educational values; but such clients represent a relatively privileged population and not the underprivileged who are most often in need of care. For proper mutual understanding, a caregiver should first learn his client's knowledge and value system - at least to a much greater extent than present practice recognises; and he should be slow to assume that his own value system is the one that is 'right'.

(c) Specialisation

Teilhard de Chardin enunciates the evolutionary law that *"specialisation paralyses; ultra-specialisation kills"*. There can be no quarrel with the *differentiation* of human skills. That word carries the connotation that the differentiated element remains in vital continuity with that from which it has sprung, as a flower or leaf is continuous with the stem and roots of the plant. But specialisation, as we practise it, presents itself as a process of fragmentation in which each specialty tends to perpetuate itself with but little regard for the whole of which it is never more than a part. Within the caring professions, specialisation requires much firmer limitation and control than we usually give it. (The excellent recommendations made in the Seebohm report are still resisted in practice in some areas, even when lip-service is paid to them). We ought, for instance, to show a preference for part-time specialist appointments over full-time; and where service requirements make full-time work essential or desirable, negotiate contracts of service for limited tenure only. Such a policy, diminishing the distance between specialists and the undifferentiated generality from which they spring, might possibly involve a slight loss of efficiency - but this would be more than compensated by a gain in effectiveness. However, the policy would imply that the current difference of status between specialist and generalist would disappear; and regrettably that means that most existing specialists will not support such a change and that generalists will have to fight for it.

(d) Setting Standards

The advantage of setting standards of attainment for students or training establishments is that it enables comparisons to be quantified, and simplifies (objectifies?) the rejection of the unsuitable. The standards we set are always intended to be minimum ones (I have never heard of a teaching establishment setting maximum standards). But once a standard is set, there is an unconscious tendency for students, tutors and examiners to treat it as a norm, as a point to aim at. Thus standard-setting puts a premium on conformity and discourages creative novelty both in students and establishments. It makes for mediocrity, because behaviour which diverges from the norm in any direction does not make for popularity (except in the world of entertainment). This objection is of least importance in instructional areas where performance can be objectively defined and precisely measured, as in tests of rote memory or simple skills which can be impersonally and mechanically performed. It matters most in those areas where the whole personality of the student is relevant to the task set. In the caring professions, standard-setting is essential for surgical skills and for legal procedures such as are needed to move a child into care or a psychotic into hospital against his will. It is valuable for diagnostic skills such as taking a person's blood pressure or setting an intelligence test. And it is virtually useless for assessing the overall competence of a social worker, psychotherapist or counsellor.

For the latter, it is preferable to rely on the admittedly subjective evaluation of a candidate by a panel of experienced practitioners who have articulated for themselves a vision of what optimum (rather than minimum) performance might possibly look like. Each such assessor would have his own idiosyncratic vision of the optimum; so it is important that assessors should meet regularly and try to share their visions with one another. Assessment would then depend upon how far candidates were judged to fall short of a theoretically unattainable optimum. Such a method might increase diversity of performance; but there is no *a priori* reason why unsuitable candidates should not be effectively weeded out by a relocation of the norm away from minimum or average performance towards the ideal. Comparability between candidates would be less measurable and more like aesthetic judgements, but would this matter? Such an approach would allow assessors to act as consultants, aiding candidates to achieve their optimum (realise their potential), rather than as judges, seeking only to eliminate the undesirable.

(e) The problem of excellence

Although observation suggests that standard-setting in other than peripheral and depersonalised areas of skill makes for mediocrity, there is ambition on the part of many to achieve excellence. This is suspect because it always means excellence in a particular and limited field of endeavour. What we should really be concerned with in the caring professions is the excellence of the whole rather than of its parts separately conceived. We should look for the wellbeing and competence of the whole man, or whole groups or communities. And there is nearly always tension if not conflict between the excellence of a complex whole and that of its parts. To achieve excellence in a particular field requires a concentration of resources - material and non-material - which are thus denied to other areas which may need them as much, or more. This is one danger of explicitly recognising a particular skill in an individual: it encourages him to strive for excellence *in that skill*, and distracts him from his proper aim of seeking excellence as a whole man, or as a member of a whole community.

It is problematic in another way: to become excellent in a skill is to become *rare.* So an excellent caregiver is likely to be psychologically and topographically distanced from his clients. When someone is in trouble, it is good practice to bring succour to him in the place where he is, and not to increase his trouble by insisting on his having to move before he can be helped. Professional caregivers do well to ponder whether they serve their clients better by being easily available, or by being unusually good at their jobs: the two do not often go together.

(f) Supervision

It is sensible for the work of a novice to be 'looked over' by someone of experience, and subsequently criticised and assessed. But the word has varying connotations in different settings. In industry, for example, a supervisor is often accountable for the *work done* by his trainees, as well as for their competence to do it. This connotation can apply also to the teaching and learning of some non-personal caring skills, as for instance when a trainee surgeon is performing an operation under supervision. But it is not at all clear that this is what supervision means in the training of counsellors or psychotherapists or social workers. Does a supervisor in such settings take responsibility for the students' clients? Possibly some supervisors would say that they do, but is their claim really justified? If a student fails in personal skills when dealing with a client, the supervisor can not 'correct' the mistake. Of course he can often prevent the student from making a similar mistake in the future; but if he were to try to correct an error by intervening himself with the student's client, he would be dealing with a different situation from that in which the student failed. In this area, the concept of *consultancy* seems more appropriate than that of supervision as it is commonly understood. Supervision implies a superior/subordinate relationship. By contrast, consultancy implies a relation between autonomous peers, even though one has greater experience than the other. Of course, even the idea of consultancy implies a measure of supervision in the sense of 'looking over'; but whereas supervision in its accepted sense seems appropriate when we think of learning non-personal skills, the concept of consultancy seems increasingly appropriate as we move along the continuum towards learning personal skills.

(g) Control and Authority

The problems discussed in the last section are a particular manifestation of the basic assumption that those recognised as teachers have a right to exercise control over students' work - a right accorded to them by those who accept student status. More generally, then, I want to suggest that while the assumption of control may be appropriate when applied to the learning of non-personal skills, it becomes increasingly inappropriate in the learning of personal skills. The latter can only be learnt in a setting in which the student is free to act autonomously, and is then enabled to reflect on his actions in discussion with more experienced practitioners. In the area of personal skills, it is the *sapiential* authority of the teacher which is recognised, and that does not connote the kind of control which is implied by the notion of *formal* authority.

This discussion serves to remind us that the desire to control is deeply ingrained in human nature and that those who teach are not immune from its unconscious influence. We need to make a deliberate effort to avoid assuming control in those important areas of learning where it is not appropriate.

* * * * *

Against this background of the concepts assumed in common by all the caring professions, we can now turn to the problem of accrediting counsellors and psychotherapists. Some psychotherapists, especially if they are medically trained, would want to draw a clear distinction between the two: they regard some of the skills of the psychotherapist as dangerous in unskilled hands - like a scalpel or a dangerous drug. I believe this view to be mistaken. The assumption underlying it is that psychotherapy is essentially directed at the solving of problems: it aims to put right what has gone wrong, and to restore the client to his *status quo ante* by mysterious methods known and safely practised only by initiates. By contrast, I believe that the essence of psychotherapy lies not in specific problem-solving, but in fostering the client's overall strength in a general way to act constructively in problematic situations. The becoming conscious of a repressed impulse or traumatic memory is a *sign* of improvement rather than a *cause* of it. Psychotherapy fosters healthy functioning and is not primarily concerned to inhibit or eliminate disorder. Its real aim is the client's autonomy and freedom rather than his conformity to a preconceived norm. It is concerned with healthy growth rather than the elimination of pathology. And this is just as true for counselling. I do not believe that counsellors should be debarred from using techniques which are allowed to psychotherapists. The important difference is that between psychotherapists and counsellors who are skilled and experienced and those who are less skilled and inexperienced.

But are there adequate grounds for regarding counselling (including psychotherapy) as a distinct and separate specialty within the caring field? Essentially counselling involves active attention by a caregiver to a person in a problematic situation, and a dialogue between them aimed at trying to clarify the precise nature of the difficulty. Counselling ends when there is satisfactory agreement between the two about this. The difficulty may prove to be one for which expert attention is needed; or one which can be resolved with easily available unskilled help or by the sufferer himself; or it may prove to be the aftermath of an unrecognised problem in the client's past, which disappears as soon as he recognises it for what it is and comes to terms with it.

Thus counselling is a process which in principle should always precede the application of problem-solving skill by an expert; and in principle no expert should be ready to apply his skill until he has taken counsel with the man in distress. It is therefore not a specialty which should stand on its own, so much as an essential precondition for the exercise of any specialty. The assumption that it *can* properly stand on its own derives from the frequency with which counselling eventuates in a resolution of the client's difficulty without specialist interference. Seen in this light, there are grave dangers to be feared in the accreditation of counselling as a distinct specialty. It will inevitably mean that practitioners in other caring fields will be identified, and identify themselves, as having diminished responsibility for being competent as counsellors themselves. And as has been seen in so many other fields, such dependency on the expert would be a tragedy. Anyone who cares for others must be ready to offer counsel, whether he is experienced and skilful or not. Michael Wilson has pointed out the importance of 'hot' counselling, for instance in hospital, and Gerald Caplan has developed a systematic theory of crisis intervention: both emphasise that those in trouble are more likely to seek help from untrained informal caregivers who are easily accessible when they are most needed. The professionals' common practice of arranging appointments at some future time when the client's crisis is already cooling is too often a matter of locking the stable door after the horse has bolted. Of course it is easier to cope with difficulties when the emotional heat has been dissipated from them. But the self-defensive delay which professionals impose means that the more demanding and more critical initial counselling encounter will remain the province of the untrained amateur.

Growing awareness of these difficulties has already led to a considerable modification of traditional practice in training programmes for counselling. The use of student placements under supervision is one example - a partial return to the apprentice system of days long past. Another example is the increasing replacement of the impersonal lecture by the seminar. And a third is the recognition that training is likely to bring about a definite if limited change or maturation in the personality of the trainee. Such developments are welcome. But it is my contention that they have been achieved *in spite of* and in opposition to the unconscious social structure of teaching establishments rather than in harmony with them; and that the future teaching of counselling requires a radical rethinking of the basic assumptions and social structure of institutions which will offer such teaching (and which will therefore determine accreditation procedures). The debate will doubtless continue for a long time, so this discussion ought not to lead to conclusions. But here are some questions which emerge from this discussion:

1. Should students who seek training in counselling be selected if they have had no prior experience in other forms of caring? That is, should all courses in counselling be 'post-experience' courses for those whose experience has been in some other caring field?

2. Should students trained in counselling be encouraged to see this as a specialised field in which they can expect to work full-time?

3. How can we structure training to demonstrate that the trained counsellor must be more ready to educate and consult with informal caregivers than he is to deal with clients directly?

4. How should training programmes seek to avoid establishing or maintaining or increasing the psychological distance between counsellor and client?

5. How can we resolve the seeming antithesis implied by questions 3 and 4 above?

6. How can we demonstrate in action a principle to which we often accord only lip-service, that counsellors and their teachers do *not* always know better than clients what clients' needs truly are?

And finally it may be worth asking ourselves a rhetorical question: to what extent is the traditional system of training and accreditation to be seen as a defence against our anxiety? How far is the structure of such a system determined by the unconscious wish of senior practitioners to avoid the uncomfortable personal responsibility of accepting and recognising competent students who will soon threaten their dominant status; and of rejecting the less competent who pose no such threat?

References:

1. J.M.Wilson ed., **Explorations in Health and Salvation** – a Selection of Papers by R.A.Lamborne, (Department of Theology, University of Birmingham), Re-issued 1995.
2. E.H.Erickson, **Childhood and Society,** (Penguin), 1965.
3. B.Bernstein, **Class Codes and Control,** Vol.1, (Routledge & Kegan Paul), London, 1971.
4. R.Dingwall, **Aspects of Illness,** (Martin Robertson), 1976.

195-4 The Accreditation of Counsellors.

WHOSE STRESS?

 . . . When a family contemplates their mentally handicapped child, and his behaviour which is so ill-adapted to the particular environment and culture in which they are located, there is an immediate presumption of something wrong or evil. And human nature being what it is, this evil, and the pain and suffering it implies, becomes the focus of attention, and tends to fascinate us and distract our awareness from the context in which it is set. Our instinct is to get rid of the evil and the pain as quickly or as radically as possible. And I want to suggest that perhaps the main task of the giver of care or help, coming into the situation from outside, is deliberately to avoid narrowing his focus of attention to the evil with which he is presented, and to look more widely at its context: not only in space (which means not only the material environment but also the people around) but in *time*. Mental handicap is something which exists over a long period of time; and when we are called in to help it is always worth asking oneself "*why have we been called in at this moment in time, rather than last week or last month - or next week or month? Why now?*" And the answer usually shows that there has been a change in the balance of stresses which is often located quite elsewhere than in the mentally handicapped person himself.

It is possible to imagine a handicapped child to be devotedly cared for, by parents and others, to the point where he can take a reasonably autonomous place in the community - but at a cost in stress for the parents which results in the breakdown of their relationship to one another; and similarly we can imagine the child to go downhill and be institutionalised, or even die - and for this experience to bring parents closer together, in harmony where formerly there had only been conflict. How can anyone evaluate these alternative possibilities? And yet an awareness of them ought to influence one's judgement about the way the child - and his parents - should be managed or treated.

The precise location of the stress within such a family constellation (which may include not only parents, but amateur and professional caregivers and others) is not always obvious. When a mother arrives in the doctor's surgery, presenting her child with some problem or other – "*I can't do anything with him, doctor*" - the wise practitioner is as likely to want to examine the mother as the child; whose symptoms may well be a reflection of her anxiety rather than of anything in his own make-up. As a psychiatrist I used to see many patients who were depressed; and as I grew more experienced I found myself becoming less likely to label them as suffering from a depressive illness calling for antidepressant pills or electric treatment: I tended rather to search for experiences of unacknowledged or unrecognised bereavement or loss, in their past history. I found such experiences often enough, and would then offer the kind of general, non-specific support, helping them to carry the burden of their grieving, and perhaps sharing in it to some extent, which any good friend or pastor might have done. But sometimes, after a few weeks or months, I would come to feel that my patient was not doing very well, and would wonder if I had been wrong to withhold the pills or electricity. Now, how did I decide that the time had come to give such medical treatment? I suspect that the critical factor was whether I myself felt that I could not take any more of their grief and unhappiness. In fact, it was my stress, not the patient's, which would determine the treatment. (I have never discovered why, in such a situation, it would be the patient who took the treatment rather than me.). . .

199 - The Context of Stress.

BREAD AND WORD

. . . Sometimes words, the communication of meanings, are enormously satisfying. When a man says 'I love you' to a girl, in words or action, his behaviour may be 'meat and drink' to her. By contrast, if he buys her a material gift, she will only find the gift satisfying if she can convince herself that it speaks a word of love to her: it is the 'word' value of the 'bread' that seems to be important here.

Medical Examples

John Masters tells of someone who, in the Bengal famine of 1943, "*saw soldiers giving bread to children with matchstick legs and arms and huge staring eyes and heads. The children crumbled it listlessly in their hands: only cooked rice was food to them, bread wasn't.*"[3]

In these days of high technology medicine, we find far too often that the material resources we make available for the treatment of the sick or for the prevention of sickness are not well received. Too often we seem to be offering answers to questions that haven't been asked. People complain that hospitals, where all doctors are trained, are impersonal; that doctors do not tell you the truth; that they don't listen to what you say; that they are more interested in your disease than in the relief of your suffering. R.A.Lambourne[4] cites three examples where the best-intentioned modern medicine has been faced with its own irrelevance:

1.   A developing country in Africa which found that the operating costs of one large teaching hospital absorbed 60% of the available health budget for the whole country.

2.   In America, medical students at one of the most advanced medical centres in the world realised that within a stone's throw of their hospital there were slums where the people got no medical help at all. They went on strike from their lectures, and started running clinics in the slums. Although in the hospital's terms their work was less skilled, it was much more effective in terms of the relief of suffering.

3.   A paediatrician went to a famous mission hospital in Africa which had been going for fifty years. The people and the church were proud of it, for every child who came there got the best possible treatment. The paediatrician looked at the infantile mortality figures in the area and found they had not altered at all over the years - the figure was 282 per thousand births. Most children died from three diseases (malaria, dysentery and one other). So he found some 15-year old girls from the mission school, taught them some simple rule-of-thumb diagnostic rules and how to weigh babies, and sent them off to run baby clinics in the villages. No doubt the girls made mistakes; and he himself reckoned to spend most of his time, not exercising the paediatric skills in which he was trained, but planning and administering the clinics and training and

supporting these girls - but together they cut the infant mortality rate to 78 per thousand in five years.

In each of these three cases, it was not actually the recipients of the service who complained. It was the professionals who found themselves challenged: it was they who saw the discrepancy between what they (or their predecessors) had *meant* to do and what they actually did.

The act of giving bread always speaks a word. Apart from those who are comatose or anaesthetised, patients always receive messages from the doctor's behaviour about the way he understands (or fails to understand) their distress. The modern hospital is a secular temple in which professionals implicitly preach a secular gospel, answering the patients' implicit question *"what must we do to be saved?"* Michael Wilson[5] has picked out various strands of this implicit gospel: he calls them assumptions. Here are five of them:

1. that the cure of disease is more important than the care of patients;
2. that patients must be passive and dependent and allow staff to take all initiatives;
3. that individuals are separate from one another;
4. that it takes experts to bring health to people, and
5. that death is the worst thing that can happen to a person.

All these are highly questionable 'words' (communicative behaviour) that accompany the material treatment (the 'bread') offered in our teaching hospitals. How can we dispense bread so that the word our prescription speaks is not a misleading one? Some patients, both in the West and in the developing world, come to have faith not in the Christian gospel; not even in the doctor; but in the drugs he offers or in the syringe which seems to act so magically - or even in the X-rays he takes as an aid to diagnosis.

Healing and Preaching

In an unpublished paper, James McGilvray[6] lists the imperatives of Christian discipleship: to preach, to teach, to baptise - and to heal; and he says that it is the last of these which always seems to create confusion. If he is right, it may be because our ideas of healing are systematised in a different 'explanatory world'[1] from that of preaching and teaching and baptising. Scientific and pre-scientific medicine both make use of 'Newtonian' assumptions about cause and effect, about substance, about force or power, and mass and weight. The laws of energy conservation and entropy remain true whatever the context in which the energy transactions take place. Drugs, surgery and bodily mechanisms are all in principle to be explained in this frame of discourse. But preaching, teaching and baptising are not amenable to such explanations. For them we need an explanatory system based on a theory of communication, dealing with information or messages rather than energy. Such a system would be concerned with form or pattern rather than with substance, with the relations between objects rather than with the objects themselves, with 'words' rather than 'bread'. It would find it was dealing with meanings, and thus with contexts and values - which the Newtonian system specifically excludes.

The difference between the two explanatory systems is fundamental. If someone gives me some material good, he is by so much the worse off. Or, if you like, I can maintain or increase the orderliness of my physical body by taking in nourishment, only by extracting a greater amount of orderliness from the environment (since energy is always conserved but entropy always increases). But if someone gives me some information, he is no poorer: indeed, the total orderliness of our joint world is now increased. Misunderstanding easily arises when we try to explain information-transfer events by using the assumptions of an energy-transfer system, for instance by talking of 'psychic energy' or the 'damming up' of libido; or when we imagine that the financial costs of running an education system reflect the quality (or even perhaps the quantity) of education made available through it. Jeremy Seabrook[7] suggests that these days even the wealthy feel poor, because the ordinary human skills through which we should express ourselves, in caring for one another in health and sickness - nursing, rearing children, cooking meals, making clothes or furniture or furnishings for instance - have been taken away from us or relinquished by us in the interests of an economic order, which then sells them back to us in the form of commodities.

Skills, like preaching and teaching, belong to the world of information transfer. But to which world do healing events belong? Jesus probably did not distinguish his preaching and teaching from his healing activity (Luke 7, 22): for him, they were all one ministry, aimed, can we say, at communicating to each person (and each participating onlooker) a confirmation of his or her unique worth and potential as a child of God, reconciled to Him and to other people. So, is Christian healing to be thought of in terms of energy transfer or information transfer, of 'bread' or 'word'? Or, indeed, as both? Or is it that the bodily healing which we seek, while explicable in energy transfer terms, is nevertheless to be seen itself as a message, a 'public effective sign' of the coming of the kingdom?[8] Or, as Michael Wilson recently suggested, as analogous to a sacrament - an 'outward and visible sign of an inward and spiritual grace'?

Preaching and teaching are addressed to the whole man, aiming to convert him, to change his point of view. Their effects cannot easily be assessed: we judge them by their fruits, but fruits take a long time to ripen. We usually reserve judgement upon any immediate changes they may seem to bring about. Did Jesus address his healing work, similarly, to the whole man rather than the diseased part? In the gospel record he is nearly always reported as having healed sick people rather than as having healed diseases. And did he view the immediate apparent results of his interventions with the same open-mindedness (or scepticism) that we apply to the results of our preaching and teaching? Would he have been interested in the mortality or morbidity statistics of his healing practice as a modern doctor or hospital might be, as a measure of his effectiveness?

Is, then, Christian healing to be seen as concerned with transforming experience and aimed at conversion or repentance as its primary objective - with bodily healing sometimes occurring as a 'spin-off'? Such a view would contrast with that which sees medical missionary work as primarily concerned with getting rid of or inhibiting disease because it is assumed to be against God's will for the afflicted - with conversion or repentance sometimes occurring as a spin-off. The practical implication of the former view will be that the medical task will be seen as essentially that of serving the nurse, who cares for people while they are sick whatever the bodily outcome; rather than one of defining and attacking disorder by special skills in which the nurse is merely the doctor's assistant.

I suppose that if we claim to be seeking wholeness for people, we must include both kinds of consideration. But what is the relation between them? Even if the two approaches are complementary rather than alternative to each other, are they of equal logical status? Or is one a means and the other an end? Do we seek to share meanings, to achieve mutual understanding (information transactions) in order to have control of those energy transactions which make for this-worldly bodily and mental health? Or do we (or ought we to) control the energy transactions as one, but perhaps not the only, means of achieving mutual understanding, of ourselves and the whole created order -which would seem to be a more direct route towards true spiritual health? . . .

References:
1. G.Bateson, **Steps to an Ecology of Mind,** (Paladin), 1973.
3. J.Masters, **To the Coral Strand,** (Michael Joseph), 1962.
4. R.A.Lambourne, '*Models of Health and Salvation*', W.C.C. Study Encounter, Vol. VII, No. 1, 1971.
5. M.Wilson, **Health is for People,** (DLT), 1975.
6. J.McGilvray, '*The Quest for Health and Wholeness*', unpublished, 1979.
7. J. Seabrook, '*Poverty as Metaphor*', in New Society, 28th. February, 1980.
8. R.A.Lambourne, **Community, Church and Healing,** (DLT), 1963.

225 - Bread and Word.

LISTENING

. . . Learning to be a good listener is an important skill for people who undertake a pastoral function, whether they are professionals - clergy or caseworkers or psychotherapists, or what Caplan calls informal caregivers - which means all those who try to be a good neighbour to those in trouble. It may sound paradoxical, but I don't want to limit the idea of listening to purely auditory functioning. A man may be very deaf and yet a better listener than one whose hearing is unimpaired; as, indeed, a blind man may be able to see meanings which are hidden from those with good eyes. When I set out to listen to a client, I try to make sure that I can see the whole of him: I avoid having a table between us. I never feel professionally comfortable trying to listen to someone who is in bed. Listening, as I am using the word, means paying attention to all possible clues I can get about the meanings which the other person is expressing, by his speech, certainly, but also by his gestures, his dress, and his behaviour. Listening is to be contrasted with not listening, rather than with seeing.

It is very much an active process, as many of you will know; and can be exhausting. (If you are a stranger to the psychology of perception, read Mrs. Abercrombie's book "The Anatomy of Judgement.")[1] The listener or observer is presented with a mass of sensory information from which he selects out certain items which he can (as we say) make sense of, or see a pattern in. Any perception involves an act of interpretation. But listening to another person has three characteristics which introduce further complications. *One is* that the other's utterances are essentially transient and evanescent, undergoing constant change in a dynamic way; so that one is trying to discern patterns in time rather than in space. If you look at a picture, or a sculpture, or a building, you may discern certain patterns or make certain interpretations, and you can come back later on and check the interpretations because the picture is still there and unchanged. But with listening, you can't go back to check, and memory is unreliable about objective detail. *Secondly*, the utterances of the other person are immediately responsive to your own behaviour: your looks of surprise or puzzlement, the way you tighten your lips, your looking at your watch or tapping the arm of the chair - will all influence what the other person says and the way that he says it. In a pastoral situation, the listener is a participant rather than an objective observer. In the very act of listening, you are saying something. Your silence speaks as loudly as your word. In a very real sense, you can't listen properly to the other without at the same time listening to yourself. In clinical practice this often results in your discovering that it isn't only your patient who has problems: you have them too. So one of the hardest things about listening is to become sufficiently aware of one's own problems to prevent them distorting one's inter-pretation of the patient's or client's utterance.

The *third* complication of listening lies in the fact that communication goes on simultaneously at a variety of different levels, as Thomas Hardy's description of the wind on the heath showed. When you encounter another person, you display certain signals of your identity: your accent or dialect, your manner of dress, your use or avoidance of gestures, will tell the listener something of what manner of man you are. You may be con-descending or deferential, wary or relaxed, which will tell the listener *how you see yourself* in relation to him. You may talk about the weather, or local gossip for a time, and this may be interpreted as a further attempt to display recognition signals, or as an indication that you need more time to discover what kind of man the listener is; or that you are *defending* yourself from the need to discuss something painful - either to you or to the listener. And as the listener hears your story unfold, he may gradually discern patterns in what you tell him, or in the way you react to him, which *you yourself are not aware of.*

The problem for the listener is to judge which of these different kinds of com-munication to respond to or how to respond to them all at once. Clinically, at least, the various communications of a patient rarely blend into the kind of harmony which Thomas Hardy heard in the wind; more commonly some of them seem to be frankly in conflict. This is perhaps why the psychiatrist sometimes gets caught out by the person who happens to say exactly what he means. Often enough the person in trouble is confused as to the real nature of his problem, and he tends to express his distress at first in terms which he thinks will be acceptable to the listener. So if it is his doctor who he goes to, he will present him with a bodily symptom, if he can think of one, even when he is half aware that the real problem lies in his relationship with his wife. If his doctor happens not to be a good listener, when he is presented with the complaint of a pain in the stomach, say, he may too soon say *"let's have a look at it"*; and thus fail to hear the more important message about the marital disharmony.

One of the advantages of good listening is that one can become aware of the significant omissions in what is offered. If someone sets out to tell you all he remembers of his childhood, and fails to mention his mother, this silence is an important communi-cation, and often deserves a response. But hearing something that isn't said is not easy.

When listening to anyone, one of the questions in the back of my mind is *"what does this man hope for*? What future does he see for himself? Where does he hope to go from here? What is his vision of the good life?" These are important questions. Jesus said to the man who had been crippled for 38 years "Do you *want* to be healed?" - in other words, "are you sure that the strain of re-adaptation to walking upright after so many years (which will be severe) is a challenge which you really want to face?"

To be a good listener is to *offer people the hospitality of your mind:* to give them a chance to feel comfortable and relaxed, to unbutton their protective garments for a while. The truly hospitable person does not force his offerings on an unwilling guest. As Dr. Dillistone has said, "*nothing is so incredible as the answer to an unasked question*". The great enemy of listening is, of course, the tendency to talk too soon and too much. In another context, Jesus pointed out that it isn't what goes in at the mouth that defiles a man, but what comes out of it. (Matthew 15, 10). This seems to be an appropriate point for me to stop talking. But there is just one thing before I do:

Listening is an act of love. Ivan Illich says "*In the prayer of silent listening, and nowhere else, can the Christian acquire the habit of this first silence from which the Word can be born. ...*" The Christian's love of God - eros - is the source of his ability to love his fellow-men - agape; and he who aspires to listen, in love, to the meaning of God's creatures, must first of all learn to listen, in love, to God himself.

Reference:
1. M.J.L.Abercrombie, **The Anatomy of Judgement,** (Pelican), 1969.

111 - Discovering the Value of Listening.

AUTHORITY AND POWER

I want to say something to start with about the nature of authority. Most dictionary definitions seem to equate authority and power, but I think we need to try to distinguish them for our purposes. Let us take a legendary example. By whose authority were the pyramids built? Partly no doubt by the authority of the rulers, who certainly had the power to back up their demands. Some of this authority and power was delegated to the overseers of slave labour. But if the slaves themselves had preferred to die rather than to submit to the authority of the overseers, there would have been no pyramids. If the slaves had refused to acknowledge the overseer's authority, he would have had no authority over them, whatever his superiors might have said; though doubtless he would still have had power, if only to do them to death. So it seems that the ultimate source of the authority which enabled the pyramids to be built lay in the slaves quite as much as in the rulers. Authority, it seems, only exists where it is acknowledged to exist.

But why did the slaves acknowledge this authority? The conditions of slavery may well have seemed so severe that death was preferable. So if slaves acknowledged an overseer's authority, it must surely have been because, at that particular moment, they were provisionally able to trust that particular overseer not to behave in such a way as to make death seem preferable. In fact the slaves' recognition of the overseer's authority depended on their judgement of the overseer as a *person*. No doubt they usually recognised his authority through fear of the power of his whip (though even this was evidently tempered by trust that he would not use it excessively); but sometimes we must conceive that a slavemaster would be so attractive a character that they would do his bidding even without the threat of the lash. In either case, whether authority was acknowledged because of fear or because of love, it would still depend upon a judgement of the *person* who was to wield it.

Authority is perhaps more usually thought of as being the *power* of a particular role or office. This is impersonal 'authority' - a kind of power which seems to work well enough in large organisations such as an army. Respect is paid to the uniform and badges of rank irrespective of the person who wears them. Pastors in dog collars may be respected by their people as having this kind of delegated authority, from God or a bishop - but it seems that the number of people who do respect this kind of authority is diminishing; and perhaps this is a good thing, just because it is impersonal, while our Christian beliefs demand that we value the personal very highly.

This kind of traditional, impersonal authority stems from a man being 'authorised' to do a job or be in a particular place or role by a superior. When your bishop or other superior authorises you to take a pastor's place, he is implicitly stating that he trusts you to act in a way which he would not disapprove; and that he is ready to take the risk that you will alter the situation you are going into, or give him a description of that situation, in a way that he may find unfamiliar and disturbing. He takes the risk that you will alter his perception of the situation (for which he is ultimately responsible) and thus make demands on him to change and adapt. In fact I am suggesting that there is a personal element, an element of personal encounter, interwoven in the source even of 'official' so-called impersonal authority.

What I am saying then is that irrespective of the differences in power wielded by people at various levels of a hierarchy, the basis of all true authority lies in the personal: in one person authorising another person to speak or behave in a way which may alter or disturb the former's understanding of the situation. Such authorisation is essentially provisional and conditional: if the man to whom I have given authority offers to disturb my understanding of the situation too violently, I will withdraw my authorisation from him. . . .

137-2 The Authority of the Pastor.

CHRISTIAN COUNSELLING

. . . We often tend - perhaps despite ourselves - to think of counselling as if it were a kind of medical treatment, administered by a doctor to his patient. The primary meaning of the noun *counsel* is 'an *interchange* of opinions, or consultation' (OED). And the primary meaning of the verb *to consult* is 'to take counsel *together*'. On this showing, the essence of counselling lies in its mutuality, as if taking place between two or more counsellors rather than between a counsellor and clients. The way doctors used to understand the art of consultation may be instructive. When I was a medical student, a doctor who wanted a second opinion about a patient or problem would consult a colleague in his own field: for instance, the general practitioner would often consult another general practitioner - and there would be a genuine interchange of opinions as they took counsel together. Naturally, the colleagues whose opinions were most sought tended to be men of experience and wisdom, so they came to be known as consultants; but the doctor who called for the second opinion remained the one who was responsible for the patient's further treatment, not the consultant. So if the consultation took place in the patient's home, the custom was that his own doctor would enter the bedroom first, and would not leave until his consultant colleague had left it. But when the NHS began, the term consultant was misused to define the senior grade of hospital specialist; and nowadays it is much less common for a consultant to be actually consulted: he usually has patients *referred* to him, which is very different. Referral is not consultation.

Counselling practice is - or should be - offering people an opportunity for consultation. It should be conceived as a forum for the interchange of opinions between two or more people, each with different but allied experience and speaking a common language. No doubt expertise in a particular field is valuable for many purposes, but it is not essential to counselling, and is often a positive hindrance to it. The possession of expertise tends to blunt humility; but a good consultation is one in which the participants share an equal readiness to reconsider their prejudices and preconceived ideas. Our teachers - or bitter experience - will have taught us that it is hardly ever useful in counselling to offer advice, because it is so rarely taken unless it merely restates what those who have consulted us intended to do anyway. Experts make statements, but counsellors ask questions; and many of us will also have learned that one of the most valuable benefits of consultation is that the naive questions, born of humble ignorance, that we ask or that are asked of us often illuminate the matter under discussion enormously - especially when the answers to them are not immediately forthcoming. Perhaps paradoxically, a good model for the counsellor is that of the twelve-year old boy, Jesus, *'sitting in the temple surrounded by the teachers, listening to them and putting questions'*.

Three streams can be discerned in the study of psychology. There are learning theorists who focus attention on the modification of behaviour. There are analytical psychologists whose main concern is with people's emotions and feelings. And there are those who study the mechanisms of perception and cognition. Psychotherapists and counsellors work largely in the emotional field, while their effectiveness tends to be judged by changes in their clients' behaviour. We are sometimes in danger of forgetting that our clinical concern with emotion is not an end in itself. It is an attempt to remove the barriers or distortions which disordered emotions can cause to perception and understanding. Counselling aims to liberate cognition: we try to understand one another; and while we may expect or hope that behaviour will change as a result, this is not our primary business. The counsellor should follow the example of Mary, who sat at our Lord's feet and 'stayed there listening', rather than of Martha, who busied herself with what Emerson calls 'an unnecessary deal of doing'.

What I am trying to establish is that if there is a polarity between knowing and doing, or between understanding people's behaviour and controlling or modifying it, then counselling focuses on the knowing and understanding, and not on doing or controlling. To use an anatomical analogy: in the brain and spinal cord, the motor nerves, which transmit instructions to the muscles and glands, form a system of pathways which is quite distinct from the system of sensory nerves, which collect and arrange the incoming information to which motor functions are a response. Counselling is analogous to the sensory rather than to the motor system.

When the Lord wanted to send Moses to bring the Israelites out of Egypt, Moses at first demurred because he was 'slow and hesitant of speech'. The Lord was apparently irritated by what he felt to be this triviality, but finally agreed to send Aaron with him to be his mouthpiece. Aaron was, so to speak, an artificial aid, a megaphone, say, to compensate for Moses' executive disability. But it was Moses, not Aaron, who heard the word of the Lord; and it was Aaron who, when separated from Moses, fell into idolatry and fashioned the golden calf. That part of our nature which is concerned with doing things needs to be constantly under the discipline of that better, and more complex part, which is concerned with understanding. Or, as a great physician taught us, *'if treatment is good, treatment after thinking is likely to be better'.* We are uncomfortably reminded that in a different context Jesus said that a man is not defiled by what goes into his mouth, but by what comes out of it.

Of course, by contrast with counselling, caring for people may be very much concerned with enabling them to do things. It is good to enable the lame to walk, to provide artificial limbs or dentures, to feed the hungry. It is also good to instruct people in how to do the things they need to do. But such caring activities are not the essence of counselling. Neither is the provision of spectacles or hearing aids, even though those do help sensory rather than motor function. Counselling is essentially concerned with the mutual processing and re-arrangement of the information and experience which people have, not with increasing its quantity nor with the activities which result from it. Its business lies with the re-ordering of perception and experience, with changing perspectives on what is already known, with increasing sensitivity, with quality of thinking and perception rather than with quantity.

With these ideas about the nature of counselling in mind, let us see how the Good News which is part of the Christian counsellor's experience will affect it. There is a sense in which the counsellor himself is the most important part of the message he conveys. He embodies a particular and unique gospel, whether it is the Christian Gospel or not. Whatever else he tries to express, he cannot help expressing *himself.* If he enters a counselling encounter without depending on his special expertise, bringing to it only his own provisional ordering of experience, and a willingness to listen to, communicate with, and learn from others so that their experience, and his own, may be creatively re-ordered - then this *is* the Good News he brings. Every man expresses his version of the gospel he believes in in a unique way; and it is this that will be manifest to others in his utterances and behaviour, in what he says and what he does not say - for better or worse. The gospel we inevitably impart is our own idiosyncratic answer to the question 'what must I do to be saved?' And even for Christians, however firm their belief, that answer can never be more than a partial expression of the Good News which Jesus brought.

It is of the essence of the Christian Gospel that we should be constantly alert and attentive to the word of God. We recognise that a basic requirement for the counsellor is that he should be a good listener. But what is it that we should be listening for? At one level we are no doubt opening ourselves to the disclosure of another's problem. And at a deeper level we are looking for a revelation of the other as a person; for it is only at this level that we can establish that rapport with him which is the essence of a creative relationship. But Christians have this further call upon their sensitivity: that at a third, more fundamental level they have to *watch and pray*. I take this to mean that at the back of the counsellor's mind there is always the underlying question, what is God doing in this situation? What is he trying to show me? What (if anything) does he went me to do, or to say?

At the deeper levels, listening and watching are not to be understood as two separate ways of taking in information, but as expressing indifferently an attitude of active and wide-ranging awareness, not only of the problem or person who attracts attention, but of the various contexts in which the problem or person can be set. We too easily forget to attend to the background as well as the figure, though both are parts of the total perception, and both are essential to it. So often the word of God comes not in the dramatic problem or symptom which is presented to us, not in the wind or earthquake or fire which so readily monopolises attention, but in the still, small voice, the intimate whisper, the superficially insignificant detail which can so easily be missed.

The question arises as to whether we have made two assertions which are incompatible: that counselling requires an attitude of attentive awareness, and that counselling is itself a way of preaching the Gospel. Can an activity which is essentially one of listening and watching be equated with the activity of preaching? My own tentative answer is that it can. No-one knows exactly what Jesus meant by his injunction to 'proclaim the Good News to the whole creation' (or even whether that text is authentic). But we do know that each man expresses the Gospel in his own unique way; and we also know that his sense of certainty is no guarantee that what he is expressing is right. We remember how Oliver Cromwell said to the religious bigots of his time *"I beseech you in the bowels of Christ, think it possible you may be mistaken"*. The Good News may be unchanging, but man's expression of it is not, and any such expression must be tentative and provisional. All attempts to fix it for the future, for instance in the making of creeds, run the risk of leading us into idolatry (it is what comes out of his mouth that defiles a man). In any case, to communicate with most of those who consult us, we have to use language and behaviour which they can understand; and often their distress, and the egocentricity which is a symptom of it, would prevent their hearing a message couched in conventionally religious language.

Thus if the Gospel is to be communicated at all, it is much more likely to be communicated by our behaviour than by our words. Now although none of us would claim that our counselling behaviour will ever be truly Christ-like, it is possible to see that the behavioural rules which we follow are such as at least not to prevent the Christian message becoming manifest. And it would seem to me that the listening and watching attitude, primarily so that God's revelation may be heard or seen, through the relationship established with the other person, occasioned by his consulting us about a problem, does at least begin to preach a gospel of which a Christian need not feel ashamed. Such a stance implies a delicacy of approach, an openness, a vulnerability, a willingness to change even if it involves suffering, a basic trust in oneself and in the other, a faith in the possibility of reconciliation and newness of life. More specifically, it shows forth God's forgiveness, and makes repentance possible. This does not need to be spelt out in words to be effective. It is of the essence of such a counselling stance that it shows the other that he is accepted in spite of whatever horrors he expresses; and because within this situation he is enabled to find a voice with which to utter them, he is freed from the continuing burden of them, and is able to relegate them to the past where they properly belong. And this *is* repentance, *metanoia*, the 'change of mind from past evil'.

Let me stress the claim that this is God's forgiveness, not man's. We may distinguish here between the humanist and the Christian counsellor. The humanist may indeed offer forgiveness by his attitude of acceptance, but his attentive awareness is likely to stay focused on the person or persons he is counselling, and to omit the deepest level of sensitivity to the word of God in the situation. At his best, he is likely to be the kind of counsellor who makes an idolatry of human relationships; who takes his love for his neighbour as ultimate but fails to leave room for the love of God. There are many such, and they may do admirable work within this limited context. But the Christian counsellor, similarly offering forgiveness, does not interpret this as his own contribution, but rather as that of his Master.

Thus there are three ways in which the Christian counsellor is called to a particular humility and self-abnegation. He is called to see his encounter with another person as one between equals, rather than between himself as strong and the other as weak. He is called to resist the temptation to use the power at his disposal to solve the other's problems. This is sometimes a function of pastoral care, of doing; but counselling is concerned with knowing, not doing. And third, he is called to realise that any benefit - to himself or the other - which emerges from the consultation is God's work rather than his own. Such humility and self-denial is hard to achieve and hard to bear. From infancy, our capacity for perception constrains us to discover, or perhaps invent, a pattern of order in what William James called the 'blooming, buzzing confusion' of sensation by which we are assailed. And we all grow up to assume that our spiritual survival, our sense of personal identity, depends like our biological survival on our being able to discern a structure in the world immediately around us and to maintain a measure of control over it. We feel unsure of ourselves unless we can display a competence which is valued by those we meet. Surely, to put aside our role as the dispensers of counsel, as those who possess skill and power, would be to leave ourselves naked and defenceless? Can the blind lead the blind? Will they not both fall into the pit? In fact, I suggest that the model of the blind leading the blind is a very appropriate image for counselling; and preferable to that of the Good Samaritan, which leaves unconsidered the important question of mutuality in loving, and reciprocity in understanding. If two blind men fall into a pit, they can still support each other, and may yet find a way out.

Perhaps such a reading of the counselling task sounds not only visionary but impractical. It is certainly intended to be visionary: *'where there is no vision, the people perish'*. Christian counselling focuses on the present and the future, rather than (as secular counselling often does) on the present and the past. The clinical approach quite properly insists on the importance of history-taking; but we must be wary of too readily assuming that because the past determines the present it enables prediction of the future too. That assumption needs two qualifications. It is only true if the environment remains the same; and in these days of ecological understanding we know the environment is always changing (except sometimes in laboratory experiments). And second, it is only true if the development of events from past to future remains uninfluenced by conscious, deliberate human choice - which is precisely what counselling seeks to foster. We seek to make the unconscious, conscious; and in human affairs accuracy of prediction is only possible when we fail to do so. The value of history is in clarifying the present (the situation as it is) rather than the future (the situation as it ought to be).

But even if our approach is visionary, I do not think it is as impractical as it may appear. Earlier we proposed that Christian counselling involves prayerful and wide-ranging awareness, not only of the other person and his problem but of the context in which they are set. Now once we admit the possibility that the context of a situation may provide the clues to its meaning and significance, we are adventuring into a whole new continent for exploration. For one of the most obvious elements of the context in which the other is set - so obvious that we constantly forget it, as we forget the daylight or the air we breathe - is *one's self*. In a counselling situation, the counsellor himself is the most important element of the other's context. Now to say this is not quite the same as reminding ourselves of the technical importance of transference relationships in psychotherapy, or of Michael Balint's emphasis on the doctor himself being the most powerful drug he can administer; for in both these cases attention is drawn to the two figures in the foreground of the picture. Our emphasis is different. We are deliberately widening our attention so as to examine its background or context. And by doing so we are led to realise that while the counsellor is part of the other's context, he must also see himself as set in other, wider contexts. And so, for the Christian counsellor, what may these be? Is it the worshipping congregation to which he regularly returns to renew his spiritual strength? Or is it that group of experienced counsellors from whom he learnt his skills and to whom he turns again when in difficulties? Or is it the family and friends among whom he finds re-creation? But each and all of these specifiable groups themselves exist in a more comprehensive context, extended not only in space but in time. . . . The series of contexts is infinite. For our present purposes, let us say that the context in which the Christian counsellor is set, and from which he draws his strength, his skills and his sense of identity, is *the communion of saints*. And within this context, as a soldier in Christ's army, we can see that it is not so impractical to engage in counselling with the kind of humility and freedom from the sense of self-reliance that I have suggested. (Is the traditional virtue of *self*-reliance still a truly Christian one, in our current social context?)

At all events, such a perspective has three practical implications. First, the Christian will be reminded that since what he is seeking is the kingdom of God and his righteousness, his holiness, his wholeness - he must always pay as much attention to wholes as he does to parts. It means that he sees the other not only as himself, but as a representative of his family, his work-group, his community. The counsellor will not only try to see Christ in the man before him, but will realise that Christ is also present in those to whom that man is related outside the counselling situation. And so he will be as ready to encounter them as to meet with him alone. Thus he will find the courage to tackle group counselling, to move into community, even though he knows that groups and communities will convict him of powerlessness in a way which the one-to-one relationship commonly hides from him. He can begin to see how a corporate understanding of health and holiness is the context which gives meaning to, and sets limits to the value of, one-to-one counselling.

The second implication of this perspective is that it makes clear that it is the system of values which the Christian brings to counselling that carries healing and reconciling power rather than his technical skill. Without Christian values (whether they are called by this name or not) skills are no more than sounding brass or a tinkling cymbal. Technical ability is valuable in solving defined and limited problems. That is what it is for. But it is a fact of experience that, from a contextual or ecological viewpoint, the solution of one problem merely transfers the stresses and strains to a different location in time or space. To cure illness in the young or middle-aged increases the burden of disability in old age. To relieve traffic congestion in some places by building motorways is to increase traffic jams where they end. By solving the problems of one generation we create new ones for their children to tackle. Problem solving is thus of only transient importance. But the counsellor's scale of values makes an enduring contribution, for better or worse, to the re-ordering of other people's experience: it alters the perspective from which problematic situations are seen, whether it makes them easier to deal with or not.

The third implication is more difficult. When we equip ourselves by learning skills and techniques, we tend to see ourselves as individually responsible for the way we employ them; and the notion of individual responsibility implies a degree of egocentricity. But as soon as we have learnt the discipline and humility proper to a soldier in Christ's army, we begin to see ourselves less as separate soldiers in his army, and rather as cells that form an integral part of his Body. We can understand the soldier to be 'in' the army, but not 'in' the commander-in-chief; but the Christian does discover himself to be 'in Christ'. And this means that we see ourselves as partly responsible for the whole of the Body, and no longer as wholly responsible for that part of it which is centred on ourselves. Our identities become Christocentric instead of egocentric. And within the constraints of love which this implies, we become paradoxically free to be as concerned with our own well-being as with that of others: you can love your neighbour as yourself, and love yourself as you do your neighbour. We come to see one another as more uniquely distinct selves even as we relinquish our view of one another as mutually independent. Sometimes the counselling encounter begins as a dance, and sometimes it begins as a duel; but in either case it should end as a dance, in which the contributions of the partners to its harmony and grace can no longer be distinguished. As St. Paul says, *"the partial vanishes when wholeness comes"*.

The question we are seeking to answer is 'how far does the Evangel impinge upon counselling practice?' Such a formulation implies that the Evangel is in principle extrinsic to counselling, and this I do not believe. The question itself illustrates the risks we run when we use words. To utter a word is to limit, define or label a concept; and the more fundamental the concept is, the greater the likelihood that putting it into words robs it of much of the meaning we intend to convey. This happens when we try to give expression to ultimate beliefs in credal statements, or try to express such ideas as loving, or caring. But the risk is diminished when the attempt to express such a concept is made with the whole of one's being and not just a part of it: a whole which includes one's behaviour and attitudes, one's history and vision of the future; and when it comprehends not only oneself but all those with whom one is in relationship. When a concept is 'lived out' in such a way, in group or community, then perhaps words may provide a crowning precision and a completeness to its meaning - for a moment in time. Jesus talked; but he only wrote once, and that was on the ground. So often, words begin to lose their contextual propriety the moment they are committed to writing, and words taken out of context are dangerous. So when the Good News is uttered, when (as we say) it is *reduced* to words, the speaker of them comes under judgement as well as those who hear or fail to hear them. But behind whatever words we use, within each of us, counsellors or counselled, Christian or Muslim, Buddhist or animist, there is a potential good news, the seed of a unique expression of the Gospel which Christians would recognise as their own. It is the task of the counsellor to act as a midwife, assisting at the birth of the Good News in those he meets; and then to wait with hope and patience for the infant babbling and gurgling to grow into intelligible speech.

To conclude: counselling can no more be separated from other aspects of the pastoral function without losing its significance than can the sensory nervous system be separated from the motor system. I have tried to avoid suggesting that I believe in counselling as a specialist occupation. There may possibly be some justification for temporary specialisation in some other fields of pastoral action -though even here my sympathies lie with Lambourne's dictum that *"what is required is pastoral care which is lay, corporate, adventurous, variegated and diffuse"*. But counselling, as I understand it, is an inherent and inescapable part of any caring encounter with anyone who is not at the time unconscious or in a coma.

Endnote: The above paper is based on the writings of R.A.Lambourne, especially those listed below.
Essential Reading:
R.A.Lambourne: *'Authority, Personal Knowledge and the Therapeutic Relationship'*, Contact, (Edinburgh), No. 25.
'Objections to a National Pastoral Organisation', Contact, (Edinburgh), No. 35.
'Personal Reformation and Political Formation in Pastoral Care', Contact, (Edinburgh), No. 44.
'Authority and Acceptance in Pastoral Counselling', Expository Times, 8th May, 1970.

181-How Far does the Evangel impinge upon Counselling Practice?

Chapter Five

FEELINGS

The experience of a panic on the docks of Singapore during World War Two impressed on James the solidarity of his own inner feelings with those of a terrified mob. Further experience of shared feelings of anxiety or guilt with individual or groups of patients led him to explore, as a doctor, the value of vicarious suffering on behalf of others.

He regarded the free inter-communication of feelings as an important factor in social and mental health. He also noted the failure of our present educational system to enable us to understand and discipline our emotional make-up as an equally important part of our humanity to logical thought.

He considered it important for adults to understand the mental mechanisms by which we defend ourselves against feelings that we find too painful or threatening. Denial, projection and detachment of feelings may damage not only our own but other people's health. It is part of normal human growth and development to understand our own minds and bodies. Unbridled feelings of aggression, violence and prejudice dog modern life whether in family quarrels, House of Commons debates or tribal conflicts.

M.W.

COMMUNICATION

. . . Communication of emotion is a biological imperative among social animals. When one dog barks, so do all within hearing distance. We cannot help expressing our feelings and we cannot help sharing them - even when we don't know whence they were aroused. . . .

Biologically then, we start with the common heritage we have with other social mammals - that we have to express our feelings, and have to have our feelings aroused by the feelings expressed by those around us. This is the raw stuff of communication and relationship: sympathy in its original Greek meaning of 'feeling with' others. Even at this animal level we must remember that the great enemy of such communication and primitive sympathy is *fear*. A little fear may draw the herd together, but a little more will scatter the herd in panic and, ultimately paralyse the individual. . . .

24 - Mental Health and Personal Relationships

TOTAL FEELING

. . .Typical of infancy is the all-or-none character of the way the child feels. The comfortable and well-fed baby's expression has a blissfulness older folk envy. And when things are less comfortable, his expression of rage is total - he puts his heart and soul into it. As he gets older, he slowly learns to master these overwhelming feelings, and is able to modulate his emotions less crudely, feeling more or less angry or content as the situation justifies. But when his emerging sense of identity is threatened, the 'total' mode of structuring experience tends to reappear. We all remember childhood occasions of anger to which our response was 'all right: that settles it, I'll never speak to him again'. So this kind of all-or-none response is more primitive and crude than our normal way of interpreting the world. Normally, the boundary between the self and the not-self is open and fluid; but the 'total' mode draws a sharp boundary between the black outside world and the white inside: it is utterly inclusive and exclusive.

Such a primitive alternative to normal functioning is not something to be rejected at all costs. It has survival value in extreme situations, and helps to preserve one's sense of identity when it is threatened. It is like the body's physiological response to fear - valuable in emergencies but not healthy if it continues when the danger is past.
. . .

112-3 The Nature of Prejudice.

ANXIETY

. . . Both anxiety and the sense of guilt carry the same basic meaning, of a threat to the individual's ego-identity or self-esteem.[2] It is the task of psychopathology to elucidate the various mechanisms by which the human being, consciously or uncon- sciously, tries to evade these very unpleasant experiences - mechanisms such as denial, projection, displacement, dissociation and so on. Such mental mechanisms are still apparently accepted as pathological: in fact, they very often seem to be pretty effective and they appear to be universal among the species, so it is rather surprising that someone has not suggested their recategorisation as psychophysiological rather than psychopatho- logical. I suppose this is because of an unspoken awareness that although they may be 'normal' in the sense of being average, they are not normal in the proper sense of being optimal. Perhaps the clergy recognise more readily than the psychopathologist that there is another, more difficult way for a man to deal with his sense of guilt - an optimal way, which is not unconscious and is not automatic. This is by experiencing repentance, - *metanoia* - a change of mind. It is characteristic of this change of mind that it is in the direction of reconciliation (with God and one's brethren); which is to say that it leads away from an egocentric context to a sociocentric or God-centred one. The man no longer judges his guilty act or guilty state as something for which he, alone and unaided, has to accept responsibility, but recognises that, being restored to communion with his fellows, the responsibility for his state and his behaviour is now something he shares with them. And similarly, of course, he finds that he is expected to accept some responsibility for the state and behaviour of his fellows.

I want to examine the possibility that the optimal way for a man to deal with the anxiety experience is also through a change of mind, a *metanoia*, of a similar kind. The word 'repentance' can be defined as a 'change from past evil'; so when the psychothera- pist seeks to help his client to 'work through' his anxiety is he really helping him to 'repent' from his anxiety?

* * * * *

Let me make some preliminary comments. Firstly, I am talking primarily about subjective experience, anxiety, and only incidentally about objectively observable phenomena. But I shall assume that anxiety always affects behaviour, however deviously; and that this behaviour can be observed and interpreted by others. (I acknowledge that the behaviour of one person is frequently unobserved or misunderstood by others, but in principle, I consider that a man cannot help expressing his experience by his behaviour except for short periods, and when he panics. Panic, of course, is the most severe form of anxiety, and its main behavioural characteristic is that its expression conveys confusing, or no signals for communication to others. However, this does not prevent it *being* communicated, since the mere absence of signals from another person who is seen to be alive is anxiety-provoking).

Secondly, we must be clear that we are concerned with neurotic anxiety, and that this is an experience directly rooted in the infant's experience of dread, antedating that stage of development when the infant can locate the source of the threat.[3] It is therefore more primitive than fear of an objectively perceived danger (whether located inside or outside the body). It is free-floating anxiety - the fear of non-being. Anxiety is re-aroused in later life by any situation which is subjectively perceived as a crisis - that is, by a situation presenting a problem which previous experience, guidance or education has not equipped the individual to solve; and this later experience of anxiety inevitably draws its patterning and quality, and to a variable extent its vehemence - from all previous experiences of anxiety back to infancy. However much the current crisis may differ in externals from former ones, the neurotic anxiety experience is the same one - it has, so to speak, an identity, even if it alters; just as I am still the same person as I was when I was a child, even though I differ in certain respects from what I was then, and might not be recognised from my photograph.

Thirdly, we are concerned with what is potential in the human phenomenon rather than what is actual. For this reason, and because we are focussing on a subjective experience, the traditional methods of objective science cannot be expected to test the validity of my hypothesis. In Teilhard de Chardin's words, we are concerned with the 'within' rather than the 'without' of things.[4]

* * * * *

When a baby experiences anxiety it expresses distress, and mother is moved to behave in such a way as to reassure it. What moves her to do so? It is clearly something much more primitive than a rational decision. Her motive is not properly described as altruistic. It is *compassionate* - a fellow feeling. She shares in the child's anxiety in some degree. If she feels nothing of this, she does nothing, and indeed, if she behaves with irritation or rejection, it is only because she cannot help feeling anxiety in response to the baby's cry - though her behaviour is inappropriate. The behaviour she usually exhibits is thus directed to the relief of the anxiety of both the baby and herself. Her reassurance relieves the baby of the feeling that his existence is threatened, and in so doing she enables his sense of personal identity to grow stronger. The basic strength of the human infant, according to Erikson, is hope: *"the enduring belief in the attainability of fervent wishes, in spite of the dark urges and rages which mark the beginning of existence."*[5]

There are of course many situations in which mother no sooner perceives the child's anxiety than she is able, through her superior ability, to abolish it forthwith by unilateral action. Such unilateral behaviour by a parent-figure confirms and validates the infant's hopefulness; and at this early stage it may be all the child needs to continue healthy development. Similarly, in the doctor-patient encounter, the doctor's diagnostic skill and therapeutic experience may justify his prescription of treatment with only a trivial degree of emotional involvement or compassion.

But hope is only the first of the virtues or strengths which a person needs to develop if he is to master later anxieties. Erikson[6] lists eight of them, each emerging as the attainment of successive stages of development. After *hope* in infancy come *will*, *purpose* and *competence* in childhood; *fidelity* marks the emergence from adolescence, and mutual *love, care* for dependents, and ultimately *wisdom*, are the virtues of adult life.

So let us move on a little, to a stage when the child has clearly gained an awareness of self, and is mastering his wilfulness. (Will is 'the unbroken determination to exercise free choice as well as self-restraint, in spite of the unavoidable experience of shame and doubt in infancy'). At such a stage, it is probable that mother will sometimes reassure her child by saying 'we don't feel so frightened (or angry or anxious) do we?' She uses the first person plural. It seems that the child is now able to experience himself as part of a group of two - a group which, so to speak, experiences anxiety mainly 'in' him. So the context of the anxiety experience is altered: from being a threat to the child's ego-identity pure and simple, it becomes partly at least a threat to a 'we'-identity. And the responsibility for the solution of the child's problem is experienced as being not 'mine alone' but 'mine as a member of this group'.

At this stage, it is clear that the childish virtues of will, purpose or competence (whichever is appropriate) will not be adequately exercised and confirmed if the parent always relieves the anxiety aroused by every new crisis by unilateral action (if she 'wraps the child in cotton wool'). Having enabled her child to experience his anxiety in a 'we'-context, she has to begin posing the question 'how will we solve this problem?', so that the child can begin to take on the responsibility of group membership by adding his own initiative to the solution. In this way, crisis becomes the occasion of learning, and progress toward maturity can proceed.

* * * * *

Having had a brief look at what may potentially happen to the child's experience of anxiety, we must consider what is involved for the mother or parent-figure who tries to help. We can note first of all that if someone is to be relieved of anxiety in an optimal way, there does have to be another person who cares. (In everyday life, no doubt many sufferers are left to cope with anxiety more or less on their own; and usually this results in the development of psychopathological symptoms by the action of unconscious defence mechanisms - as, for instance, Freud demonstrated in his 'Psychopathology of Everyday Life.'[7] Possibly, older children whose ego-strength is in any case likely to be increasing through the general processes of physical and emotional growth, might occasionally learn to solve new and critical problems on their own, without the current support of a caring person; but for them to do so without developing some quirk of character or behaviour which betrays the presence of an unresolved anxiety must be rare).

To respond to an anxious person's signals of distress by caring for him is not an inescapable biological imperative. Certainly, it is common enough in maternal experience; but as we saw, mother's behaviour is directed as much to relieving her own anxiety, aroused by the child's distress, as it is to relieving the child's distress itself. Anxiety is catching, and its expression is repellent rather than attractive. Unless there is a prior bond of love or commitment to an anxious person, most of us will try to avoid him, or seek a quick escape from the infection of anxiety. If we do not literally cross the road to avoid him, we find ourselves remembering an urgent appointment, or we buy the sufferer a drink, and perhaps have one ourselves. In the consulting room, the doctor or psychiatrist finds himself prescribing a sedative instead of making time to listen to the patient's story.

But in my own case, for instance, I do have a professional commitment to the anxious person; and however much my immediate reaction may be to escape from the contagion of anxiety, the very fact that the sufferer has appealed to me for help means that my self-esteem is jeopardised if I fail to help him; and since it is often the case that, as an onlooker, I can see possibilities of solving his problem which haven't occurred to him, there is a conflict between my desire to escape and my desire to help. This experience appears basically similar to that of the mother with her child. But, as we have seen, once the child has achieved a separate ego-identity, the unilateral solving of the critical problem by mother denies the child a necessary learning experience; and the same difficulty arises in any other care-giving or therapeutic situation.

For the helping person, therefore, the implications of all this seem to be that he must be able to form a bond with the sufferer so that together they form a 'we'-group; and that he must (temporarily) have the ability to experience and tolerate the other's anxiety until he understands, and until the sufferer also understands, how the problem may be solved; and he must have the strength not to allow himself to use psychopathological mechanisms to cut short the process.

So far so good. But what are we to say about the situation when the helper sees *no* solution to the problem presented by the anxious one; or, if he thinks he sees it, finds that the solution lies far outside the competence of either of them? This is the common experience of social workers and social psychiatrists. The 'we'-group of two, helper and sufferer, is a context which is too narrow for most real-life situations other than that of mother and infant. We find that all the members of a family, or primary group, tend to be involved in the anxiety and crisis of the individual; and in turn, we find that the crises and problems of families and primary groups are themselves involved in those of the community at large. Some of us, committed either professionally or through love of our fellows, have learned to tolerate some of the anxieties of individuals; and some fewer of us are beginning to learn the harder task of tolerating the anxieties of families and small groups. Some of R.D.Laing's recent essays[8] show what a hard task this can be. But how many of us can look at the anxiety and panic of our whole generation without escaping into psychopathology?

You will remember that we are looking for optimal ways of dealing with anxiety rather than average, pathological ways. The value of an optimum is that it can sometimes be a true norm - a fixed standard by which we can evaluate, if not measure, the sub-optimal phenomena of experience and behaviour with which we are in daily contact. Stephen Neill has made the point that in this proper sense of the word, normal human nature is best exemplified by Jesus of Nazareth.[9]

Let us consider what may have been his experience of anxiety. Since he was fully human, he no doubt had infantile and childhood experiences of it but we cannot usefully guess at them. We can guess that in his baptism he was affirming his common humanity, and his willingness to share in the anxieties of his fellows (which, as we have seen, is a primary condition of ability to help others). His experience in the wilderness must at the least have exercised his capacity for withstanding anxiety; and indeed, we can see, in the account of the temptations, how the devil invited him to evade the challenge of affirming his true self, his sense of identity, by sub-optimal techniques - or mental mechanisms.

During his ministry we are told of several occasions on which he went apart from the multitudes. No doubt, as the records say, he went apart to pray, but we can guess that these would be times when he felt that 'virtue had gone out of him'. This is a common enough human experience and we can fill it out a bit. When we have this feeling, at the end of a session when we have been involving ourselves in caring for anxious people, what does it mean to us? That we feel exhausted, emotionally drained. We become irritable and uncertain of our judgement. If circumstances forced us to carry on without rest or refreshment to our spirit, we would feel that our ego-identity, our self-esteem would be threatened. In fact we would suffer, albeit transiently, from anxiety.

Jesus cared for individuals, sharing their anxieties as a parent. Surely he suffered from this shared anxiety. His ministry to individuals led him to criticise the scribes and pharisees - the social establishment of his day, which, as always in human history rejects and excommunicates those whose anxieties it finds intolerable. And then, when his experience of the social factors underlying individuals' anxieties was ripe, he went up to Jerusalem, to the seat of the temporal and ecclesiastical power. He wept over it; and thereafter followed the experience in Gethsemane and the crucifixion.

What are we to think of his experience in Gethsemane? Throughout his ministry he had shared the anxieties of those who had sought his aid. He had risen above the temptations to escape from anxiety by magical (dissociative) means (making stones into bread), or by using worldly power, or by a self destroying gesture (by throwing himself down from the temple parapet). In going to Jerusalem he faced the ultimate challenge to his self-evaluation as the bringer of Life, God's Messiah. In the garden he experienced 'horror and dismay', and his 'heart was ready to break with grief'. Was this because he was afraid of the cross, afraid of personal death? Or was it because the load of anxiety and sense of guilt which he had so willingly shared with the rest of humanity had become too great to be borne by one human being?

* * * * *

Such an attempt as this to guess at the vicissitudes of another person's subjective experience makes clear the inadequacy of our language for the purpose. I started with a definition of anxiety as meaning a threat to *ego*-identity or *self*-esteem. When discussing anxiety in the growing child I talked of it becoming, at least partly, a threat to a 'we'-identity; and now I find myself talking of the experience of Jesus as that of anxiety, though here we must guess that its meaning was his fear lest chaos should continue to be the lot of that humanity with which he had identified himself, his fear that his prayer 'that they may all be one' should remain unanswered, or answered negatively.

I am not happy to be using the same word for these three very different experiences. But they seem to have an identity in the same way that the words infant, boy, adolescent, man can all be used of the same individual. The three different experiences are really, perhaps, the same experience in the context of different stages of development.

* * * * *

Let me finally go back to the question I posed at the beginning. Is the problem of 'working through' anxiety really the same as the problem of 'repenting' from a sense of guilt? I would suggest that it is. Since a sense of guilt is a derivative of anxiety, this would not be improbable on *a priori* grounds. It seems to me that the change of context, from ego-identity through successive stages of 'we'-identity, are each of them occasions for metanoia, for a change of mind, in each of which anxiety is experienced in a new perspective, each leading forward to a greater maturity, a greater integrity of personality, and - paradox of life itself - to a readiness to accept ever greater burdens and thus risk the new-found integrity anew.

References:
2. E.H.Erikson, **Insight and Responsibility**, (W.W.Norton), New York, 1964, p.86.
3. S.Freud, **Introductory Lectures on Psychoanalysis**, (Allen & Unwin), Revised Second Edition., 1943, p.341.
4. P. Teilhard de Chardin, **The Phenomenon of Man**, (Fontana, Collins), 1965.
5. E.H.Erikson, **Insight and Responsibility**, (W.W.Norton), New York, 1964, p.118.
6. loc.sit. p.119.
7. S.Freud, **The Psychopathology of Everyday Life,** (Hogarth Press), 1901.
8. R.D.Laing, **The Politics of Experience**, (Penguin), 1967.
9. S.Neill, **A Genuinely Human Existence**, (Constable), 1969, p.35.

71 - The Context of Anxiety.

VICARIOUS GUILT

. . . I want to draw attention to two other ways in which guilt feeling may arise, neither of which stem primarily from the moral fault of the sufferer. The first is that since guilt feeling is emotional, it will tend to spread, as if by contagion or infection, from the sufferer to others, irrespective of its origin. We know this is true of such emotions as anxiety, cheerfulness or sadness. In such cases, emotional expression is often overt, so the tendency to spread is easily understood. But since people usually try to hide (hardly ever entirely successfully) the expression of guilt, the initial conscious response of those around tends to be one of puzzlement. However, the fact that the meaning of emotional behaviour is not consciously recognized by others by no means lessens the likelihood of emotional contagion occurring. On the contrary, it increases it. If I enter a roomful of people who are all gloomy, I am likely to feel gloomy myself - precisely until I consciously recognize that the others are miserable and take some action either to cheer them up or at least to avoid their influence on me. So unacknowledged guilt is likely to be especially contagious. This hypothesis is not easy to verify, because few will admit to feelings of guilt which seem to them entirely irrational. It is more likely that people will rationalize their feelings as being due to some specific cause: plenty of other more respectable labels are easily available. We can say we feel anxious, or inadequate, or even ashamed -more easily than that we feel guilty; and can in turn rationalize our anxiety, inadequacy or shame in inappropriate ways. But the hypothesis of 'free-floating' guilt may be of value as an explanation of why so many seem to be obsessed by it despite the remarkable efficiency of the mental defence mechanisms, such as denial and projection, which enable us to repress the guilt feeling aroused internally by our own instinctual acts and intentions. Those whose sins are most flagrant rarely seem to feel particularly guilty: it is the more saintly among us who seem to have a well-marked conviction of 'sin'.

The second way in which guilt feeling may be induced without moral fault is when we become aware of other people acting in a way which conflicts with our own moral standards. We usually call this shame, but is there really a difference between shame and guilt, except in the degree to which we feel isolated from our fellows? A simple illustration would be a class of small children in school when the teacher demands to know who stole the purse out of one of their coats in the cloakroom. It is likely that several of the children would show the outward signs of guilt - blushing, lowering of the eyes and so on; and perhaps equally likely that the objectively guilty one would not be among them! Here is another example, which perhaps illustrates both mechanisms. Just before the fall of Singapore in 1942 I was attached as the military doctor to a ship evacuating refugees from that port. At the time there was no enemy activity within ten miles, but for some reason there was a total breakdown of order on the quayside and a situation of panic occurred. Along with a member of the crew, I was tied to the bottom of a companionway, pulling one refugee after another across a gap of about three feet between the quay and the ship until the moment she sailed. Most of the refugees were British and (I was younger then) I felt deeply - ashamed? guilty? - of the disorderly behaviour and unnecessary panic they displayed. We then sailed for fourteen days across the Indian Ocean, unmolested, and throughout the voyage one after the other of the passengers came to me expressing, or rationalizing, their guilt or shame at what had occurred. For what it is worth, I can only testify that my feeling in that situation was one not of shame but of unmistakable guilt. Although I was literally separated from those who were panicking, and was too busy to panic with them, I identified myself with them, unconsciously I suppose, and could not help sharing in their feelings subsequently. Doubtless an ingenious spiritual counsellor or psychotherapist could discover within me all sorts of moral faults with which to rationalize my guilt feeling then; but by what criterion could I come to prefer his explanation to the one I am suggesting? The conventional psycho-analytic explanation of situations such as this is that the sight of others' behaviour arouses an instinctual wish in oneself to emulate them, and that this is the source of the guilt one feels. Even if this is true, one's guilt feeling in such a situation does not originate from a personal moral fault: its source lies externally.

However that may be, these two sources of what we may call *vicarious* guilt feeling may help to account for many cases and situations which classical explanations seem to fit inadequately. One immediately obvious implication is that guilt feeling does not inevitably point to individuocentric moral turpitude with its connotation of lowered self-respect; on the contrary, it is an indication of one's capacity for common human sympathy. And, since if I am affected by others' behaviour, they also are affected by mine, the recognition of vicarious guilt feeling *enlarges* the field of my moral responsibility: instead of holding myself to be wholly responsible for my own moral behaviour, I have to recognize that I am partly responsible for that of all those with whom I identify or am in communication. The concept of vicarious suffering is of course well recognized both pastorally and theologically; and if suffering can be vicarious, why not guilt feeling? . . .

77-4 Vicarious Guilt Feelings.

DEPRESSION

What is the difference between 'feeling depressed' and 'suffering from depression'? Jack Dominian is aware of the difficulty of the question, but in this book he limits himself to describing the 'current approach of medical science to depression'. He does it very well: he faithfully portrays not only the content of what most doctors think about it, but also the manner of their thinking. So he writes as if depression is a disease entity, rather than a quality of feeling which is sometimes so severe as to need medical help. This is indeed what medical science does: it shifts attention from the person who feels depressed to the depression which a person feels. The perspective allows for more or less satisfactory investigation and explanation of the non-personal factors in the sufferer's condition, but even in Dr. Dominian's hands it becomes confusing when we consider grief and mourning. Are such experiences only predisposing causes of depression or are they depression itself? He writes of mourning as having a 'depressive quality permeating through its component elements', which suggests abnormality, but continues 'and yet the process is undoubtedly a normal one'. Elsewhere he says that the process of grieving can benefit by being shared with other people. Quite so; but do the feelings of those who share also have a depressive quality? And if so, when the sharer is a medical man (as he may be), why will he prescribe antidepressants for the sufferer but not for himself? Such questions put in doubt the adequacy of a conceptual model which focuses on the disease instead of on the person. Dr. Dominian does not neglect the personal, but his use of the medical model inevitably makes it subsidiary rather than primary.

The book is interesting to read and will be of value to non-medical counsellors and others, not least because of the questions and doubts it will raise in the reader's mind.

174 - Review: Jack Dominian, 'Depression: What is it? How do we cope?'

SYMPTOMS OR SIGNS

... A man may feel ill, and his doctor may or may not make a diagnosis of disease. Feeling ill and being diseased are two quite different things. One is subjective and the other objective and it is fallacious to assume them to be correlated with one another in most cases. Out of 100 people, about five will neither feel ill nor have anything objective wrong with them. At the other end of the scale, some 20 or 23 will have a diagnosed disease and will feel ill or at least know subjectively that they are not well. But for the rest - about three-quarters of them - feeling ill and being diseased do not go together. Many of them will have symptoms - headaches or muscle pains or feelings of tiredness or irritability - which don't take them to the doctor and which he would not diagnose as disease if they did. Conversely, if a doctor were to examine this 75% he would find all sorts of diseases, mostly minor but some more serious, which were not giving any symptoms at all. (This is the justification for some of the screening techniques which doctors suggest at times.) Doctors are trained to pay particular attention to objective signs of disease, and to be rather mistrustful of the subjective symptoms which patients report to them. They tend to dismiss symptoms as trivial unless they find objective signs which confirm that disease is present. It is persons who have symptoms, and bodies which show signs. This often accounts for patients' dissatisfaction with doctors; and sometimes leads to less than good care for those who are dying. When a disease process is beyond medical reversal, it is the treatment of the person and his symptoms that matters, not further ineffectual treatment of his disease.. . .

191-4 Little Bends in the Truth.

HUMAN LIMITATIONS

... What we take in through our senses - eyes and ears, noses and skin - is only a tiny fraction of the whole truth even of our close surroundings. Our sense organs are only sensitive within a range that is peculiar to the human species. We can't see ultraviolet or infrared light waves. Bees can see ultraviolet but can't see red. We can't hear very high pitched sounds, but dogs can, and so can bats. Different species have different samples of the whole truth to deal with. Nature saw to it that our evolutionary ancestors developed just the particular kinds of perceptual equipment that they needed to survive in the particular environments in which they lived. Of course, humankind has become so clever that we can improve on nature in some ways: we invent technical devices to measure

FEELINGS

wavelengths and record them on dials so we can partly overcome some parts of our sensory inadequacy. . . .

191-3 Wholeness and Truth.

A CHANGE OF FEELING

How does a severely handicapped child feel when he is first put on a horse? Till then his view of the world has been largely from below; he has had to be dependent on other people looking down on him from above. Furthermore he has experienced himself as a failure in almost everything he has tried to do. But once he is seated on a horse, he sees the world - and himself - from a new and uplifting perspective. Now he is the one who is looking down on other people from above - six feet above contradiction like the parson in his pulpit! If he enjoys the experience as many do, he is likely to show rapid all-round improvement for several months.

But then the novelty begins to wear off, and after this first rush of improvement there is nearly always a year or more in which further improvement seems slight or absent. Do not be depressed by this. Experience suggests that between 18 months and 2 years after this first exciting experience, improvement in many children will start again, more slowly but more steadily and may then continue until the child reaches whatever peak of which he may be capable.

A similar pattern of change is often found in older people who undergo a major upheaval in their lives, such as moving to a strange country, getting unexpected promotion at work, a crippling accident, or bereavement. It takes about two years for the experience to be properly digested and for such people to become familiar with their new sense of who they are. It seems the new experience sows the seed of a new *sense of identity*, and this seedling becomes established in the first few months, but it takes about 2 years before it produces the fruit of a more mature and wiser personality.

So, have patience. It takes a long time for 'horse therapy' to show its full effect.

210 - 2 The Case for Continuity.

IDENTITY, DISCRIMINATION AND PREJUDICE

Scene: A predominantly black youth center in Birmingham, 1978. Two young black people are playing table tennis. One, about to serve, suddenly stops, puts his hands on the table and says to the other "The thing is, man, are we really the children of God, or not?"

How does a black youth really feel when he faces a white policeman in one of our inner city areas? How would I feel if I were really in his shoes? It is never very easy to see things from the other man's point of view. It always requires a deliberate effort, and often we feel too busy, or too anxious, to make the leap of imagination that is necessary. Christian people set a high value on compassion or sympathy - two words whose original meaning is feeling *with* others. They imply that we should strive to feel as others do, but usually we make the opposite assumption, that others feel as we do. Of course, we can never be sure that we really feel as another person does, however hard we try. But even if we have to accept this inevitable uncertainty, it is still very important to make the effort.

In our western society, both the academic and scientific traditions teach us to deal with problems dispassionately. It is a very effective method in dealing with objects which have no feelings, requiring us to suppress or disregard any subjective feelings of our own which would impair our objectivity. But where problems are concerned with other human beings, we ignore their subjectivity - their feelings and attitudes and their sense of who they are - at our peril. So in this chapter we will consider discrimination, identity and prejudice: three concepts which find their significance at the place where subject and object meet, in the sphere of interaction between oneself and others.

Discrimination

Discrimination is in danger of becoming a dirty word, because we so often assume it to imply discriminating against someone or some group. But its dictionary meaning is to distinguish between things, and in this sense to say that someone is dis-criminating is to pay him a compliment. It is necessary for the human animal, as for all others, to be able to discriminate between his own kind and other kinds, who may be predators or prey. Discrimination is fundamental to survival not only of the individual, who must eat but not be eaten, but also of the species, which requires the individual to find a mate and ensure reproduction. But we are the only species which has the capacity to think about and conceptualise the discriminations we make. We alone can choose whom we will regard as 'us' and whom we will see as 'them'. When occasion arises, we are able to change these categories: in the light of experience, friends may become enemies, and enemies, friends. Although there is biological evidence that there were once six different races of human beings, as shown by such things as skin colour and blood groups, they are all able to interbreed and have done so; so that now there is certainly only one human species. Of course, we can, if we wish, distinguish particular groups of people as what Erik Erikson calls *pseudospecies*: in some primitive languages, the same word is used to denote a member of one's own tribe, and a member of the human species. Foreigners are not categorised as human.

Born, or adopted, into a family who nurture him, a child at first accepts them as his own kind, and in the process of growing up will learn to discriminate between acceptable and unacceptable others. If the child or his family feel threatened, the dis-crimination will tend to be uncompromising, rigidly inclusive and exclusive. But when child and family feel reasonably secure, the boundary between 'them' and 'us' is less defensive and more flexible, discriminations are made more sensitively and, so to speak, allow for various shades of grey to soften the boundary between black and white. And in making such positive and negative choices among other people, a person necessarily comes to identify himself at the same time as he identifies others. He develops a *sense of personal identity.*

Sense of Identity

The sense of identity constitutes the core of each person's experience. He only communicates it to others indirectly and implicitly, except perhaps in the privacy and intimacy of a love-relationship. It is subjective, and it is unique; so objective generalisations such as I am making here are likely to be experienced as partial and superficial at best; or as irrelevant; or, at worst, as derogatory and dehumanising. Whatever statements can be made are *guesses* about how other people experience themselves, and if applied to a particular person or group should be employed tentatively, with sensitivity and imaginative sympathy.

For the growing child, his sense of identity is modified and differentiated with his discovery of new skills and capacities, and their recognition and acceptance by others, providing provisional answers successively to such implicit questions as "what can I hope for?" "what can I imagine myself to become?" and "what am I competent to control?" With the advent of puberty, these partial elements of identity come together in an often turbulent and always critical way; and the so-called adolescent identity crisis consists of the effort to integrate the parts into a whole. Attempts to do so are often manifested as 'experimental' identities in the period before maturity.

The range of identity-options open to a young person is very much affected by the way other people in his social environment validate or reject such life-styles as he offers. If none of those he feels able or willing to adopt meet with approval from those around, he may experiment with 'negative' identities, such as those of drop-out, delinquent or sick patient. When we label particular lifestyles or behaviour patterns in these ways, we are at risk of uttering self-fulfilling prophecies: give a dog a bad name and he is more likely to bite. In a rapidly changing society where the cultural norms and life-styles of parents hardly retain their relevance to social survival for the two decades their children need to reach adulthood, adolescent identity confusion may almost be regarded as normal; and this imposes on us a responsibility to provide young people with a 'psychosocial moratorium' in late adolescence, during which we continue to be supportive while suspending judgement upon (and diagnosis of) the life-styles they provisionally adopt.

Prejudice

There is always a considerable difference between the description of a man given by his friends or acquaintances, and the way he would describe himself. We are rarely aware of our own shortcomings until other people point them out to us. It is understandable that to preserve his sense of identity and self-esteem, a man will try to exclude such negative elements. So if a person does find himself afflicted with attitudes or impulses which his self-respect will not accept, he tends to project them outwards on to some other agency. In less scientific cultures than ours, such an agency would often be an evil spirit or the Devil. When St Paul said *"The good that I would, I do not, but the evil that I would not, that I do",* he found himself impelled to go on *"it is no more I that do it, but sin that dwelleth in me"* - as if sin were an agent independent of himself. Unlike St Paul (who still accepted responsibility for his own sinful actions), and especially in our western world where only a few believe in evil spirits, most of us have an unregenerate tendency to project the evil we encounter in ourselves on to some convenient group of people from whom we have already discriminated ourselves. *They* are evil, *we* are good; *they* are dirty, *we* are clean; *they* have destructive impulses against which *we* must protect ourselves; it is never *we* who provoke conflict, it is always *them*. *They* are beasts, dogs, pigs: *we* alone are human. Thus those whose culture, behaviour or skin colour are most obviously different from our own present us with readily available 'scapegoats' on to whom we load our own evil; and herein lies the origin of so-called 'racial' prejudice - which really springs from the same roots as any other kind of prejudice.

The tendency to prejudice is thus deeply rooted in human nature and is aroused whenever we feel our sense of identity or self-esteem to be threatened, from whatever cause. To be prejudiced against someone or some group is to make a judgement which disregards their rights. It is therefore *unreasonable* - however ingeniously we may rationalise it. Our choice of scapegoat is not related to the threat in a rational way: it depends on logically irrelevant factors, such as their unfamiliarity or foreignness, and their visibility. Prejudice is likely to be more of a problem the greater the difference between the majority community and the strangers in appearance and behaviour; and the greater their number relative to the majority. 'Racial' prejudice may thus be more obvious in inner city areas than in rural ones; but the tendency to it lies deep in the hearts of all men everywhere. We may not be able to rid ourselves of prejudice entirely (a good test is to ask ourselves "how would you like your child to marry one of them?") but when we behave towards strangers with respect, courtesy and hospitality, their unfamiliarity is lessened, and it is easier to control our tendency to make scapegoats of them.

Threats to identity

It is only when one's sense of identity is threatened or challenged that one is likely to pay attention to it. As we said earlier, in conditions of reasonable security, the boundary of the self is fairly yielding and flexible and transactions across it, incorporating new elements and relinquishing existing ones, proceed smoothly. When apparent threats provoke defensive measures, these take the form of clarifying and hardening the boundary, so that it gains strength at the cost of flexibility and sensitivity. The implicit question "whom do men say that I am?" is rephrased more explicitly as "who the devil do they think I am?"; or, since people seek confirmation of their identities in groups of their peers, "who do they think we are?" or "who do they take us for?". Boundary trans-actions become marked by hostility and a tendency to treat outsiders as not fully human - as non-persons. The black youth does not see the policeman as an individual person, but as 'the fuzz'. And the same is true for the white man, threatened by finding himself among the alien group: he calls them 'cattle' or some other collective, undiscriminating, non-human term of abuse.

Depersonalisation

Such examples show how we react to anxiety by *depersonalising* others, and thus hinder communication with them. But a sense of insecurity is not the only source of such depersonalisation. Communication, properly understood, is a two-way process. And we communicate with one another by the totality of our behaviour, not only in words. There is thus a limit to the number of people any one person can truly communicate with. In a complex society such as ours, social structures are necessary which unintentionally raise barriers to communication because the transfer of information can only be indirect, one way at a time, instead of being mutual as is possible in a face-to-face encounter. Such barriers exist whenever such structures try to deal with more than 500 to 1,000 people at once. They therefore exist in all bureaucracies and in all mass media, where audience participation is not immediate and automatic; and less justifiably in far too many institutions such as schools, hospitals and factories. It is always depersonalising to be 'talked at' in a setting which prevents people from being able to make their voices heard. And, of course, it is minority groups who suffer most from this. Some of this kind of depersonalisation is therefore inevitable in our society, and it points to the importance of providing places and situations in which people can voice their opinions publicly, informally, and freely. The value of small group meetings of ten to fifteen people is well recognised nowadays; but there is little recognition of the need for places where several hundred people can meet in a similarly unstructured way. We lack a modern equivalent for the *forum* which served as a focal point in Roman communities.

Social Bereavement

A man's sense of personal identity is shaped and nourished by his experience of interaction with his local culture. If the culture is lost, for any reason, those who were sustained by it are likely to suffer from what G.N. Appell has called social bereavement.[1] As with individuals, this means that they go through a period in which they feel sad, angry or bitter, thinking with longing of the past and fearing the future; they are restless and unable to function with their normal efficiency. Typically, an individual's mourning lasts not less than one or two years; for a group of people it may take several decades. When the lost culture is devalued by those around them, it may take longer still, for they are less likely to recognise their misery as grief if there is pressure on them to repress it. Pastoral counsellors try to enable those who mourn to reflect on both their good and bad memories of the lost one - and to forgive the bad. Appell, pointing out that social bereavement threatens people's identity and self-esteem, says that it is important to provide the means whereby those who are thus afflicted can view their own past, and see that it was a *"meaningful and important experience on which to build the future"*.

In the context of our multicultural urban society, it is plain that many of these generalisations about identity, prejudice and discrimination apply to both black and white, to those long resident in a locality as well as to recent immigrants. Those labelled as 'oppressed' by some people are seen as 'oppressors' by others, but both are likely to be culturally dispossessed. It may be that what is expressed as racial tension and violence is at least partly an unhealthy response to social bereavement on both sides; and that the Christian church which offers counselling to individuals who mourn may find an analogous role in helping culturally bereaved groups to recognise their need to do their 'grief work' as well. And just as the bereavement counsellor will only be effective if he shows interest in, and respect for, the dead, so we should all learn to show more interest in and respect for the cultures which people have lost and upon which their sense of identity depended - and still depends.

Cultural Identity: Segregation and/or Integration

The feeling of being culturally dispossessed or alienated, then, affects groups as well as individuals. This raises the political question of whether the interests of such groups are better served by a policy of integration or segregation. We should beware of the tendency we commonly have to interpret these possibilities from the viewpoint of the *short-term* interest of the *majority* culture: to favour integration may imply that the minority would be seen as less problematic to the majority if they were scattered; or to favour segregation might mean no more than 'out of sight, out of mind'. If either solution is imposed by a majority on an unwilling minority, the latter's sense of alienation can only be increased.

A satisfactory political outcome will only be reached when the identity-needs of the minority are taken as seriously as those of the majority. Essentially, this means that a policy must be open-ended and permissive, allowing opportunities for change over a long period. It can be expected that those (of both minority and majority) who feel their identities to be most threatened will tend to segregate themselves; and that it is only as they come to adopt new identities based upon their former culture but incorporating such elements as enable them to tolerate their present social environment, that they will be able to integrate themselves in it. A family faced with the arrival of a new baby has analogous problems. It has to provide for some degree of temporary segregation for a new arrival be it in mother's arms, or cot, or nursery; and this means that other family members have to accept some degree of displacement from the space they formerly occupied. It therefore has to cope with a certain amount of discomfort, and often (for instance) jealousy of the baby. The long term aim, of course, is the integration of the newcomer; but this cannot be forced and depends on sensitive management of all the difficulties and disturbances that are entailed. And the precise shape of the eventual integration (or lack of it) cannot be predicted in advance: it is nearly always significantly different from the original hopes or daydreams of the parents!

Politically then integration and segregation are not to be seen as mutually exclusive alternatives. Policy should be directed in the long term so as to encourage integration to occur; but this implies that in the shorter term, it must also allow segregation to occur when it seems tactically necessary or desirable. Policy decisions must be such as to keep tactical options open rather than to foreclose them. In all this the majority culture has the greater responsibility. As in the family, it is with the majority that the power lies, and it is the majority which establishes an environment which either permits or obstructs the newcomer's movement towards integration. The behaviour of the British people in past generations does not suggest that they will find it easy to develop this kind of flexible policy. Historically, we have been a class-conscious society, each class believing in keeping itself to itself, thus making for segregation; and in the days of Empire the British overseas were notorious for their segregation of themselves from the local communities or countries which they believed they served by ruling. The current situation in this country will demand considerable 'conceptual repentance' from many of us if we hope to negotiate with our immigrant minorities in a Christian way.

Beyond Identity

The notion of cultural identity offers us a convenient way to speak of those elements of personal identity which are shared by members of a particular culture, but in the end it is personal identity with which we are concerned. Jesus said *"If anyone wishes to be a follower of mine, he must leave self behind"*. Erik Erikson[2] says *"man's development does not begin or end with identity, and identity must become relative for the mature person"*. As Christians, the ultimate aim of our concern for a man's sense of identity, at any stage of his life, is to help him to affirm a self of sufficient value to be a worthy sacrifice when he comes to relinquish it.

References:
1. G.N. Appell, *'The Plight of Indigenous Peoples: Issues and Dilemmas'*, in <u>Survival International</u>, 1977.
2. E.H. Erikson, **Childhood and Society**, (Penguin Books), 1965; **Identity, Youth and Crisis**, (Faber),1968.

112-5 Identity, Discrimination and Prejudice.

Chapter Six

INSIGHT AND OUTSIGHT

Early in his professional work as a psychiatrist James experienced a clash between his medical training in objectivity - standing back, as it were, and focussing more and more narrowly upon the signs of disease in an individual patient separated from their home and family environment: and his psychiatric need for subjectivity - sympathetic involvement with the person who was appealing to him for help, entering into their situation, feeling with them and broadening his vision of their situation in terms of their relationships. He described his profession as '*social psychiatry seen from within*'

James always sought to balance these two perceptions - that which he saw with his eye, and that which he saw with his heart - outsight and insight. In Shakespeare's play, King Lear says to Gloucester (who has cruelly lost both his eyes): *"No eyes in your head … yet you see how this world goes."* He replies: *"I see it feelingly."*

The importance of balancing these two ways of perceiving human behaviour extended into his work with small and large groups of people in which a leader or consultant needs to be both a good participant member of the group, feeling its feelings; but also to be able to stand back from the group and assess it's mood and purpose.

James' ability to feel and interpret feelings made him a notable pioneer of the therapeutic community approach to the promotion of health, and an effective if disturbing educator.

M.W.

INTERIOR ASPECT

… The psychiatrist is already aware that his understanding of the person requires him not only to make a dispassionate assessment of the externals - the bodily mechanisms and the behaviour; but also to enter into the interior world of the person with empathy, or, more simply, compassion. It is our failure to pay attention to the interior meaning of human situations which is responsible, I think, for much of our failure to deal with the externals of human distress. There are complaints, for instance, that the dedicated medical man in the mission hospital, trying to preach the Gospel by practical works of love in healing, finds to his dismay that the gospel he has taught has been one of scientism - a belief in and reliance upon modern secular science, with its objective concern for externals, rather than upon the love of God within. This is an old difficulty. Of the ten lepers in the Gospel account, nine were relieved of their external sickness - but only one understood the interior meaning of the healing activity of Jesus and turned back to glorify God.

What are some other implications of this idea, that all entities have their own interior aspect, their own separate conscious centres? It implies that there is a scale of centredness, extending all the way from an inorganic mass, wherein there are as many small centres, acting at random to one another, as there are atoms - up through the biological series, in which centredness, consciousness, is graded according to the capacity for spontaneity which is shown, - to reflective man. This illuminates the observation that some animals are ruled by instincts which compete with one another in a largely automatic way. In Teilhard's terms, each instinct would indicate a separate 'centre'. This would remain true of the human infant, who is likely to be governed by instinct for some time until maturity supervenes. The implication is that each separable instinctive tendency has its own 'consciousness', and that only when these are integrated together and fused can one display true spontaneity and maturity. In the psychiatrist's jargon, one would say that these separate 'consciousnesses' are to be found in what we call the unconscious - and can become unified and integrated by being brought into consciousness.

While traditionally science has limited itself to the study of external appearances, nevertheless I think that this notion of the 'within' of things enters into the construction of scientific theory. The observer makes a reflective survey of his data, and continues to contemplate them until they fall into a meaningful pattern, which he then proceeds to test as his hypothesis. But this kind of science remains meaningless unless there *is* a conscious recognition of a meaningful pattern. This seems to suggest that phenomena do form patterns of complexity which our consciousness recognises as real (if not actual, to use Erikson's distinction) - patterns which become part of our conscious experience. The pattern, therefore, seems to be the *interior aspect* of the complex phenomena which we contemplate.

The relevance of this consideration may be illustrated by the example of an African peasant who wants his crops to grow. He consults his priest, who advises him to sacrifice a sheep to the god of the crops. By sacrifice, and prayerful ritual, he affirms an at-one-ment between himself and the lords of nature, and waits for the crop with a quiet mind. Now the European agricultural missionary comes along and advises him that irrigation and manure are more effective than killing sheep as a means of getting the crop to grow. Looked at scientifically, from the outside, this is surely true. But is it of no human importance that the man no longer has to take the solemn steps of prayer and contemplation and indeed sacrifice, of some kind, to ensure his at-one-ment with the cosmos at the level of reflective thought? We know what the *result* of his scientific education may be. But what is the *meaning* to him of the new, secularised situation? Greater material benefit, certainly; but what is his place in the universe? By the pagan and ignorant sacrifice of a sheep he had affirmed his allegiance to his god and thus expressed his reconciliation to the world around him.

This example can be translated into the larger framework of the political and economic problems of modern society. Objective scientific prediction can indicate that a certain line of action will be effective. Often we cannot take the action; and even if we can, and do, events falsify the prediction, or leave us dissatisfied. How far do things go wrong for us, as experiences, because we neglect the process of contemplation and reconciliation between the interior aspects of events? It seems to be an aesthetic process that is lacking, whether it is cast in religious terms or not. It isn't merely the objective study and measurement of the problem we need: it is the need to stand and stare, to soak ourselves in the real meaning of the problem and its proposed solution, to enter into it with compassion, empathy, as if we were looking at a picture or listening to a symphony. Gerald Durrell once said on a television programme that if you wanted to be a successful collector of wild animals *"half an hour spent standing in front of a cage looking at the animal was never wasted"*. Not because of what the animal did in objective terms, but in order to understand it - in fact, to know it from within.

    . . . One last quotation from Pierre Teilhard de Chardin: *"There is less difference than people think between research and adoration"*.

61 - The Phenomenon of Man.

A PARTICIPANT OBSERVER

    . . . Sigmund Freud maintained firmly that he was a scientist, and he was certainly well schooled and practised in the traditional methods. He believed in the importance of remaining detached from his field of study; and I have read somewhere how he was at pains to discuss how a consulting room should be arranged, so that the free flow of the patient's thoughts should not be affected by any uncontrollable change of demeanour on the part of the therapist. Furthermore he called his method "psycho*analysis*". But from the moment he took seriously the fact that a relationship grows up, inevitably, between patient and therapist, the fact that there is mutual interaction - what he spoke of as trans-ference and counter-transference, he and more particularly his followers have been involved in what seems to be a progressive, if reluctant, retreat from the established and traditional bases of scientific method as we have outlined them.[1]

    For here we have a situation in which it is manifestly impossible for the observer to remain detached and external to the field which he is studying. Psychotherapists try to counter the difficulty by insisting on the need for the therapist to know himself - to be objective about himself, for instance by having a lengthy training analysis. But he, of all people, is aware that none of us are truly aware of our-selves except in the most fragmentary way. And since this therapist, who tries to be objective about himself and his patient together in the consulting room, is the same person who wakes up in the morning with a headache, worries over the mortgage on his house, and is involved in the lives of other patients as well as of his own family - it is clear that the field of study, far from being the controllable, closed system that scientific method requires, extends throughout the life-space and life-time of at least two people. And, of course, the field is never limited to two people anyway. Once you begin to take relationships between people seriously, and realise that current relationships depend upon conscious and unconscious memories of previous relationships, the field of study in which you are now a participant observer is most decidedly an open rather than a closed system.

    There is something reminiscent of King Canute on the seashore in contemplating the way scientifically trained psychotherapists have gradually given in to the logic of this situation. The first analysts strove so hard to try to control the situation and confine it to the therapeutic hour. The patient was even discouraged from discussing his treatment outside the consulting room. But the situation refused to be confined. When the inevitable need arose for observation to be extended to parts of the field outside the consulting room, the psychiatric social worker appeared. This breach in the wall has steadily widened, as the therapeutic task has spread throughout the casework professions. At every stage workers have shown an upsurge of anxiety at their failure, trained as they are in scientific method, to define their fields of operations. Currently, this is expressed in arguments about the 'limits of agency function'.

The next step in the blurring of the boundaries came with group therapy; and we saw practitioners arguing the merits of closed groups, with a defined and consistent membership, as against open groups, where members could come and go with greater freedom. Inevitably, it is the open group that has proved the more viable. After group therapy came the notion of the therapeutic community: a whole ward or hospital being regarded as the relevant field, with the whole staff - doctor, nurse, social worker, and even ward maid and hospital administrator - participating in the therapeutic process along with the whole body of patients as co-workers.

I must emphasise that this progressive extension of the field and blurring of its boundaries has not come about absentmindedly nor in a spirit of therapeutic empire-building. The self-esteem of the therapist as scientist has been threatened at every step; and indeed the psychiatric journals are full of accounts of research projects in which doctors have reasserted their allegiance to scientific method. Statistical methods have been refined, personality inventories and questionnaires have been prepared, control groups have been inveigled into co-operation. With depressing frequency, the outcome is that the conclusions, if interesting, are of doubtful scientific validity, while the more rigorous and convincing the research methods, the more banal and trivial are the conclusions.

The fact is that the progressive advance of this non-science in therapy, this increasing involvement in participant observation, is positively humiliating to the scientifically trained therapist. Progressively, he loses control of his patient and the situation, progressively he becomes less able to measure and quantify, progressively he becomes less able to predict the outcome of his patient's illness. And yet his empirical and pragmatic concentration upon what seems to be best for his patient leads him on. What seems to be best for his patient. Not what seems to be worst for his disease.

Psychoanalysis, and the whole study of human relationships which is founded upon it, is based on an acceptance of the whole patient as he is, partly healthy and partly ill. Every doctor respects his patient, but his respect does not prevent his interfering with bodily mechanisms, with the physical integrity of the organism, in a way which the patient need not necessarily understand. But the psychotherapist, as participant observer, eschews any such interference from outside. By allowing a relationship - a channel of communication - to grow up between his patient and himself, he is enabled to share in the patient's problem and thus to understand its significance. He learns to be compassionate, in the original meaning of the word, rather than dispassionate (though since he is still a scientist, he may be dispassionate as well). Thereafter, he confines himself to making interpretations; seeks to make explicit the realities of the situation and to share his insights with the patient. Sometimes, indeed, a shared understanding of some aspect of the problem will lead them to agree that the therapist, rather than the patient should do something active, but whatever he does or says to alter the situation will itself be shared.

The remarkable thing is that this process of sharing, and of clarifying the meaning of the shared situation, proves to be the very bringer of health itself. The prescription is not altered for different diseases. It is non-specific, like the fresh air and good food which are not only of value for the treatment of tuberculosis. And, like them, the prescription brings health to the therapist as well as the patient.[2]

So far as I know, the question of whether individual psychoanalysis is regarded as a treatment for disorder or treatment for the patient has not been critically discussed, probably because in the field of psychiatry or personality the disease or illness or disorder is even less conceptually separable from the sufferer than is the case with physical disorder. I suspect that many authorities would indeed regard psychoanalysis as treatment directed at disorder, while being inclined to regard group or community therapy, and case-work, as being rehabilitative or resocialising.[3] I do not hold this view. To my mind, individual psychoanalysis is just as concerned with non-specific health-building as is relationship therapy in any other context. (To speak technically, I would say that the recovery of repressed traumatic memories is a *result*, rather than a *cause,* of the increased ego-strength gained by the patient within the transference, for instance). All relationship therapy is, of course, fundamentally distinct from those other methods of treatment, such as behaviour therapy or the various physical methods, which are aimed at altering a particular part of the personality, which has been defined as undesirable and something to be rejected.[4]

* * * * *

Let me now recapitulate some of the contrasts between the scientific and the non-scientific approaches to the problems people bring us. The scientist remains a detached and dispassionate observer of what happens in a defined field. This is to be compared with the participant observer, looking at a situation from within it - and finding it to be an open system, with indefinable boundaries. The participant observer is himself one of the objects of study, one of the variables in the situation. He cannot remain dispassionate and impersonal, because he has to develop a personal relationship with his patient or client; so he must allow himself to be, in the proper sense of the word, compassionate: he has to 'feel with' the other person. In sacrificing the god-like detachment of the scientist, he can no longer maintain rigorous control of the field, and because he can no longer ignore or discount the uniqueness of the phenomena with which he is involved he is relatively unable to count, measure or predict. He has to look at the situation, including himself, as a whole. He cannot take parts of it for separate consideration out of context, except by adopting the scientist's role which, by definition, detaches him from his participant relationship to the whole. He regards relationships as sacrosanct, as the very stuff of life; as contrasted with the scientist, who cannot control or analyse any living thing without disturbing and breaking its relationships to its surroundings, and thereby killing it or maiming it or restricting its freedom to be itself, even if only temporarily.

One other contrast is worthy of mention. Whereas the practice of the scientific approach leads to ever increasing specialisation, the non-scientific approach appears to lead away from it. What began as a highly esoteric activity in the consulting rooms of the pioneer psychoanalysts is now the concern of case-workers, nurses, welfare officers and counsellors of many other kinds; while in the hospital, lay administrators are likely to find themselves in the therapeutic community meeting; and in the factory, the foreman is likely to find himself attending a course on human relations. This generalising process is not to be seen as one of diluting professional skills because of the shortage of trained experts. It results from an entirely realistic acknowledgement of the significance of different people in the pattern of relationships which is of importance to the patient's or client's health. The foreman can be far more influential for a man's health than a psychiatrist who only sees him for an hour or less once a week - or less.

The measures advised for the treatment of a patient with tuberculosis were no doubt the outcome of prolonged empirical study of particular cases by practising physicians. Fresh air, adequate food, rest and exercise started by being a prescription for the individual, then became regarded as general measures of preventive medicine with implications for legislators; and are now regarded as the birthright of every member of a civilised society. In psychiatry, we have hardly as yet moved beyond the first of these stages; but at least one professor of mental health has put forward what looks like a practical preventive programme,[5] and as his teaching, and that of those who follow him percolates through to local and national health authorities, we can look forward to the second stage. It seems to me entirely likely that, as time goes on, the fundamental needs for mental health will come to be provided in civilised countries (if there are any left) as willingly and readily as those for physical well-being are now. . . .

References

1. W. R. Bion, **Experiences in Groups**, (Tavistock Publications), 1961, p.104.
2. R.D.Laing, New Society, 1st. October, 1964, No. 105, p.12. Vol.1, '*Families of Schizophrenics*'.
3. R.N.Rapoport, **Community as Doctor**, (Tavistock Publications), 1960.
4. T.S. Szasz, **The Myth of Mental Illness**, (Paladin), 1961, p.10.
5. G. Caplan, **Principles of Preventive Psychiatry**, (Tavistock Publications), 1965.

66-2 The Participant Observer.

PARTICIPATION AND OBJECTIVITY

. . . As a psychiatrist, I have always been more interested in sharing experience with those who consult me than in controlling their behaviour. But since I am a mental hospital doctor, many of my patients have in fact come to see me (whether of their own wish or not) because of disordered behaviour, and I must count myself lucky to have discovered, as often as I have, that when I am able to understand and share my patient's experience, his behaviour has tended to alter in a way which other people seem to approve. What happens is that as the patient tells his story, and I try to put myself in his shoes, I find myself thinking increasingly "Well, if I'd been in your shoes, that is just what I would have done, or felt".

So I leave the consultation having expressed sympathy, but quite confused as to what constructive advice or help I can offer. And then when I next see him, I find that quite unexpectedly, and unpredictably, the behavioural difficulty has changed, or altered in some way for the better. It is a constant source of astonishment and wonder to me - a perpetual miracle. This kind of situation can be contrasted with all the other kinds of psychiatric treatment which don't apparently depend on the sharing of the client's experience: attempts to control disordered behaviour by the use of drugs, or conditioning treatment, or by the use of one's magical authority as a doctor. These latter kinds of treatment often appear to be much more clearly explicable in terms of cause and effect. They can be thought about objectively and dispassionately, in a manner which is recognisably scientific, whereas any observations about the process of sharing experience are necessarily those of an involved participant in the process. Hence my title - Participation and Objectivity.

It seems to me that the special characteristic of group work, as contrasted with other settings in which we can try to conceptualise processes of caring for people, lies precisely here, that it is to be found at the inter-face between participation and objectivity. In the group, one tries to create a situation in which it is safe for the experience of each member, and of the group as a whole, to be taken seriously as something worthy of communication; and in which the behaviour of each member - and of the group as a whole - is taken to be a reflection of such experience rather than as something to be controlled or manipulated or directed without regard for its inner significance. The traditional psychoanalyst claims that his special interest is in his patient's inner world: he takes *"subjective experience as a central object of study"* (Rycroft). The pure behaviourist, or the authority figure in a traditional institution, on the other hand, is likely to concern himself only with the outer world - with what is 'outered' or uttered - and he will tend to be more concerned to control what is uttered than to understand its meaning as a communication. . . .

. . . So it seems to me that the particular skills of the group worker are those which enable him to stay afloat in the turbulent waters which are to be found where two mighty streams meet: on the one hand there is the river which we recognise under such terms as participation, involvement, experiential reality; while on the other there is that colder stream which we associate with words such as objectivity, detachment and historical actuality.

The difficulties and uncertainties of being a group worker are familiar enough. However carefully I try to communicate my experience to a group, its other members seem capable of making the most perverse interpretations of what I try to convey. And however clearly another seems to be expressing a certain experience, I often find out subsequently that I have misinterpreted him and that he meant something entirely different. The feeling of powerlessness, of being unable to control or direct the group, is the commonest feeling I have in groups which I am supposed to be leading or conducting. The group seems to make me feel that my participation in it is either useless, or something to be guarded against and feared. And yet, as we all know, although at any one moment I am likely to be filled with uncertainty and confusion, yet over time the group I am concerned with needs me, and is incomplete and probably incompetent if I am temporarily absent from it. . . .

. . . *Participation*, then, opens to me a wealth of shared experience. It enables me to share in communal fantasies and myths and to be involved with my fellows in a truly compassionate, fellow-feeling way - which is certainly not always desirable or realistic, of course. It has its own warmth and it confirms me in my sense of personal identity. Its dangers lie in its subjectivity. At the tribal level it limits me to animistic and anthropomorphic beliefs, attributing personality to elements of the environment and to a centring of the universe upon myself or my tribal group. It solves no problems except personal ones. It enables relationships to deepen into love, it is creative, it is hopeful, and it allows for the growth of awareness and consciousness and complexity. But by itself it solves none of the problems which arise between man and his environment. It does not prevent famine or flood, nor does it mend a broken leg. So, by itself, it does not prevent (though it may ease) the experience of evil.

Now let us turn to survey the course of our other river, that of *objective actuality*. How does it arise? I suppose one learns very early in life about the unyielding nature of inanimate objects. At first, no doubt, one anthropomorphically endows them with an evil spirit at the tribal level; and at the individual level many a child has complained about the 'baddy chair' which has barked his shin. Nothing very objective about that, you may say. But I suspect that the developmental basis of all objectivity is in fact the mental mechanism of projection.

Primitive man consults the witch doctor and says "I feel bad". The witch doctor, being at that undifferentiated stage a participant member of the group, and thus sensitive to primitive sympathy or compassion, feels bad too. So he searches around for something other than the person, the self who is complaining, on to which the badness can be projected. It may be a demon or evil spirit; or in more modern times a bad habit, a bad tooth, a bad appendix or whatever. So long as the medicine man can point his accusatory finger away from the actual person in front of him, who has engaged his sympathy, both he and the patient will have a sense of relief, at least for the moment, whether his diagnosis is right or wrong. Basically, this mechanism still seems to underlie modern medicine - an almost obsessive search for new diseases which can be labelled, defined, and then, hopefully, got rid of. . . .

. . . The hypothesis I have been outlining, therefore, can be summarised by saying that the objective impersonality of much modern social science research and the dehumanising effect of many aspects of institutional social structures come from the same roots (and may, therefore, be expected to have analogous advantages as well as disadvantages) - while both of them are to be seen in contrast to, if not necessarily in conflict with, that other stream of human social development which I have labelled participation. On the one hand we see an association of ideas such as objectivity, cool detachment, clarity of definition and boundaries, analysis, exact measurement, categorisation, and control; while on the other, we link participation, warmth of relationship, involvement, hopefulness, love, spontaneity, and heightened awareness.

Conflict between the two approaches arises, I think, because the practitioner of scientific method (whether he works in a laboratory or as manager of an institution) learns his craft in dealing with infra-human or inorganic phenomena. Objectivity and detachment are obviously important in such a context to avoid such pitfalls as anthropomorphism. Also, his accuracy of measurement depends upon his concentrating on similarities and repetitions of phenomena and thus on ignoring the uniqueness of each one - a serious limitation of his method in the eyes of the group worker when dealing with human beings. The social scientist, indeed, takes much trouble to ensure the randomness of his sample before he can trust his measurements; he has specifically to exclude any tendency of one specimen to relate to another, trying to see each person as if he were a social isolate; while the group worker as participant regards relationship as something to be nurtured and fostered. Thus when the social scientist reports on human behaviour, his findings are likely to be trivial or banal the more statistically convincing they are. Furthermore, his insistence on clarity of definition and his analytic method (which is necessarily divisive and reductive) means that he has to concentrate on part-structures and part-functions rather than 'seeing things whole'. His method makes him report as if he had 'tunnel vision' - only seeing what is at the end of the tube of his microscope or telescope. On the other hand, the scientist or authoritarian manager is likely to criticise the practitioner of participant methods for his lack of detachment, his apparent failure to define the boundaries of his field of study, and his inability to produce objective evidence or proof that his methods are effective.

The scientist is essentially concerned. with what *is*. He looks for facts. The group worker, the participant, is inevitably concerned not only with what *is* but also with what *ought* to be. He is concerned with what is only potential, not yet actualised. He is like a midwife, standing by and offering moral support while something new is being born.

In fact, of course, neither of these two tendencies in human development can do without the other. In the long term, differentiation in development is the very stuff of progress toward maturity, and it belongs in the stream which I have labelled objectivity. Looked at objectively, however, what we tend to see is not so much differentiation, which seems desirable, but specialisation, which seems less so. I think this is a distinction to be taken seriously. Differentiation of an amorphous social body or group implies that its various parts develop special functions, indeed, but it also implies that the parts remain participating members of the whole in spite of their special functions. Specialisation, as we see it in the world around us, all too often seems to imply dissociation of the specialised part from the whole body, so that we are troubled by barriers to communication between specialists, or between the various parts or departments of the authoritarian institution. So in our group work, whether with children in care or with other staff members who are our peers, we find ourselves involved in just this problem, of encouraging each individual to become special in his own way, while discouraging any tendency for him to become dissociated or to lose his capacity for participation. We have always to remember the principle that each of us is partially responsible for the whole, rather than wholly responsible for a part of it.

At this point I would like to lay aside the model of the confluence of two streams which we have been playing with, and replace it with the more organic model of a plant or a tree. For, in the light of historical development, it is clear that participation is much the more primitive and ancient of the two. It is the vital stem, arising from the roots of our nature as social beings, from which grow the branches and flowers of differentiated excellence and actualised and outered perfection. The flowering of civilisation and culture, the flowering of personality in the individual, will only continue to occur so long as the flowers or branches are not cut, so long as dissociation of the specialised bits does not occur. It is the participant approach to problems, woolly and open-ended and subjective as it often appears to be, which is the source and the constant replenisher of the vitality and significance of all specialisation.

66-4 Participation and Objectivity.

PARTICIPATION

. . . There are four characteristics of scientific method which are learnt by students at an early stage. They are:

1. Definition of the field of study.
2. Analysis: the breaking down of complex phenomena into simpler elements, either in thought or in actuality.
3. The search for regularities or recurrences.
4. The adoption of a detached and dispassionate viewpoint.

All four of them imply a readiness to break or ignore the relationships which the observed phenomena would naturally have with the environment around them. Typically the method tries to establish facts by taking things out of context, and treating them as if they existed in a closed system - a system which excluded the observer. This is what I mean by objectivity.

Of course the method has paid enormous dividends over the past few centuries and is a fundamental investigative technique without which our kind of science would not exist. Nevertheless, like other good things such as health, security or riches, there is a risk that it may become an idolatry. Perhaps it already is: many people not only treat the universe *as if* it were a closed system, which has its value as method, but are misguided enough to believe that it actually is a closed system and therefore doomed to thermodynamic decay: whereas since they are themselves actually within the system they are forever debarred from knowing whether the universe has boundaries or not. Teilhard says:

> *"We are continually inclined to isolate ourselves from the things and events which surround us, as though we were looking at them from outside, from the shelter of an observatory into which they were unable to enter, as though we were spectators, not elements in what goes on."*

Any closed system is a human artefact, to be taken seriously but not too seriously. In reality all things exist in relation to one another, and the breaking of relationships implied by objectivity sets a term to its usefulness. Quantum physicists studying very small particles are already aware that the observer can no longer be excluded from the field of study because the act of observing itself affects their observations.

To the extent that psychotherapy consists of attempts to improve interpersonal relations, scientific objectivity, necessarily breaking or ignoring such relations, is of only limited use. In group therapy an important relation for members of the group, both individually and corporately, is with the therapist, who is inevitably a participant in the group process rather than a dispassionate observer. The scientific observer - including the clinical scientist - could believe himself to be in control of his field of investigation because he could always analyse it and disregard those elements which he could not control. The psychotherapist, as participant, can do no such thing: he learns to wait for the right moment for an interpretative intervention (a moment which cannot be predicted and which may never come) - and to accept the vulnerability and frustration which this implies.

I suspect that it is no accident that psychotherapist and quantum physicist share this sense of objectivity's limitations. Both of them are trying to deal with single entities: either the single particle on the one hand, or the single person, or group seen as a single whole, on the other. This concern with the single entity means that they are not able to depend on the predictability of statistical laws. To use a Teilhardian phrase, they '*escape the slavery of large numbers*', and find themselves in a world where cause and effect tend to get confused and where their only certain means of being able to dominate a situation is to get out of it and thus break the relationship. In fact, the model for the observation of persons, far from being that of the dispassionate scientist manipulating events (holding certain variables steady so as to see how others may change) - this model is better seen as that of a dance, wherein each partner responds to the other so nearly simultaneously that neither can claim to be the initiator, in which mutual awareness and consciousness grows as complexity of response multiplies itself, and the participants are no longer concerned to 'know about' each other as the scientist knows about things: they more truly come to know each other to the extent that they become, in the scriptural sense, more nearly '*one flesh*'. Indeed, participant observation at its best is an act of love. . . .

66-7 Becoming a Participant Observer.

HEARING AND SEEING

Too much noise makes you deaf. This sounds like a glimpse of the obvious. But I do not mean sheer quantity of noise: I am thinking of the meaning the word has in information theory, to indicate an excessive or unorganised variety of input. In this sense, if we have to listen to unfamiliar information which we are unable to organise and make sense of, we seem to be deaf to it, we can not hear it, even though it is not particularly loud.

Some years ago I took part in a seminar with some industrialists and social scientists working in industry. The social scientists raised a question. They said "we are called in by managers when they are in difficulties with problems in the field of human relationships. When we are lucky we can make a fairly definite diagnosis and suggest some fairly straightforward courses of remedial action. But all too often, we then find that the managers who consulted us seem quite unable to take in the relevance of what we report to them, and however civilly they treat us, they make us feel we have been wasting our time". The seminar went on to discuss the social scientists' problem: but the observation I want to draw attention to is the inability of the managers to hear what is being said to them even when it is something to their advantage.

Let me jump now to the matter of sex education. It is widely agreed that it is desirable, if not easy, to give children information about sex as part of their general education. But I suppose most psychiatrists have met young adults who can give convincing evidence of having been exposed to reasonable sex instruction in earlier life, but who have failed to take in fundamental elements of such teaching. A vivid example I once read was of an intelligent woman who, at the time of her second pregnancy, still believed that the afterbirth had to be replaced in the womb for further pregnancies to be possible. Of course psychiatrists have plenty of explanations, in terms of emotional blocking and so forth, of why people fail to hear the information they need; but it is the fact that they do, and not the reason why they do, which I want to emphasise.

Here is a third example. When I worked in a mental hospital, I not rarely found that if I offered a tentative suggestion as a possible way of tackling a problem, it would be turned down by my colleagues more or less out of hand; but that after many months one or more of them would of their own initiative produce almost exactly the same suggestion and it would then lead to action. Of course I would initially feel that they were unable to hear what I was saying; and sadly, I could never be sure whether their subsequent enlightenment resulted from my having sown the seed, or from their having rediscovered the idea on their own.

In such situations as these, it is likely that at first we hold those who don't hear what is told them as responsible for the failure of communication; but that we then wonder guiltily whether as doctors or teachers (the words are synonymous) we ourselves were responsible for not expressing our meaning more clearly - whether, so to speak, we have been too 'noisy'.

Vision as well as hearing suffers from this kind of limitation. Given a particular constellation of visual stimuli, we see only what we are ready to see, and are often unable, at least for a time, to fit the elements of what lies before our eyes into an unfamiliar pattern. Mrs Abercrombie's book '*The Anatomy of Judgement*' (1969) gives a number of good illustrations. Visual perception shows more clearly than auditory that we can only perceive things from one perspective at a time. Faced with the simple kind of ambiguous picture which psychologists have made familiar, we may find it possible to switch from one perspective to another quite quickly, and see for instance the outline of two faces at one moment and a vase a moment later. But when we deal with more complex patterns of stimuli, (e.g. a pattern of snow and rocks which can be seen as a picture of a man) the time needed to change perspective seems to increase; and when we deal with extremely complex situations such as the way a person perceives himself, his sense of personal identity, the time needed may be much longer, and may need to be thought about in terms of a growth process. Such a change, brought about by the need to readjust after a bereavement for instance, may take 18 months or longer to achieve. . . .

. . . In summary, then, it seems that my problem is this: when I try to communicate a liberating idea to someone and he fails to hear me, is it because of a technical failure of my skill in diagnosing his need, or in uttering the right words at the right time so that he can hear them; or is it that, however sure I may feel that the idea I express is the right one for him, the truly liberating idea is never in fact known by anyone except the man who needs it; and that all one can do - all one should do - is to respond to another's need with wide-ranging attention to his situation in its context, trusting, but never being sure, that the support this gives him will enable him to discern, autonomously, the idea that is right for him.

161 - 1 Too Much Noise Makes You Deaf.

KALEIDOSCOPE

(Formerly entitled "Mind, Health and Community". 10 week course in the first term for the Diploma in Pastoral Studies.)

-oOo-

The seminars have laid little stress on providing new information, but have striven to encourage students to change perspectives on 'facts' they already know - e.g. by experimenting with different real or imagined contexts.

The series has usually begun with discussions of 'crisis theory' and 'therapeutic community' as these form a bridge between my apparent 'expertise' as a psychiatrist, and pastoral and/or counselling practice. Both lay stress on:

patterns of health and normality rather than of illness;

corporate as well as individual aspects of caring, and

the importance of amateur/lay/fellow-sufferer involvement in caring and healing as contrasted with that of experts.

Discussion then follows the group's apparent interests, and will try to cover such topics as authority and leadership; community and group morale in church, institutional life and the family. I look for opportunities to talk about guilt feelings (vicarious guilt), evil and sin (solidarity in sin) and mental mechanisms such as projection (scapegoating). If this sounds like social psychology, it *is* social psychology - examined from within, as experienced in day-to-day life, rather than from a detached, academic stance.

I also try to introduce insights from biology and physiology, ethology, systems theory and social anthropology, as well as psychotherapy, where relevant, to encourage students to develop their theological doctrine of man in a multidimensional human context.

I discourage the taking of notes!

The authors from whom I am most conscious of drawing (apart from R.A.L. and M.W.) would include Gregory Bateson, Berger and Luckman, Buckley (Sociology & Modern Systems Theory), Gerald Caplan, M.R.A. Chance, E.H. Erikson, E. Goffman and Konrad Lorenz.

242 - Kaleidoscope.

Chapter Seven

AMATEURS

As a layman in the Christian church James was sensitive to the role of laity, and to the ministry of the whole people of God in society. He repeatedly reminded his audiences of the literal meaning of the word 'amateur' (one who loves). And he often urged ordinary people not to opt out of situations which so-called experts like to take over: but to value the gifts of their humanity, their health, their capacity for solidarity with all sorts of people, and their potential for supporting individuals, as well as for raising the morale (and therefore the mental health) of the community in which they lived or worked.

On his retirement at the age of fifty-five he deliberately let go of his professional and leadership roles in order to inter-relate with others as an amateur.

M.W.

HEALTHY PEOPLE

. . . When we become acutely ill - physically or otherwise - we all of us need 'mothering'. Typically, doctors and nurses treat us like babies: they put us to bed, wrap us up warmly, make diligent enquiry into the functioning of our bowels, and feed us on slops. We are encouraged to forget all our responsibilities, and any attempt at initiative on our part is frowned upon heavily. For short-lived illnesses - influenza, measles, or an operation for appendicitis - this 'return to infancy' is satisfactory to all concerned; and as soon as we begin to show initiative and a desire to take control of our own lives again, everyone knows we are better, and the doctor stops coming to see us.

But many patients have illnesses of a different kind - long drawn out affairs, lasting months or years - which medical skill can't do much about. What is to be done when a patient is left with a disability that the doctors can't do any more for? The answer we give nowadays is rehabilitation. This means that we stop focussing our attention on the illness, and try to get the patient to make the best use of what health he has left. All too often you find that at this point - when the doctor stops paying attention to the illness, he loses most of his clinical interest in the patient, and hands him over to someone else - remedial gymnast, or occupational therapist, or someone like that, whom he thinks knows more about health than he does, even though they may know less about illness. In a way, it is an admission of failure by the doctor. Medical science cannot remove your disease. What can you do with the health that remains to you?

The sad fact is, of course, that the classical pattern of 'treatment' - the removal of independence and initiative and treating you like a baby which we mentioned - becomes, after a time, a positive hindrance to the recovery of health in itself. If you treat people like babies for long enough then they will tend to behave, to some extent, like babies. They will want everything done for them, they will be frightened of a world they are unfamiliar with, they will just 'try to be good' and only do as they are told. This sort of pattern of behaviour is known as 'undue dependence' or 'institutionalisation' and -

whatever the original illness may have been - physical or otherwise - this illness, caused by treatment, is always a mental illness, an illness of the mind. And it can't, by its very nature, be cured by medical measures. If we begin taking a clinical interest in this disease we simply make it worse: the dependent relationship of patient to doctor is simply increased. The only advice the doctor can give is "go away and make your own decisions. This is your life and you must live it. I've done all I can for you".

So this kind of illness is one of the chronic kind that can't be treated medically. It has to be tackled by trying to increase the remaining capacity for health. In this case, mental health.

Mental health, you must remember, doesn't only mean the absence of mental disease, any more than physical health means only the absence of physical disease. The best practical way of tackling mental health is to think of it as a problem of morale. We all know the difference between a person or a group of people with good morale and one with bad morale.

Now morale depends on two things: your sense of security and your sense of purpose. When you are acutely ill, the sense of security is what you are most concerned with. You need to be comforted and looked after and relieved of responsibility: you need other people to do the fussing around. But when all this has been done, and you are beginning to recover, then you need to recover your sense of purpose. You begin to say, "what shall I do today?" Think what happens if you put a sick dog in a cage. He will lie down in the most comfortable spot. But what happens if you put a healthy dog in a cage? He sniffs busily around and explores every inch of it and does everything he can to get out: *he* isn't impressed by the security it offers him.

It seems to me that you can usefully apply these principles to your work in hospitals. Some of the time you will be ministering to the patient's sense of security, helping him, making him comfortable, relieving him of responsibility. Perhaps you think this is all you are doing, and in the acute ward it may indeed be your main function - though, of course, none the less valuable for that. But in the chronic wards, and with the long stay patient, you are doing a great deal more whether you realise it or not. Because, you see, you come from outside. You give patients some sort of a link with a real world where people do things, and go about their ordinary lives without being bossed around by nurses and doctors. You stimulate them into thinking about a wider environment, by your casual conversation and questions, and by the very clothes you wear. You are a chink in the prison wall, so to speak.

This, I think, is the real importance of your work among long stay patients. It isn't important that you give a patient a cup of tea. Most of my patients are up and about, and I'd just as soon they had the initiative to make their own tea. But it *is* exceedingly important that they should be reminded of the real world beyond the hospital. That is really good for morale.

The more ordinary people (perhaps I should say healthy people - not ordinary) that my patients can see the better. There are about 200 in Rubery who are never visited. I like them to see outsiders who are friendly and who take a real interest in them as persons. So often when I am taking round visitors to the hospital we just stand at the door and look - and then make some remark about the furnishings. But the W.V.S. with their trolley of little things to sell can really talk to the patients. And with the money they make on the trolley they can takes parties of patients out for trips, or send them on holidays. These kinds of ways of re-introducing patients to the world at large, then, are one of the main ways in which you folk can help morale.

Another valuable way is by asking patients to do little things for you. Nothing restores morale like the feeling of being wanted, and doing something for someone else. At best, our patients are given occupational therapy where they are nearly always doing something that the hospital wants them to do. It is a great thing for them to he asked to do something for someone outside the hospital.

I see my job, as a medical superintendent, as being mainly concerned with morale. Trying to foster initiative, trying to get the patients to start doing things, talking about things, exploring the abilities they still have, to take an interest in the world again. Often this kind of approach evokes criticism of the hospital set-up. It isn't always constructive criticism, but it is none the worse for that. Perhaps the only way to get out of prison is to break down a wall or door - especially when no-one can find the key. So if you find that your friendly attempt to encourage a patient's initiative brings forth a flood of bitter invective and hostility against doctors or nurses or the hospital - or even relatives - don't be alarmed, and for heaven's sake don't try to dam the flood. Don't believe every *word* the patient says, but don't reject the *emotion* he is expressing.

It is a real emotion, and a real response to a real situation, whatever mistaken ideas he may have about other people's motives. And you know, - if you can induce a patient to blow off steam to *you*, who are going away home at the end of the afternoon - think how much emotional wear and tear you are saving the nurses and other patients, who otherwise would have to cope with it!

Emotion - of this or any other kind - is frightfully catching. It is impossible for any social animal - and human beings are social animals - to keep his emotions entirely to himself for very long; in fact much mental ill health results from people's attempts to do so. So the morale of any one person depends upon the morale of those around him - in the ward for instance. I tell my nursing staff that they can't hope to improve the mental health of any individual patient beyond the general level of mental health of the group of which he is a member. Institutionalised patients always tend to isolate themselves from other people to some extent, and it is a great help to morale if this isolation - these 'barriers to communication' can be broken down. So if you can get one patient or one group of patients involved in doing something for - or something with - another patient or another group - you are making an important contribution to their health too.

And finally: in any group the *leader* is all-important to morale. The ward sister and nurses are themselves the victims - to some extent at least - of the same process of institutionalisation that has such bad effects on the patients. With patients battering away at their emotional stability on the one hand, and doctors doing almost the same thing on the other, it is their sense of security rather than their sense of purpose that is threatened and anything you can do, as representatives of the wider community outside the hospital, to make them feel that you appreciate their work will have at least as much value for ward morale as what you can do for the individual patient.

17 - Address to Women's Voluntary Service.

CARE BY THE COMMUNITY

... When I worked in a mental hospital, I realised for many years that we were trying to look after many people in hospital for whom we were unable to do anything constructive; and that indeed the hospital organisation - its social structure - was probably doing more harm than good to many of them. Let me indulge in a bit of arithmetic. In the hospital in which I worked, we admitted 1200 patients a year. The average length of stay of each admission was about six weeks. So each bed would cope with about eight admissions a year - six eights are forty-eight, leaving the bed empty for four weeks. So in order to cope with 1200 admissions a year, we needed 1200 beds divided by eight - which comes to 150. But actually we had about 800 beds in the hospital - and over 600 of them were occupied by people who had been patients for longer than two years.

Well, I am very doubtful whether any amount of medical skill was really helping those long stay people. Many of them were certainly crippled and disabled, but medicine was no more help to them than it would have been, if they had lost an arm, or an eye, or had gone deaf. They would nearly all have been more sensibly housed in group homes like yours than in hospital wards. What is a ward, after all? The word means a place where people are guarded, and really very few of them needed guarding. The nurses used to get very cross when I told them that since they worked in wards they should be called warders!

Of course, if all that 600 had been living in group homes with 5 people in each home - our community would have needed 120 of them. So I think there is a great future ahead for associations like yours!

I know you appreciate that it has to be the non-medical people - the community at large - who organise and maintain group homes. It's no use expecting hospital doctors and nurses to take the responsibility for them. If you were to do that they wouldn't be able to help themselves turning group homes into little hospitals - or little wards - and the inhabitants would finish up just as badly off as before. I understand your association has the 'strong backing' of the hospital authorities. I'm glad to hear it; but if you take my advice you will be very careful not to let it become so strong that you lose your independence of them. Doctors and nurses are jolly good chaps and girls but they are trained to look for what is bad and try to get rid of it. They aren't trained to look for what is good and to try to foster and nurture it.

Social workers on the other hand *are*. Their training - especially that of residential social workers - is directed towards the *sustaining of personality*; and this is likely to be much more use to you. So if by any mischance you do have to depend on a statutory agency, try and make it a social service agency rather than a medical one. They are more likely to sustain your corporate personality as a Group Homes Association than to take you over and alter the way you function.

The fact that group homes and Day centres and similar community care organisations are so obviously and so badly needed in this day and age is, if you think about it, an indication that things have gone badly wrong with the way our caring services have been allowed to develop over the past few hundred years. Hospitals were originally founded by non-medical people, just like yourselves, who were anxious that the community should care for its casualties and its disabled. But they have grown further and further away from the community that gave them birth, until now, to enter a hospital - general or psychiatric - is for most people just like entering a foreign country, where everyone talks a strange language and where the natives (that means the staff) indulge in all sorts of strange rituals and odd behaviour which no uninitiated person can understand; and they expect you to behave in a peculiar way too. . . .

. . . Now perhaps we should reflect upon the lessons we can learn from the mistakes of our ancestors, as we begin to move into the new era of community care. At the moment, it does look as if the new movement will help to correct the isolationism which has characterised traditional medicine. Small homes scattered throughout the community do not run the same risk of isolation as large hospitals - unless, like some children's and old people's homes, they are sited miles out in the country. It is important that they should be scattered. In the new university medical centre in Birmingham there are plans to set up more than two thousand beds on one site. This is going to mean two thousand sick folk, two thousand or more staff, and at least another thousand visitors, students and so on - five thousand people all with their attention riveted on sickness. I can't believe this will make for a healthy community. It is certainly going to be a symbol - a monument to the pathology of a mass society - however good it is going to be technically. So keep your group homes scattered, not more that two or three within shouting distance of one another. But I wouldn't mind betting that someone will suggest to you before long that it will be more economic, or more administratively convenient, to have several of them on one campus. Don't listen to them.

Secondly, encourage outsiders to visit your homes. One of the more disastrous developments in hospital practice of recent years has been the niggardliness of its hospitality - imposed by fiat from above in the interests of national economy, I hasten to say, not by the inhabitants of the hospitals themselves. It is very important that all caring institutions, large and small, independent or statutory, should earmark funds for hospitality, and should welcome visitors, and welcome the naive questions and comments of outsiders about what they are doing. This is the best safeguard against unreal rules and regulations and customs which otherwise tend to grow in even the most devoted of caring agencies, like barnacles on a ship's bottom.

Remember that it is *always* anxiety provoking to care for people - any mother knows that in dealing with healthy children, let alone sick ones. And the risk is that we spend ourselves trying to relieve our anxiety by mistakenly trying to be perfect. Dr. Donald Winnicott, (1974) the well-known child psychiatrist, used to say to anxious parents that a child didn't need a perfect mother - he needed a mother who was just 'good enough'. Our group and community homes have to be, not perfect, but just good enough.

Let me expand this a little. I am saying that you should not strive too hard for excellence in your group homes. The ultimate reason for your interest in group homes and day centres is to help the community in which we all live to be a more healthy one. Now a healthy society is one which goes on growing until it comes in sight of the limits to its resources, whatever these may be, physical or psychological or social. And the healthier it is the earlier it will become aware of these limits. But if resources are limited, it is clear that any one element of the social fabric can only be given the resources it needs to do its job excellently if they are denied to other elements in the social fabric. The excellence of the part has always to be subordinated to the good of the whole. The pursuit of excellence is dangerous. . . .

. . . Now you may feel that - as in the army or industry - strategy is an exalted matter for managing directors and governing bodies, not for ordinary people like us. I am sorry to disillusion you. If we are thinking about health care strategy it is quite untrue. If you leave it to managers or directors or politicians, they will design a strategy which they hope will make *them* healthy - but because they can only see a limited distance, like anybody else, they will leave some minority out of account and that minority of unhealthy people will infect and become a burden on the rest of us. I expect you are thinking that health care strategy is a matter for the doctors. It isn't. If you leave it to people like me all you will get is a medicated society. Or if you leave it to the experts in public health all you will get is a sanitated society. When it comes to health care strategy there simply are no experts. Your voice in this field is just as important as my voice; and the voice of the long term patient in hospital and the voice of the man who is unemployed is just as important as either of ours. Our responsibility is to enable these unregarded voices to be heard, not to speak for them. . . .

. . . To finish with, I want to leave you with this thought: it is better for each of us to see ourselves as partly responsible for the health of our whole community, than to see ourselves as wholly responsible for only a part of it. Group Homes are valuable not as an end in themselves, but as a practical and useful way of reminding us of our duty to consider the strategic problem of how to enable the whole community to become healthier.

138 - 2 Aspects of Community Care.

MENTAL HEALTH IS EVERYBODY'S BUSINESS

The Methodist Conference at Nottingham last year (1972) adopted a motion 'calling upon the Methodist people to co-operate with the staff of local psychiatric hospitals and the National Association for Mental Health in the rehabilitation of long stay psychiatric patients. ...' This is a splendid resolution. It goes on '... in particular to:

provide outings for such patients, inviting groups to church events and into their homes,

co-operate with Local Authorities and Councils of Churches in the provision of group homes,

investigate the possibility of the provision of non-nursing homes after the style of the Methodist Homes for the Aged.'

As I say, a splendid resolution. But you will notice that there is nothing in it about mental *health*. It is perhaps unlikely that very many of the long-stay patients who are to be offered this kind of help will get completely well. But some probably will, because most mental hospitals contain some patients who are only ill because they have been too long in hospital. Now what happens to those who get better in these splendid new homes? Will they really be able to find a new status as healthy people? Or will they still be regarded, and regard themselves as ex-mental patients? If they seek to emigrate, or to take out insurance policies, or to take certain kinds of employment, our kind of society will often ask the question *'Have you ever had a nervous breakdown?'* - and reject those who admit to having had one. There are a good many elements in our society which prevent those who have once been ill from ever being recognised as healthy again; and the wording of this resolution makes me wonder if there is a risk that it will perpetuate the labelling of people - as long stay patients or as ex-patients - in a way which diminishes the likelihood that they will ever be seen as normally healthy again. Labelling people can be a very risky business: if all my friends and acquaintances decided to label me as mentally ill, then, let's face it, I would surely *become* mentally ill.

Now I certainly don't want to discourage the Methodist Church from taking steps to improve the lot of the long stay psychiatric patient. But I do think it is important that the Church - not just the Methodist church but the Church with a Capital C, should try to clarify the context in which it sees this kind of what I call 'Samaritan' activity as making sense. The parable of the Good Samaritan helps us to understand who our neighbour is. But when I try to translate it into twentieth century terms in Britain, I sometimes have a horrid picture in my mind of lots of well meaning members of church congregations waiting anxiously by the side of the Jerusalem to Jericho road for some poor man to be set upon by thieves, so that they can go to his assistance. Is this unfair? Isn't it really more centrally important for the Church to set about fostering the growth of a healthy society, than for it to concentrate on the detail of setting up an ambulance service? It is only in the context of a healthy society that a service for those who are unhealthy makes sense.

When I worked in a mental hospital, well-meaning visitors would sometimes bring offers of help. They would come to me and say, "what can we do for these poor people?" Few people ever came to ask, "what can these crippled people do for the community?" And, to my shame, I never really found a way of enabling our long-term patients to regain their self-respect by actually doing something which they felt was socially useful. And yet the most important disability they all had was that they *felt useless.* And when any of us feel useless, and people offer to do things for us - it simply confirms our feelings of uselessness and makes them worse.

So here is one of the primary characteristics of a mentally healthy society. It is a society in which each member - every member - is able to maintain his self-respect, by feeling that he is filling a role which society respects and values. A healthy society isn't one in which no-one is ever sick or chronically disabled, because that would be a society in which no-one ever took risks or made mistakes - and it would die or disintegrate through boredom. But it would be one in which those who were temporarily or permanently in-valid or useless in one way, were recognised as being valid and useful in other ways. . . .

. . . I think that perhaps what I am trying to say to you, rather indirectly, was summed up much more pointedly by Jesus when he asked *"Why do you look at the sawdust in your brother's eye with never a thought for that plank in your own?"* Who are these people we so complacently label the mentally ill? They are our brothers and sisters, our neighbours. They are at the very least performing a prophetic ministry for society at large in demonstrating its unhealthiness if it has to extrude them into institutions or even specially designated homes. We, on the other hand, fail to recognise the insanity within each of us which has allowed us to create and maintain so insane a society. Every human being who stays in a mental hospital reproaches the rest of us with our blindness and deafness and failure to understand what they are trying to express.

So let me finish by saying this. I do not believe that the Conference resolution last year will lead to a significant result unless every Methodist in every congregation has visited and re-visited his or her local mental hospital often enough to recognise the real people, to recognise the humanness, of those whom the Conference categorises as long stay psychiatric patients.

129 - Mental Health is Everybody's Business.

THOSE WHO LOVE

Amateurs in the field of health care tend to underrate their importance. Most health care in this country and every other one is given by amateurs. Mothers look after their children when they have measles and mumps, wives look after their husbands when they get influenza or indigestion, daughters look after their elderly parents when they get forgetful or feeble. The professional and expert service given by doctors, nurses, social workers and other therapists never were and never will be more than the tip of the iceberg of the army of people who care for the health of others. . . .

. . . The attack on disease usually needs an expert because he does unpleasant or dangerous things like giving drugs with nasty side-effects, or giving anaesthetics and cutting people up; or in the field of mental illness he gives electric shocks or drugs which numb your faculties. But the business of comforting and strengthening people doesn't need expertise: it uses safe measures which are as pleasant for the giver as for the receiver - rest, good food, exercise, fresh air, warmth. These ways of treating the sick are really the elements of *hospitality,* and they constitute a field in which the amateur can always be of help. People think of an amateur as one who is not as skilled or as clever as the expert. Actually the word means *'one who loves'.*

Professionals always concentrate on what is bad and try to get rid of it. But amateurs act on St Paul's suggestion: *"Whatsoever things are pure and lovely and of good report, think on these things."* Professionals are trained to be dispassionate and impersonal in dealing with evil. Amateurs can allow themselves to be compassionate and personal because they focus not on evil, but on the good, on the things that enable people to be more truly human. These are the words Canon David Jenkins uses to describe those who help us to be more human: the artist, the fool (or clown), the monk (who sacrifices everything for the vision he is committed to), the sufferer, and of course the lover. He says that '*the expert, the efficient, the achiever, the operator, are no doubt necessary in a technological society but they are not ultimately involved with being human*'.

Of course, the expert and the amateur are not necessarily different people. Experts, trained to be dispassionate and impersonal in their attack on disease, can often transcend their training and be also compassionately concerned to enable their patients to be more fully human. But it isn't something they are taught in school, it is something they only learn by experience - and by becoming more truly human themselves at the same time. Amateurs, not trained out of their natural compassion, their natural tendency to 'feel with' a sufferer, still have to learn, by experience, how to be objective and impersonal about what is evil without being infected by it.

In the field of mental illness, the two approaches can still be distinguished. The expert takes a lot of trouble to make a diagnosis, to tie a label on the disease, and then to try to get rid of it. But his technical disease-attacking procedures in this field don't add up to a great deal: he either makes people drowsy with tranquillisers or shocks them with electricity: in medieval times, and earlier, they did the same thing in different ways - they used poppies or mandragora for drowsiness, and snakepits or cold water douches for shocks. But we also use psychotherapy, which is health-enhancing rather than disease-attacking. The psychotherapist respects the patient's humanness, and listens to him to try to understand what he means rather than to understand what is wrong with his mental machinery. He sees mental illness as an indication that the patient has difficulty in communicating his meanings. Communication, of course, is a two-way process, but to be frank I don't believe that psychiatrists are any better than anyone else at making themselves understood - but they are good at listening.

Now I don't suppose many psychiatrists would agree with me about this, but I am going to suggest that when they use their skills of listening, and trying to understand what people are trying to communicate, they are really acting as amateurs rather than as specialists. If you are a disease-attacking expert, it doesn't really matter whether you know your patient as a person: you don't have to 'love' him. A surgeon can cure people without even knowing their names. But a psychotherapist won't be much good unless he knows and *loves* (not necessarily likes) his patient or client. And if he is more skilled at psychotherapy than a layman, it is because he has had *more* experience than the layman and not because he has a different *kind* of experience. So I believe that the art of psychotherapy - of taking relationships and communications between people seriously - can be practised just as readily by laymen, amateurs, as by professionals. I don't mean that it is easy - it certainly is not. But anyone who has spent 20 years trying to take relationships and communications seriously, because he is committed to helping people, and himself, to become more fully human - is likely to be just as good at it as a professional like myself. . . .

. . . As I have said, the amateur looks for the healthy part of people and tries to foster their growth. He leaves it to the expert to try to get rid of the bad bits when necessary. But let me add this: *if you don't pay too much attention to illness, a lot of it will just go away.* This sounds like a paradox. But here is how to resolve it: if you don't pay too much attention to illness a lot of it will just go away - *provided you pay a lot of attention to the building up of health.* So if we had an effective and sufficient body of amateurs, there would be less need for experts. We couldn't get rid of them altogether, but we would be able to make the curative services - the hospital services for instance - much less expensive and of more manageable size.

So, then, the amateur is one who stresses the importance of loving people; whose techniques are harmless and akin to those of hospitality; who is compassionate with persons rather than dispassionate about things; and who is more interested in building up health than in attacking disease. He is also one who recognises his own need to become more healthy. There is an illusion in the expert-client relationship that the expert has all the health and the client all the sickness, the expert is the one who knows and the sufferer is ignorant. But the amateur recognises that although the sufferer is sick in one way, he is healthy in others, and may therefore have something to teach the helper about his own health. . . .

. . . At the *face-to-face group* level, it means that all those involved, helpers and sufferers alike, seek to share one another's burdens. This is the principle of the therapeutic community: that all the patients and all the staff, of whatever grade, are recognised as being part of the group's therapeutic potential. This means that it is accepted that sometimes the ward cleaner will speak the healing word instead of the nurse or doctor; and that sometimes the bearer of health to one person will be another patient who is even more sick. The professionals do not claim to be the sole dispensers of health. Such a community has no autocratically imposed rules. It often looks like anarchy to the casual visitor; but what saves it from anarchy is that all the members (patients and staff alike) meet together regularly to discuss and if possible resolve problems openly and honestly, respecting one another's differences but insisting that the health of the whole community is the only basis on which the healing of individual component members can be built.

At the level of society at large, or of any group so large that regular face-to-face meetings of all the members are impracticable, there is still much room for the amateur. At this level, it means insisting that the general task of health building is something that cannot be safely left to the experts. If you ask the doctors to arrange your health service, they may give you a medicated society; or if you ask the public health specialists they may give you a sanitated society. Only if you allow everyone to have a voice - and especially those who suffer from society as it is now - the delinquent, the mentally sick, the alienated and the dispossessed - will you get the information you need in order to develop a strategy for a healthier society in the future. It means that when you find sickness rates rising, you pay at least as much attention to raising the morale of those affected as you do to the provision of more caring services. When there is an epidemic of drug-taking in a community or section of the population, you don't only set up special units for the treatment of addicts: you also try to discern the causes of their disaffection. If you fail to do this, then even if you are successful in cutting down the number of drug addicts, you will find that you have an increase in some other symptom of social distress, such as violent crime, or suicide, or something else which may be worse than the addiction. It means that you pay a great deal more attention to information and opinion gathering than we commonly do, and that you give much more time and effort to reflection upon what is really needed to improve people's health before you rush into ill-considered, impulsive action. Faced with problems of sickness we all of us imagine someone sitting on our shoulder and urgently whispering to us 'don't just stand there *do* something'. This is very often if not always the work of the devil. I want to say to you, stop and think: always think of what the middle term and long term outcomes of what you propose to do may be as well as what the short term benefits are. It is bad to be panicked into running away from problems you don't understand. It is almost equally as bad to be panicked into action before you understand them. Often it is wiser, and more healthy, to with-stand, to stand with, what is puzzling, rather than to change it into what may well be an even more intractable puzzle.

160 - Amateurs in Health Care.

CARING INSTITUTIONS

. . . The kind of caring institutions we create in each generation reflect our beliefs about our society's weaknesses. In Victorian times, poverty was seen as one of the worst evils from which people suffered, so we shaped institutions to relieve the distress of the poor. Then later we came to believe that illness was an even more pressing evil, so we put more effort into medical institutions to relieve the distress caused by illness. But as time has passed, we have found that the institutions we set up with such good intentions have taken on a life of their own; and that the resources we put into them are swallowed up by the demands of the institution itself to survive and grow, instead of being used to relieve the distress for which they were intended.

We are becoming increasingly aware that, in our time, one of the major evils is that hospitals and other institutions tend to dehumanise the people who come to them; and that this applies not only to those who seek their aid, but also to those who staff them. Now, of course, I'm sure that this isn't true of the Manor Hospital; but if we were celebrating the centenary of some other hospital, we might wonder whether what we were really celebrating was not so much the fact that it had survived for 100 years, but rather the fact that so many of the staff and patients who had lived and worked there had managed to preserve their humanity, in spite of the bureaucratic rules and restrictions which seem inevitable in such places, but which are so imprisoning or destructive of the human spirit.

Often, we like to think of our caring institutions as modelled on the parable of the Good Samaritan. We try to care for the sick and disabled instead of passing by on the other side like the priest and the Levite in the story. But there are one or two important ways in which we have *not* followed the parable. St. Luke's gospel says *"A certain Samaritan, as he journeyed, came where he was* ... He came where the wounded man was. And this is just what our modern hospital staffs do *not* do. Doctors and nurses in hospital are not mobile enough. They have lots of technical apparatus and machinery and record systems and they are immobilised by them. We doctors expect people to come to us when they are in trouble, instead of us going to them. And this is usually wrong. When people are ill and distressed, the last thing we should ask of them is that they should have to leave their own familiar surroundings and home comforts, and have to cope not only with the illness but with the extra strain of having to adapt to a strange environment. Yet this is what we do.

So here is one element in my vision for the future of the Manor Hospital: instead of seeing it as a place to which patients are brought in, it should become primarily a place from which caring people go out, to look after people in distress *where they are*. I suppose you would still need some few beds, for homeless people for instance; so I picture a hospital where there would be many staff and few inpatients; but where the staff would be even more reluctant to stay within the walls of the institution than patients are. Perhaps the hospital should send seventy of them out, two by two like Jesus did. Such a hospital would be basically a training and resource centre for a genuine community nursing and medical service, rather than a place of residence for the sick. Of course, at this moment hospitals depend on X-ray machines and operating theatres and complex apparatus which can't be moved; but in the next 50 or 100 years there is no reason why all that stuff can't be miniaturised, like computers and transistor radios; and then the machines can fit into the nurses' and doctors' bags like the stethoscope, and be carried around in their cars or on a trailer. We must surely all look forward to the day when doctors and nurses are again masters of the machines they use instead of their servants as they are for the time being.

This brings me to another way in which we don't follow the parable of the Good Samaritan. *The Samaritan wasn't a professional*. He is not presented to us as one who was specially trained to know what was good for other people. It was the priest and the Levite who were supposed to be the experts in those days. Our modern hospitals are staffed by experts - trained professionals. We may allow unqualified people or even volunteers to do some of the humbler jobs, but we don't allow them to be actually responsible for the care offered to the sick. But why not? One of the commonest complaints about hospitals is that they are not home-like. We take the criticism seriously, and try to make them more friendly and comfortable; but however hard we try, no-one is ever likely to mistake a modern hospital - or a modernised old hospital - for anyone's home. If we really want to achieve a home-like atmosphere in a hospital here is what we should do: we should arrange for all the administrative functions such as the building maintenance and furnishings and cooking and sleeping arrangements to be the responsibility of *amateurs*. And we should see that professionals only come in to see the patients or residents when invited in by the amateur-in-charge. In fact we should value the professional as an adviser, but discourage and resist any attempt he may make to take over control.

Here then is another element in my vision for the future: that the places in which people are cared for when they are sick or disabled should be under the control of amateurs instead of professionals. We wouldn't call the heads of such establishments by the same titles we use at present: we wouldn't call them administrators or superintendents or number nines or tens or chairmen of staff committees - we would call them simply, *householders*.

I expect many of you - especially the professionals among you - will regard these ideas of mine as impractical nonsense and rather too frivolous for the occasion. How can we leave serious matters like caring for the sick in the hands of untrained amateurs? How can we expect them to make responsible decisions about the way the sick should be treated? Well, I must remind you that the vast majority of those who are sick or disabled, even seriously, are at this moment being looked after, not in hospital, but at home by amateurs. The word amateur means 'one who loves'. So parents are looking after sick children, wives are caring for husbands, daughters are looking after elderly parents. Institutions and hospitals only care for a tiny fraction of the sick or disabled or dying. If, in spite of this, we were rash enough to claim that such amateurs don't exercise the kind of responsible care which we professionals do, then my answer would be that people can only learn to be more responsible if we encourage them to accept responsibility. The professional's task should be to help the amateur to exercise his capacity for responsibility, instead of doing as we usually do now, and trying to take over all the responsibility ourselves. At present, far too much of professional practice - in hospital and elsewhere - encourages the sick and their relatives and friends to have a quite unhealthy dependency on the expert . . . .

. . . Interdependence is a far healthier state to be in than either dependence or independence; and if ever we are to have a really healthy health service in this country, we have got to lay far more emphasis than we do on reciprocal caring, on bearing one another's burdens, on mutual support, on dissolving this artificial barrier we erect between the sick and the well. The healthiest among us is partly sick and doomed to die; while the least healthy of us still has some contribution to make to the wellbeing of us all. We all need caring for, and we all need to care for others. ...

192-1 Manor Hospital Centenary.

Chapter Eight

GOD OF GOOD AND EVIL

In probing the mystery of good and evil James drew both on his knowledge of perception, and his clinical experience in helping people to face up to an evil situation, and by with-standing it to make something good out of it. Perhaps nothing is more needed in our society today than men and women who refuse to opt out of difficult and hostile situations but 'stay with it' and suffer on behalf of others.

These pain-bearers of society - such as family doctors, mothers of families, probation officers and teachers - are the cement of community. James deliberately trained himself to bear anxiety, guilt and embarrassment, for the common good of all. In himself he tried to transform such bad experiences, and use them as raw material for the creation of wholeness in family, hospital, church congregation and local community.

James believed that a new awareness was growing in society that in the long term *we cannot in fact get rid of evil:* but must learn to live with it, transform it, and make good out of it. This involves a journey from one state of being to another, an inner journey of *becoming*.

James was a contributor to the Institute of Religion and Medicine working party on 'Exorcism'(187-2). Rejecting a dualist approach to good and evil he described wholeness as inclusive of both the sick and the well. He thought and lived the insight that Jesus, the suffering servant, faced and endured evil to the utmost. Easter Day does not cancel Good Friday: they are a complementary revelation of wholeness.

M.W.

EVIL INTO GOOD? (Sermon Notes)

Suppose you own a pond on which a water lily is growing. The lily plant doubles in size each day. If the lily were allowed to grow unchecked, it would completely cover the pond in thirty days, choking off the other forms of life in the water. For a long time the lily plant seems small, and so you decide not to worry about cutting it back until it covers half the pond. On what day will that be? On the twenty-ninth day, of course. You have one day to save your pond. (A French children's riddle).

So there seems to be a sudden *change of state*, from what seems good to what seems evil: a change of state as radical as that of ice turning to water, or water to steam.

In this second half of the 20th C we may be witnessing an analogous change of state in the social field: social temperature rising (each 'atom' moves faster - electronics, transport, fashions, habits).

A particular aspect: up till now, when we have labelled or experienced something as bad or evil, we have tried to separate our-selves from it. Golden Bough: witchdoctor's job to *expel the evil* either publicly (rituals, rain dance etc.) or privately (medicine man). Shaman differentiates into ruler (evil that humans can manage), or priest (evils that need supernatural help), or doctor for sickness. And then magician, alchemist, scientist became society's problem-solvers (= evil-expellers). So successes of modern medicine have been those of disease-eradication. [Nowadays - hospices for the dying].

O.T.: the scapegoat, bearing away our evil into the wilderness. Transgressions were blotted out; enemies were utterly consumed. After the exile, repentance involved separating themselves from their foreign-born wives and children. Rules against defilement and uncleanness.

Echoes in N.T.: *"If thine eye offend thee, cut it out and cast it from thee". "Pure religion is this ... to visit the fatherless and widows, and to keep himself unspotted from the world".* But since the 1950's, we are beginning to find that this attitude of separating yourself from evil, while still useful in small things, is not working too well as a general principle: it's an assumption we can no longer take for granted. There is no wilderness left: it's now our neighbour's garden, or nature reserve. Excommunication is no longer an effective sanction against wrongdoers: we don't hang people, or transport them to penal settlements; nor can we persuade turbulent young folk to go off to the colonies or join the army and keep away from us. Even our physical rubbish, dirt or waste is too vast in bulk for nature to deal with, so we suffer from pollution. In fact, by trying to solve problems, we just make bigger and harder ones. The motorway eases traffic flow in one place, but concentrates bigger jams at another. Curing the illnesses of the young means more sickness among the older which is less easy to treat.

So we begin to have forced upon us the idea that in future we are going to have to *live with* evil instead of eradicating it or expelling it: to live with it until it somehow 'changes its state' and becomes part of the good. We have to become *reconciled* to today's evil: tomorrow's greater good is more likely (not certain, but more likely) to result from reconciliation between today's good and today's evil, than it is from the eradication of today's evil.

Is this a new idea? Or have parents, especially mothers, always known that we have to live with unsolved problems, and uncorrected naughtiness or waywardness in our growing children, or with their pain and unhappiness - and our own - in the likelihood (not the certainty) that all this discomfort is character-building, a necessary part of the maturation process, both for them and for us?

The Exodus - symbol of dealing with evil by separation from it. The Cross - symbol of dealing with evil by staying with it in the *hope* of reconciliation.

187-4 Sermon Notes: Evil Into Good?

THE NATURE OF EVIL AND HUMAN RESPONSES

. . . Modern Christians differ in their beliefs about the reality of the Devil, even though they may share common assumptions about the reality of evil. To believe in the Devil (and evil demons by derivation) is to believe that he is a living entity showing at least as much adaptability, intelligence and capacity for communicating with people as human persons possess (though not constrained by what we all assume to be the natural limits of space and time). Belief in a personal Devil and personal demons was part of the world view of the writers of Scripture and of the man Jesus. Demons were recognised as beings with whom one could converse and who were able to respond to one's utterances. This writer does not now hold such a view, though he might have done had his life experience been different. The assumption he makes is that evil is better described as those parts of our experience which have not yet become good, or that we are not yet able to see as good*. But disbelief in a personal Devil does not imply disbelief in the personal nature of God or the Trinity. To be a person implies at least some capacity for communication, for the integration of parts in a whole, and for self-awareness. The perfection of oneself as a person is a human aspiration, but one that cannot be achieved by a person in their lifetime. It is a vision of the best we can conceive for ourselves. Any human conception of God, however inadequate it may be in other respects, should therefore include, as it should transcend, a description of God as personal. But in my view, if demons are thought of as personal, they cannot be wholly evil; since I assume that a capacity for communicating with persons is itself good. Their capacity for responding in a personal way to persons who encounter them or feel they are possessed by them shows that in principle they are capable of change; and this imposes on us a Christian responsibility to try to ensure that any change is for the better. I assume that, if they exist, demons cannot be totally beyond redemption.

The tendency of humankind to personalise and externalise what is perceived as evil has existed throughout the history of the species, and appears early in the development of every child born. The toddler bruising himself against a chair is as likely to blame the 'baddy chair' as his own clumsiness. Perhaps analogously, although medicine does not now invite us to personalise the external agents we blame for disease, such as bacteria or poisons, it is often assumed (at least by non-medicals) that the only proper focus of treatment is on the elimination of such agents. Thus a bacillus is regarded as *"the"* cause of tuberculosis and, now that we have specific drugs which kill it, we are at risk of forgetting that (as our fathers knew) it is a disease which can be cured by fostering the strength of the sufferer. They used to prescribe *"ample fresh air, plenty of good food, bodily and mental rest and exercise undertaken in graduated fashion"* (Price 1946). When someone encounters something they judge to be evil, there are always two aspects to the confrontation: the object or process which he encounters, and his response to it. And the evil nature of the encounter may be modified either by manipulation of the object or process, or by some interior change in the way he interprets it or responds to it. It is in the light of this second, perhaps less obvious possibility, that this chapter is written. . . .

. . . Until the second half of the twentieth century it has always been possible for us to imagine that progress toward a more perfect world would best be made by trying to exclude evil elements from the present one. Material waste or dirt could be channelled or dumped far enough away from human habitation for the natural process of decay to

---

* Carl G Jung would not have approved this assumption. He said "as long as Evil is not (regarded as) a living entity, *nobody will take his own shadow seriously"*. But even so he acknowledged that "as shadow. Evil was not absolute and final, but redeemable and ... an instrument of enlargement of human awareness" (Van der Post. 1978).

deal with them. Evil or troublesome members of the community could be constrained to leave their country for their country's good. Heaven could be conceived as an island of ordered perfection lying in a sea of chaos called Hell. But with the advent of worldwide radio communication, supersonic air travel and rapid population growth, this picture of the world is being radically changed. We are finding that our material waste spoils not only our own but our neighbours' physical environment. Other countries are no longer willing to accept those people whom we wish to exile; and we do not find internal exile, in mental hospitals, prisons or concentration camps an ethically unambiguous alternative. There is now no wilderness into which the scapegoat can be despatched, bearing away our evil, for the wilderness has become our neighbour's garden. Wars across national frontiers are being replaced - or supplemented - by urban guerrillas and terrorists; and when a member of the British Government triumphantly celebrated the first commercial flight of Concorde by saying that between sunrise and sunset it has *"shrunk the world to half its size"* (Shore 1976), many of us felt shivers of apprehension at the implication that tomorrow we will all feel twice as crowded as we do today. Our new understanding of ecology brings us to realise that whenever we deal with evil by solving a problem in one area of life, the resulting shift in the balance of forces produces another, often more difficult, problem elsewhere. In the medical field, the prevention or cure of illness in younger people means that more of them live on to present problems of intractable degenerative disability when they are older. When we hear of an exorcist commanding evil spirits to *"return to the place appointed them"* (Exeter Commission 1972), the Christian of today has to ask what kind of appointed place can be imagined where such demons could do no further harm to other parts of God's creation. It seems clear therefore that we are being called to discover ways of living with the evils we experience, as an alternative to avoiding or getting rid of them.

The dilemma was recognised rather earlier in the psychological field than in the material. It was the early psychoanalysts who took the first steps towards showing us how evil experience could sometimes be lived with and turned to good account as a contribution to greater personal maturity; and, building on their foundations, students of child development have shown us that in fact the growth and flowering of human personality, from infancy onwards, will not occur unless the child experiences what seems to him to be evil at successive stages of development, and succeeds not merely in containing it, but in transcending it. Intra-personal conflict is an essential stimulus to the maturing of the personality; and to 'wrap a child in cotton wool', denying him the experience of evil appropriate to his age is to distort or stunt his development. In groups and families, the psychotherapist can see each member separately trying to escape the evil that he feels by projecting it on to others. In small groups, one member is often unconsciously selected as the scapegoat for all; and the process of group psychotherapy is largely concerned with enabling individuals to find strength to 'withdraw their projections' back into themselves, so that each takes responsibility for his own share of the evil experience of the group. . . .

. . . If in God's providence it is not only possible but preferable to reconcile evil with good by staying with it and suffering it instead of seeking to destroy it or banish it, how are we to understand its transformation into its opposite? There is a difficulty caused by our language. To be properly understood, the noun evil should be thought of in an adjectival sense. There are people, objects, events and conditions which we may judge to be evil; but when we use the word as a noun we should remember that this is only a convenient form of shorthand.* But we still have to understand how the evil quality attaching to a person or event - or to a demon or spirit if *we* think in those terms - can be transformed into a quality of goodness. If evil is qualitative rather than substantive, then it is as impossible to conceive of absolute evil as it would be to imagine absolute blueness or redness which referred to no concrete reality. A phenomenon may be more or less evil; and thus our problem becomes the more comprehensible one of seeking to explain how a person or event which seems more evil than good can be transformed into one that seems more good than evil. An answer to the difficulty immediately presents itself: a phenomenon which appears evil in one perspective may appear less evil or even good if viewed from a different perspective. What seems unmistakably evil (or good) to a child may be seen quite differently by its parents. Reconciliation can occur when two enemies, each seeing the other as evil, are enabled to 'see each other's point of view'. Such a change of perspective, a 'change of mind from past evil', is precisely what is meant by *metanoia* or repentance.

But the apparent simplicity of this explanation is deceptive. It is no easier to change one's perspective on the real world (except as such changes are evoked by the gradual processes of growth) than it is to repent of one's sins. Part of the difficulty in practice lies in the fact that what is seen as evil often tends to fascinate the person who perceives it: it concentrates attention so narrowly on itself that we become unaware of its context and our surroundings. Of course there is biological survival value in the inborn tendency of the human species to pay concentrated attention to what it sees as evil. It is as valuable as is the arousal of the nervous system to prepare the body for fight or flight in the face of threat. But the continued arousal of such mechanisms when the danger is past leads to pathology. They are 'energy-expending'; and at other times they normally give place to 'energy-restoring' mechanisms which allow of rest, repair and further growth. Human beings are also endowed with a capacity to learn; and although it may seem difficult it is nevertheless possible to teach ourselves to make a deliberate effort to pay attention to the context of the evil with which we are faced - its context in time as well as in space. (No deliberate effort is needed to make us pay attention to the evil itself: that comes quite naturally to us.) So often it is the context that determines the meaning of what we perceive. Events can look very different from what they seem at present when we contemplate their possible outcome in the medium and long term (their context in time); and what seems to be unequivocally evil in one member of a family often reveals quite a different significance when it is seen in the context of the family and its interaction as a whole. The degree of certainty and conviction with which we label an event as evil - or good - is unreliable, at least until it has been tested by reference to a

---

* The same comment applies to other abstract nouns which derive from qualities of action or feeling, words like love, or sin, or anger. Unless they are being used metaphorically, they are to be understood as referring to loving, sinning or angry persons. See John Macmurray's argument that 'knowledge is primarily a dimension of action' (J. Macmurray, 1957)

range of possible contexts.

Since the argument presented here appears to question the objective reality of evil it will doubtless be resisted by some. Many of us have at some time found ourselves in situations where the sense of evil is so overpowering, so inexplicable and so foreign to us that its autonomous existence seems certain and obvious. There are many intelligent people, including Christians - for instance in African traditional societies - whose understanding of evil is that it results from the activities of ancestral or other spirits (Appiah-Kubi, 1975). Those among us whose Christian belief in the supernatural does not include belief in such occult forces might nevertheless come to believe in them if we were to find ourselves alone and isolated for any length of time among a community for whom animistic beliefs were the norm - particularly if our morale was lowered by sickness or anxiety. Our sense of certainty is subjective, and is no guarantee of objective truth. Even healthy people can be affected by hallucinations (false perceptions) occasionally, and by delusions (false beliefs) more often. T.S. Kuhn (1970) has shown how man's interpretation of the objectively real can be drastically altered by an opportunist rather than a logically predictable acceptance of a different or novel set of ideas. . . .

. . . Staying with evil in the hope of reconciliation implies taking a risk of being corrupted or overcome by it, and we must recognise that it is no part of a Christian's duty actively to seek martyrdom. Having stated our grounds for believing that it may be *preferable* to stay with what seems to be evil, we have to acknowledge that the limitations of the human condition often make it impossible in practice. Here are three examples: the experience of pain and suffering can at times be strengthening and ennobling, but there are limits to the amount of suffering we should willingly tolerate in others, if not in ourselves. Second, when we recognise temptation, it is often wiser to avoid it altogether than to seek to face it and bring it under control. And third, in order to stay with a situation of great evil in the hope of achieving a greater long term good, it may be essential to deal summarily with lesser evils which conflict with such an aim. The principle of reconciliation does not lessen the importance of acknowledging evil to be a dangerous enemy. Sometimes it is indeed best to flee from an enemy, but at others it may be better to confront him. But confrontation may be of two kinds. It does not necessarily mean 'facing with hostility and defiance' (OED). It can also mean facing up to an uncomfortable reality which has hitherto been avoided. An army may confront another with the intention of destroying it, but an ambassador may confront a hostile monarch with the intention of seeking an accommodation with him. In newspaper accounts of industrial disputes the opposing sides often seem to confront one another with hostility and defiance. But a parent or schoolteacher or psychotherapist may confront someone with 'home truths' with compassionate rather than hostile intent.

The perception of what seems to be evil thus faces the Christian with an often difficult choice between three decisions: whether to flee from it, to confront it with hostility, or to bear with it in the hope of its conversion into what seems good. The third of these courses of action, like the other two, does not deny that evil is to be seen as an enemy; but perhaps it was this keeping open the possibility of reconciliation that Jesus had in mind when he taught us to 'love our enemies'. As Christians, we believe that the cosmos was created by God. If demons exist, then they too are part of God's creation. If they are personal, they are God's children even though they may be disobedient. Are we not then called to co-operate with his loving redemptive purpose for them, as we are for the rest of the created order?

Thus far we have dealt with some reasons why it may be preferable to stay with evil rather than to avoid it. We have noted that to remove it from one place may merely transfer it to another; and that some experience of evil is a necessary condition of children's growth toward maturity. We have also contrasted the Old Testament deliverance model of the Exodus with the New Testament model offered by the life, death and resurrection of Jesus. From such considerations arises the possibility that, although humankind continues to find evil detestable and threatening, it may have a much more positive role to play in God's economy than we find it comfortable to recognise. Theologically, the traditional understanding of the Fall of man from a pre-existent state of grace has been challenged by the Irenaean view that man's fallen state is a mark of his immaturity, and that he

> *"having been created, should receive growth; and having received growth, should be strengthened; and having been strengthened, should abound; and having abounded, should recover (from the disease of sin); and having recovered, should be glorified; and being glorified, should see his Lord."* (Irenaeus - quoted by Hick 1966)

The traditional model sees the work of redemption as a restoration of man to his *status quo ante* by the elimination of sin and evil. It is paralleled in the field of medicine by such treatment modalities as the excision of a diseased part of the body, or purging, or giving antibiotics for infections; and in the longer term, 'rehabilitation' after illness. They are directed toward restoring the patient to the condition he was in at the moment he became a patient. Rituals of exorcism or deliverance often appear to have a similar aim. However necessary such clinical or ritual interventions may be, they imply an inadequacy or failure of the sufferer's strength to cope with the evil unaided. Whether from a theological, medical or demonological perspective, the traditional model leaves uncon-sidered the possibility of growth through suffering; of the person being not merely as strong as he was before, but actually stronger as a result of his evil experience. It does not concern itself with *newness of life*.

By contrast, the model we associate with Irenaeus implies that man's spiritual growth toward maturity depends upon his experiencing evil, and being stimulated by it, and learning how to cope with it. In this view, the state of grace which man seeks lies, and has always lain, ahead of him. Not only does such a 'growth' model provide a much more satisfactory fit with the facts of science recognised by modern man, and with many of the health-promoting (as contrasted with disease-attacking) activities of medicine. It also enables us to see our encounters with evil as having creative possibilities, challenging us to contribute to humankind's collective task of building the world for God. We are no longer condemned to a dispiriting defensive battle in which the initiative lies with the enemy. The suffering which evil brings us is as real as ever, but is no longer seen merely negatively, as retributive punishment for Adam's sin, but as a price to be paid, willingly if not gladly, for the movement we strive to make toward the realisation of the kingdom of heaven. Belief in evil demons stems from an ancient world view which was ruled by fear. When the Lord delivered the old law to Moses, the people 'trembled and stood at a distance'; but from that time on, the refrain that runs through the whole of scripture is *"Do not be afraid"*. *"Be strong and of a good courage"*, said the Lord to Joshua; and the life, death and teaching of Jesus hammers home the message . . . .

. . . The views expressed in this chapter about the nature of evil do not provide any proof of the non-existence of evil spirits; but perhaps they add weight to the experience of those priests who find that very many of those who come asking for exorcism turn out on investigation to be suffering evil experience for which meaning can be found in other ways than by invoking demons. But there remains the question as to whether exorcism has a value in the small minority of cases in which (a) the sufferer believes himself to be possessed by a demon and (b) those ministering to him can find no other explanation for his suffering. And these, of course, include those who are capable of tolerating their own ignorance and keeping an open mind, as well as those who share the sufferer's belief in demons. In this situation, some would say that those who do not believe in demons should not exorcise since by doing so they would appear to endorse a belief which they think to be wrong. This is the position taken by the sixty-five scholars (CIO 1975). But there are analogous situations which cast some doubt upon the finality of this argument. After the war in the Pacific in 1942-1945, Allied planes landed on islands in the south seas bringing relief to the inhabitants who had been suffering from the blockade imposed by the Japanese. Some of these people had never seen an aircraft before, and interpreted their deliverance from evil as a supernatural visitation by a great bird from the sky who came bringing good things - the so-called 'cargo cults'. But the undesirability of their beliefs would not have justified the Allies in withholding airborne supplies from them. Similarly, it has been found by Christian medical missionaries in some parts of the world that their patients come to have faith in the syringe the doctor uses for injections as the source of their deliverance from evil, rather than in the Christian gospel which the missionaries tried to preach. But would they therefore be justified in not using the syringe? There are other examples of the difficulty. Parents often respond to the trivial injuries of their small children by 'kissing them better'; and physicians often respond to the (not necessarily trivial) complaints of their patients by prescribing a 'placebo' (an inert substance of some kind). In these four situations, the fact that the giver believes that the recipient misinterprets the source or nature of his deliverance does not stop him from continuing to provide that deliverance. The conversion of recipients away from an inappropriate deliverance model is to be seen as a longer-term problem requiring different considerations from the urgent need for relief from distress. The position taken by the sixty-five scholars is understandably addressed to the long term rather than the short-term problem.

If exorcism is to be rejected even as an emergency response, we should seek other grounds than that it appears to endorse an erroneous belief. As Dingwall (1976) says, *"If we wish to further a moral crusade in favour of our definition of wellbeing, then it is clearly vital to be able to articulate it with the theories of those whom we are trying to persuade".* So how can Christians who hold the kind of view expressed in this chapter articulate it with the views of those who believe in demon possession? A blank denial that demons exist is unlikely to convince those who do believe in them. Indeed, one of the working party's witnesses pointed out that if the Church were officially to proclaim its disbelief in them, those who felt a need for exorcism would simply seek help from other, perhaps less desirable, agencies. A possible way forward in this difficulty is the one I have tried to explore earlier in this chapter. It leaves the question of the existence or non-existence of demons open, but tries to shift the focus of attention away from the demons who are the putative *cause* of the evil and on to the evil experience itself. Causal explanations of evil experience are never single and probably always incomplete. The experiencing person is as relevant a 'cause' of it as is the objective 'reality' which he encounters; and modification of either may resolve the distress. More generally, since evil experience results from the coming together of a number of causative factors, a change in any of them, or in the balance of them, can remove its evil quality.

Perhaps then the essence of a ministry to those who believe themselves to be possessed is to focus attention on the person and his subjective experience, instead of looking only for its causes. We can only come to an understanding of another's experience by allowing ourselves to *share* in it, but we should be slow to accept any particular explanation for it. Perhaps we should adopt the stance of one trying to appreciate a work of art, rather than the stance of a scientific investigator. This is the method of many who exercise a deliverance ministry. They establish a personal relationship with the person in distress, thus sharing their suffering to a greater or lesser extent; and then seek for appropriate measures to withstand or relieve what is now their *joint* distress. And such measures may involve the use of prayer and sacraments, or expert attention from doctors or psychologists - or it may be that the non-technical loving care and support of a good neighbour is all that is needed. When an exorcist successfully brings relief to a sufferer, it is at least possible that his success is more the result of his having established a personal relationship with him than it is the result of his having used the 'correct' ritual to drive away a demon.

Rites of exorcism (at least within the western Christian tradition) appear to have the following undesirable features in common:

1. The adoption of a passive role by the man who believes himself to be possessed: he plays no active part in his own deliverance.
2. The focus of attention is on the *cause* of the evil experience (the demon or demons) rather than on the experiencing person.
3. The assumption that *one* causative factor (the demon or demons) is of over whelming relevance to the man's evil experience.
4. For the Christian, the derivative assumption that the healing activity of the Holy Spirit can in this situation *only* be mediated through the exorcistic rite.

Of these characteristics, the first three are commonly found not only in exorcism but also in more conventional forms of deliverance from evil such as are exercised in the medical field. As we have seen, such an approach is always a second best, aimed at restoring the man to his pre-existing state rather than at his further development or growth. By focusing attention on the disorder rather than on the person who has it, this approach is always at risk of depersonalising the sufferer, and this, of course, is a danger which the Christian must take particularly seriously. But it is the implied limitation on the freedom of the Holy Spirit to act in new, unexpected and creative ways which would seem to be the most telling objection to the practice of exorcism.

The essence of the task of the Christian minister is to mediate God's love for humanity; and this implies that the focus of attention must continually be on *persons* - the personal self and the personal other. It is within the *personal* relationship between God and humanity, and thus between persons, that deliverance from evil experience is to be found.

Bibliography

M.I..J. Abercrombie,	**The Anatomy of Judgement,** (Hutchinson), 1960.
K. Appiah-Kubi,	*'The Church's Healing Ministry in Africa'*, <u>Contact</u> (Geneva), No. 29, 1975.
P. L. Berger & T. Luckman,	**The Social Construction of Reality**, (Allen Lane), 1967.
Church Information Office,	**Exorcism,** Statement on behalf of 65 signatories, 1975.
R. Dingwall,	**Aspects of Illness,** (Martin Robertson), 1976.
Exeter Commission,	**Exorcism,** (SPCK), 1972.
J. Hick,	**Evil and the God of Love**, (Macmillan), 1966.
T.S. Kuhn,	**The Structure of Scientific Revolutions,** (University of Chicago), 1970.
K. Lorenz,	**Studies in Animal & Human Behaviour,** Vol. II, (Methuen), 1971.
J. Macmurray,	**The Self as Agent,** (Faber), 1957.
F.W. Price,	**A Textbook of the Practice of Medicine**, (7th Edition, Oxford Medical), 1946.
W. Sargant,	**Battle for the Mind,** (Heinemann), 1957.
P. Shore,	speaking at Heath Row Airport, London, 21st. January, 1976.
L.Van der Post,	**Jung and the Story of our Time,** (Penguin), 1978.
J.M. Wilson,	*'Exorcism'*, in <u>Expository Times</u>, July 1975, LXXXVI, No. 10.

187 - 2 Nature and Existence of Evil.

ON DEALING WITH EVIL

. . . How does a man deal with bad experience?

(1)   A very common way is simply to *deny it*. When we first hear bad news, we often say *"Oh, no, I can't believe it"* or *"I don't believe it"*. We shut our ears or our eyes to the obvious. The alcoholic will deny that his drink is doing him any harm long after he is aware of quite obvious symptoms of deterioration.

(2)   And there are other more subtle ways of evading the problem. *One is to find someone or something other than one's self to blame.* When the Lord asked Adam if he had eaten the forbidden fruit, he said Eve had given it to him; and when the Lord turned to Eve, she said the serpent had persuaded her to eat it. This 'passing the buck' doesn't get rid of the evil, any more than denying it does; it only seems to make it a little easier to bear at the time. In pre-scientific times, it was usual to blame demons or evil spirits, and men tried to exorcise or propitiate these supernatural agencies by rituals of various kinds.

(3)   Another way in which this mechanism of blaming works is when a group of people makes a *scapegoat* of someone. If everyone in a group is feeling upset, it often happens that one member is picked on, and blamed for *all* the evil experience of *all* the members, instead of for the small fraction of evil for which he may really have been responsible. Of course, if this happens, the one who is scapegoated tends to behave worse: if you give a dog a bad name he is much more likely to bite someone.

If we think about the behaviour of the apostles at the time of the Last Supper, it seems very likely that Judas was a scapegoat for the twelve. They were despondent, because Jesus had made it clear to them that he wasn't the kind of leader who would liberate the country from the Roman oppressors. He acted like a servant, and washed their feet. The apostles were worried about the problem of leadership, and wrangled among themselves about who would be chief. When Jesus told them he would be betrayed, one after another of them asked *"Is it I?"*. And yet in spite of all this uncertainty about themselves and their loyalty, none of them made any move to stop Judas going out and leaving them. It almost seems as if they allowed Judas to be the betrayer - on their behalf. As if all their bad feelings were projected on to him.

(4)   Beside the techniques of denial, and blaming or projection, there is a fourth common mechanism which we can call *dissociation*. By this means one's mind seems able to split off the evil part of experience from the rest, so that it is no longer recognised as being part of the self, and the self is relieved of responsibility for it. In this way we can on occasion manage to forget evil experiences, though sometimes the part which is split-off gets back at us when we are off guard, and gives us neurotic symptoms or nightmares. St. Paul gives us what I think is an example of this mechanism in his letter to the Romans. He says *"The good which I want to do, I fail to do; but what I do is the wrong which is against my will; and if I do what is against my will, clearly it is no longer I whom am the agent, but sin that has its lodging in me"*. He talks of sin as if it had a separate life of its own, like a demon or evil spirit. In an age which no longer believes in demons, the psychiatrist would want to say that sin can't be an agent: Paul himself really was the agent, who was himself responsible for his sinful actions.

The thing, which all these unconscious mechanisms have in common, is that they are ways in which the self tries to escape from the evil experience. Some people fly to alcohol, or to drugs, or to gambling, or to suicide, to escape the realities of life.

(5)   But there is another way of coping with bad experience which is quite different from these because it doesn't involve running away, but requires us to face up to the evil, *to with-stand it.*

This way is not easy. It means 'working through' the experience, exposing oneself to it as it really is. The process is usually painful, and needs courage. Most importantly, this method of coping is unlike the other ways because it requires a change of mind, a change of attitude. You won't be the same person after it as you were before. You will have learnt something about yourself. Your personality will have grown or matured to some extent.

One experience which most of us have to go through at some time in our lives is that of the death of someone we love. The suffering of the pangs of grief is certainly an evil: in the New Jerusalem, according to John's vision, *"there shall be an end to death, and to mourning and crying and pain"*. This experience is not the result of sin unless it is a sin to be born, for in human terms there cannot for long be birth without love, nor birth without death. How do we cope with grief? Do we listen to those of our friends who tell us to "go right away and have a change of scene?" Do we seek the doctor's aid in finding oblivion through sedatives? Do we try to lose ourselves in work, and carry on as if nothing had happened? Or do we look for someone to blame: 'if only' the illness could have been diagnosed sooner; or 'if only' his employers had been kinder to him; or perhaps we blame ourselves 'if only' I had been a little more patient with him. . . . All these are examples of evasive tactics, aren't they? Actually they are rarely entirely successful. Sooner or later, if we are to remain healthy, we have to face up to the real situation. We have to accept the loss, and allow the wound to heal. We have to weep on someone's shoulder, and get the weeping over. We end up perhaps a little sadder, but certainly wiser.

The word '*repentance'* most nearly expresses what is involved in this process of facing reality. Usually, of course, it is limited to the notion of sin rather than the wider notion of evil: we don't usually talk of repenting from grief. But, after grieving, we have to 'come to our senses', like the prodigal son. The psychotherapist talks of 'working through' anxiety or grief or depression, but I think the process is very much the same. It means confronting the true situation in which we find ourselves, and not being sidetracked by evasions. It means accepting the possibility of a change in one's personality to something more mature, at the cost of some suffering, some 'growing pains'. It means accepting responsibility for your actual experience, whether it was something you sought for, or whether it was something you would have avoided if you could.

I have said that repentance (in this wider sense) is usually painful and difficult. In fact it is so difficult that I don't suppose it often happens if someone is left to themselves, and has no-one to whom they can turn for support. We really do need a shoulder to weep on when we mourn.

When we are faced with evil, as I said at the beginning, we tend to narrow the focus of awareness so that we become self-centred or egocentric. Now the only stage of life when self-centredness can perhaps be regarded as necessary for health is in the first few months after birth, before the baby becomes aware of its mother as another person. *From that moment onwards, the healthy child learns progressively that he can only manage to deal with what he feels to be evil if he accepts the help and support of other people.* At first, when he feels distressed, he relies entirely on mother to come to his relief; but in every child's life there comes a point when mother expresses her sympathy for him by saying "Oh dear, we are in trouble, aren't we?" In saying "we", rather than "you", she enables her child to learn that he is a member of a group - in this case a group of two - and that his evil experience is something which can be shared by others in the group. And then mother goes on to say "How shall we deal with this trouble?" And this enables the child to learn that the solution of what is now a shared problem doesn't lie with mother alone, but with him as well. He realises that he can add his initiative to their joint search for a means of relieving - not only his own distress, but hers also, because she shares it with him. . . .

. . . It is this widely-based idea of the mature self which is threatened by what I called the constricting fascination of evil. And yet, the wider the group or community with whom a man identifies himself, the more likely he is to experience evil, including sin, originating outside his individual self. He will find himself taking a share in the responsibility for other men's sins, feeling a vicarious guilt on their behalf - even when they do not know they are sinning. This is what Jesus did: he identified himself with the whole of humanity, and so shared the responsibility for their sins; and this is what led him to say on the Cross "*Father, forgive them; they do not know what they are doing*".

So it seems to me that all men share in the responsibility for all the evil experience of humankind. We share the responsibility; but that doesn't mean we are called upon to apportion blame. I see our human efforts to fix the blame for wrong doing on those responsible for it as a backward-looking divisive and evasive tactic, distracting attention from humanity's real task. We all bear one another's burdens of guilt feeling and bad experience, whether we like it or not. It is part of the human condition. The choice we have is either to avoid facing up to it, choosing to keep our limited image of our present selves free of the risk of change and free of the risk of growth too; or to face it boldly, sharing the pain and the risk of failure - but also the chance of further growth - with all other people; seeing ourselves, as St. Paul saw us, as part of the whole creation, groaning now, but waiting with eager expectation for God to make us his children and set our whole body free.

91 - 2 On Dealing with Evil.

WHOLENESS

The concept of wholeness is not a scientific one. It is not meaningful to speak of wholeness objectively, since the speaker can never, even in imagination, detach himself from it. Wholeness is an inclusive concept: it includes the person who thinks it.

I have suggested in other papers that the possibility of thinking meaningfully about this unscientific concept arises from the periodic experience of an infant of being warm and comfortable and well fed and safe in mother's arms. Such experience probably never lasts long, if only for physiological reasons, but in the intervals between such brief experiences it remains an enduring memory, and for the healthy individual, an undying hope and expectation. In its absence, during the large part of life in which we are actively striving to alter the situation in which we find ourselves, it remains at the back of our minds, colouring all our immediate goals whether in play or at work; it is a fantasy which we constantly try to make real, whether we see it as a golden age in the past to which we would return, or as a beatific vision of a possible future.

Once past infancy, all our other experiences tend to give shape and structure to this vision, and because our experience changes, the vision itself is iridescent, dynamic, constantly changing and developing. Initially the experience is both boundless and unstructured - a conception of infinite goodness, we might say; but the pressures of the outside world immediately begin to challenge both its infinity and its goodness. So the development of the vision thereafter is likely to depend on the balance between experiences which the child regards as good and those he sees as bad. If bad experience predominates, he will try to defend himself and his immediate surroundings by drawing hard and fast battle lines against a hostile world, across which all transactions are seen as conquests or defeats. He will see things as totally black or totally white; and the all-or-none character of this 'total' kind of discrimination will cause it to be a rather blunt conceptual instrument for dealing with the world, while the strength and vehemence of his defences will limit the growth and differentiation of his vision.

If on the other hand good experiences outweigh the bad, then defensive works and manoeuvres are seen as only of provisional and temporary significance, exploration across the temporary boundary lines is possible and the world is seen as at least potentially 'whole', inviting a more flexible, sensitive and friendly approach. Over all, the experience of each of us contains a mixture of the two elements. Unless we sometimes interpret the world in a 'total' way as a hostile wilderness and look to our defences, we would be unlikely to survive; but unless at other times we interpret it as a 'wholesome' garden to explore, we would be unable to develop towards maturity.

Experience in the 'total' mode remains egocentric from infancy onwards; and this kind of vision, of the self at the centre of an island of good, fully under our control and sharply demarcated from a hostile environment, means that other people outside the boundary are seen as objects to be manipulated and are not seen as fully personal. It is only experience in the 'whole' mode which allows us to recognise other people as fully human, personal beings like ourselves. Wholeness is necessarily something we share, not something we compete for.

If then we see ourselves as surrounded by other persons who have similar needs and rights to our own, we can begin to realise that in order to retain a vision of wholeness for the world, the best I can hope for myself, or for others, as parts of that world is that we should be not perfect, but just 'good enough'. Movement towards the perfection of the whole depends upon each of its components being not perfect, but just good enough. We must learn to see ourselves as each being *partly* responsible for the whole creation; not - as we do when experiencing in the total mode - as being wholly responsible for just a very limited part of it.

This conclusion, that each of us should aim not at personal excellence, but to be just good enough, seems somewhat paradoxical, and perhaps it is only in this second half of the twentieth century that we can begin to understand it properly. At all previous periods of history, it has been possible to conceive of a perfect society (and analogously a perfect individual) as one from which or from whom all elements which make for imperfection have been expelled. Heaven could be visualised as an island of goodness surrounded by a sea called hell. It is only now, in an age of instant world-wide electronic communications that we can see that no society can any longer exile its deviant members unless another society is willing to accept them. We cannot despatch the scapegoat into the wilderness, bearing away our evil, for the wilderness has become our neighbour's garden. Thus we are called to a new view of humanity. The mechanical view of the universe current two or three centuries ago would have seen no difference between a part of the machine which was perfect and one which was just good enough. Either a part fitted into its proper place or it was cast out and disregarded. The organic view, popular in the last century and this one, takes the organism as its model. It allows for greater complexity and more variability among the parts of the whole, but it still sees efficiency as depending on the expulsion of waste which can be ignored. It is only a truly personal model of the cosmos which enables us to see that in future we have to *live with* our waste, evil, dirt or disorder - in human terms our delinquents, our deviants, our rebels.

What this new view implies we will have to discover as the future unrolls. It was Freud whose insights gave us some hope that the evil experiences we would like to be rid of can be redeemed, so that tomorrow's greater good could emerge from the reconciliation of today's good and today's evil, rather than from the expulsion of today's evil. It is interesting that this discovery in the personal field came before we were faced with the analogous problems of environmental pollution in the organic and physical fields. But the ecological view, which takes the environmental context of the person or organism or event as seriously as it does the person or organism or event itself, is being forced upon us in all fields. The recycling of waste products is a growing industry; the containment and redemption of terrorists and hijackers is a growing problem.

It will be interesting to see what shifts of emphasis for Christian doctrine this rather novel insight will produce. For the future, it is clear that we have to live with conflict rather than hope to settle it, since we find that to settle it in one situation is to arouse it in another. In the language of systems theory, a complex adaptive system (such as a living organism or a human society) must contain (and maintain?) disorder if it is to remain adaptive. In theological terms this means that conflict and evil are for the rest of time inescapable elements of the world in which our Lord is incarnate. Our task is to learn to live with them and redeem them, not to abolish them. Jesus told us that his coming would bring us not peace, but a sword. The wholeness we seek must *include* evil, and sickness, and death. Enemies they may appear to be, but our very survival depends upon our learning how to love our enemies, to love evil and sickness and death. And - though it is still difficult to conceive how - this must mean that we have to discover how to care for them and cherish them. In the words of John Macmurray, the positive includes its own negative, and is constituted by it. Evil is an essential part of goodness, sickness an essential part of health, death an essential part of life. We cannot have one without the other. So reverence for life, health and goodness implies a derivative reverence for death, sickness and evil.

So far I have discussed a human view of wholeness rather than the wholeness of humanity. It would seem that the notion of wholeness can no more be limited to the whole of humankind than it can be limited to one person. Humankind is a *part* of the created order, and however important a part it may think itself to be, the human species is under the same imperative to limit itself to being just good enough as is each of its individual members. We are right to see ourselves as God's stewards, responsible to him in our time for his created order; but if we are God's stewards we are also the servants of his creation. We have to look after it and care for it, and this may at times imply that we have to put its interests before our own, and to accept the limitations thus imposed to our striving for personal excellence, individual wholeness.

What does all this imply for our day-to-day concerns for humanity in its sickness? Many of its implications are to be found in Michael Wilson's book *Health is for People*. Here I will only give some unsystematic examples born of my personal experience as a mental hospital doctor. A concern for wholeness meant that, faced with a person or a group of people in trouble, I had to make a deliberate effort to see the disorder *in context*. The effort had to be deliberate because one's natural reaction was to concentrate attention on the problem rather than its context - on the figure instead of the background. The evil before your eyes tends to fascinate and narrow your span of attention. But it is a major evil in modern medicine that we so often pay more attention to the disease than to the person who has it. It is a common complaint that hospitals and doctors are too impersonal in their dealings with patients. Our primary task is usually seen as the cure or alleviation of disorder, but it should not be: our primary task should be the care of people while they are disordered, and the cure or relief of the disorder should be secondary to this - a means to this end instead of an end in itself. Doctors too often defend themselves from difficult situations by using the magic spell of the words 'doctor-patient relationship', which they think allows them to isolate themselves and their individual patients from the cold blasts of real life in community. The contextual emphasis is just as important when one has to deal not with a disease but with a person: he has to be seen and understood in the context of his family, and the family has to be seen and understood in the context of the local community. These successive exercises in ecological thinking are not comfortable, and often make us increasingly aware of our own powerlessness to alter evil situations; but they do shed new light on many of our established habits of thought and practice. We do not always immediately treat the pain of which a patient complains: we look to see if suffering it for a time may not bring greater health both to him and his family or group. This would be true in many instances of people complaining of depression after bereavement. We do not always remove the person with difficult behaviour out of his family and into hospital: it may help more to have a few talks with him and his wife or parents together. We learn to ask ourselves 'why has this man begun to complain now, today, rather than any other time?' - which often suggests ways of altering the context in which his disorder is set which would be more helpful than simply prescribing something for his disorder.

We may feel it more appropriate to encourage or initiate community protest about bad housing, or about faulty hygiene or safety precautions in a local factory than to confine ourselves to treating the casualties caused thereby. But such initiatives take courage, which we often lack. Within an archaic mental hospital, we may see our task as striving to diminish the harm the institution does by depersonalising the people in it, rather than retiring behind closed doors to do psychotherapy with one or two of them. And at another level, it may be more important to try to integrate the hospital community - staff and patients - with the residents and other institutions in the locality, than to run the hospital as a 'happy ship' behind its isolating walls, even though this may mean that the hospital community remains in a state of morale little better than that of the perhaps depressed area around it.

The practical implications of this shift in perspective are often not easily accepted. It may indeed contribute towards the wholeness of man if the spastic child is cared for at home rather than allowed to deteriorate in an overcrowded and understaffed hospital - but the neighbours may not like it. It may be healthier and more wholesome for patients in a mental hospital to be responsible for the cleanliness of the ward in which they live - but the resulting untidiness can be agony for the nursing staff and a grave affront to visiting dignitaries. Those among us who see ourselves as healthy are challenged by such encounters to think out what we really mean by health or wholeness. Wholeness is inclusive: it includes both the sick and the well.

But who among us can see ourselves as truly healthy? If we take our search for the wholeness of humankind seriously, we have to recognise that we are all partly healthy and partly sick. This carries implications. One is that those labelled as sick have a contribution to make to the health of all of us. In our geriatric wards, where so many folk feel useless, it may be more important to ask the question "what contribution can we help them to make, crippled as they are, to the community of which we are all members?" than to say "what more can we do for these poor souls?"

Another implication is that professional caregivers, however skilled they may be in problem-solving, are no better guides to wholeness than anyone else. Health is not a matter for experts. Inasmuch as both caregiver and sufferer are seeking wholeness, their encounter with one another is a matter of the blind leading the blind. It is only problems with which experts deal, and wholeness is not a problem. Problem-solving is not to be regarded as an end in itself, but as a means. Since all human beings die, medical problem-solving, even at its best, only achieves a shift of the problematic from one time of a human life to a later one, or to other people. And this is true in other fields of technology. The establishment of a new transport facility implies a build-up of traffic at its points of termination. In the national economic field, the illusory attraction of perpetual growth is merely an attempt to evade facing up to this fact of life.

So to conclude: we have to recognise that the search for the wholeness of humanity is a responsibility of us all, sick and healthy as we are in varying degrees. It is not often that those of us who think we are for the moment healthy are the best guides: at such times we ought constantly to be asking ourselves "at cost to whom am I healthy?" – "who is hungry that I may be fed?" Rather, those who contribute most to it are likely to be those who consciously and deliberately shoulder their share of the burden of the world's pain and sickness and grief; those who represent in themselves the condition of fallen humanity, but who accept their representative function with courage and hope in the light of the vision which inspires them. They are those who bear pain and sickness, as they bear joy and satisfaction, not just for themselves but on behalf of all humanity.

Bibliography

On Health:	J.M. Wilson,	**Health is for People**, (DLT), 1975.
On Developmental Psychology:	D. W. Winnicott,	**Playing and Reality**, (Pelican), 1974.
	E.H. Erikson,	**Identity, Youth and Crisis**, (Faber), 1971.
On Ecology:	B. Ward & R. Dubos,	**Only One Earth**, (Pelican), 1972.
On Philosophy:	J. Macmurray,	**The Self as Agent**, (Faber),1957.
		Persons in Relation, (Faber), 1961.

121-8 The Wholeness of Man.

A PERSONAL MODEL

. . . I turn to a third area for dialogue between theologian and psychiatrist. John Macmurray suggests that in the 17th century man's model for the universe, and for himself, was a Cartesian one, mathematical and mechanical. This worldview is well celebrated in Joseph Addison's hymn 'The spacious firmament on high'. But the model proved inadequate because it gave no account of spontaneity, of change generated within the elements of creation and not just from outside. Macmurray says that in the 19th century it came to be superceded by an organic model, the cosmos conceived as an organism, with its own internally generated rhythms of change, of birth, growth, decay and reproduction of elements to ensure continuity. Most current thinking is still dominated by the organic model - one which includes mechanical understanding of part functions but transcends it in its understanding of wholes. But he then suggests that for various philosophic reasons (notably because it gives an inadequate account of the Self, failing to distinguish between the I and the Thou), this organic model needs to be replaced by (or subordinated to) a personal model - a model of 'persons in relationship'. It   is likely that recent thinking by psychotherapists would support him here. For instance, the organic model gives an insufficient account of how we ought to deal with what we categorise as dirt, disorder, waste or evil. Organisms take in what they need from their environment and discard or excrete waste products. At any time before the 1950s it was not unreasonable to visualise the good society - or the good man - as one from which all evil or disorderly elements had been excluded. In clinical work this was exemplified by purging and amputations. In Judaeo-Christian religious thought it was exemplified by rituals of purification, of transferring evil to a scapegoat, and in general by separating oneself from evil and aiming to keep oneself 'unspotted from the world'. But at least since the time of Freud, psychiatrists have realised that since they were dealing with sick persons and not just with their sickness, they could not so easily amputate badness from a man's mind or experience; and they have had to discover ways in which patients could learn to live with - and indeed to make constructive use of - those painful parts of present or past experience from which they sought deliverance. With the development of group psychotherapy and social psychiatry, we have seen more clearly how unfailingly easy it is for people to project their evil experience on to others, and for them to collude with one another to make a scapegoat of one who is made to carry the burden of the whole group's badness - and be extruded from the group into the wilderness. Sometimes the scapegoat is one of themselves and sometimes he is the man who is ostensibly their leader, but the projection process is the same. So the therapeutic task is increasingly interpreted as enabling people to withdraw their projections, to take responsibility for their own share of the group's badness, whether it arises from their own fault or that of another. Sharing one another's burdens of evil experience is no longer just a pious fantasy but a conscious and realistic social objective.

This apparently novel idea, of learning to live with evil instead of trying to eradicate it, is not confined to psychiatrists. Ecologists are teaching us the same lesson. But perhaps the idea is not so novel. If the Old Testament model of deliverance was the

Exodus, when the Israelites were separated from evil, in the New Testament we have a different model in the Cross. Jesus made no attempt to keep himself unspotted from the world: he kept company with publicans and sinners. He was 'in all things tempted like as we are'. He refused all opportunities to escape from evil, but suffered it and stayed with it right up until his death.

But this rather satisfying congruence between the inductive findings of the psychiatrist and the more deductive approach of the theologian should not blind us to some rather problematic consequences. If, as I am suggesting, tomorrow's greater good is more likely to come from a reconciliation between today's good and today's evil, than it is from the eradication of today's evil, then evil and the suffering it entails seems to play a much more positive role in God's economy than many theologians have so far accorded it. To quote John Macmurray again, "*the positive includes the negative and is constituted by it*". This suggests that the good includes evil as an essential constituent. But this will scarcely appear to most people to lead to a fruitful kind of debate until there is more general acceptance of a world view which is not just mechanical, nor just organic, but is truly personal.. . . .

217 - Church and Psychiatry.

SERMON: HEALTH ENHANCEMENT

. . . But the enhancement of health is different. It respects the life that is there. It requires the doctor to be compassionate rather than dispassionate. It often leaves the diagnosis of the disease rather vague. It is unscientific. It is not a specialised job for doctors only - in fact doctors aren't trained to do it, they just learn about it with experience. And the best textbook for the enhancement of mental health is not to be found on the medical bookshelf - it is the bible.

Psychotherapy partakes much more of this approach than of the attack on disease. It deals with the whole person; it doesn't attempt to cut out bad bits of the mind, but explores ways of transforming the bad into something good, of persuading or enabling people to accept things about themselves which they had previously rejected or found intolerable. Two of its findings are especially important to us as Christians. One is that you can't be healthy in isolation. Your relationships with other people are vital parts of your humanity. So healthy activity means taking a viewpoint which transcends one's own egocentric one. The healthy person is he who acts in the interests not only of himself, but in the interests of all those with whom he is in relationship. He is a person who aims to be dependable rather than independent. This finding of the psychotherapist, of course, is no more than a faint echo of the bible's emphasis on loving your neighbour; and of the saying of Jesus "*If anyone wishes to be a follower of mine, he must leave self behind...*" " *Whoever cares for his own safety is lost; but if a man will let himself be lost for my sake, he will find his true self.*" (Matthew 16, v. 24/5)

The second discovery of the psychotherapist is that a man needs to learn to reconcile himself to his own unconscious roots. Most of us still feel rather affronted at the suggestion that we do not know ourselves. But we don't. The dark side of our nature, that which we experience in dreams and nightmares and madness, always seems alien to us. Who is the dreamer who dreams my dreams? I don't recognise him. In so many ways the things he dreams up are beastly, antisocial, irrational. But he *is* part of me. In fact, this dark and earthy, animal-like part of me which I am so loth to acknowledge contains the springs of my whole life. The roots of my personality lie hidden there; and the modern theologians who lay stress upon God as the 'ground of our being' are trying to express this truth in their own terms. God made us, and God loves us, conscious and unconscious alike. The roots of a rose plant are hidden in the darkness of the earth, and are nourished by decay, manure, and dirt. Yet the beauty of the flower is entirely dependent on the roots, and if they are separated from the plant, the flower dies. . . .

. . . The study of evolution is, in a sense, the study of our roots. Since man has descended or rather ascended - from the animal kingdom, it is possible to see a parallel between the need for the individual to become reconciled to the 'beastliness' in his own unconscious, and the need for humankind as a whole to become aware of, and reconciled to evolutionary roots in the animal world. I think the recent upsurge of interest in animals is a sign of modern people's need for this. Some of you will have read Joy Adamson's book *'Born Free'* (1960) in which she tells the story of Elsa the lioness, or you will have read Konrad Lorenz's book *'King Solomon's Ring'* (1952). Or you will have seen some of the natural history films on television. All these seem to be expressions of this urge to find mental health for the modern community by becoming aware of humankind's biological roots. Underlying them is the same vision as Isaiah had, which was read to us in the lesson. (Isaiah 11, v. 1 - 10)

'The wolf shall dwell with the lamb, and the leopard shall lie down with the kid; and the calf and the young lion and the fatling together; and a little child shall lead them'. . . .

64 - The Enhancement of Health.

SERMON: FOR REMEMBRANCE DAY

Every year Remembrance Day comes round to remind us of our inability to solve the problem of evil. Those whose deaths we are commemorating fought because, at the time, they, and we, were convinced that there was no other way of dealing with the evils for which the country's enemies seemed responsible. But in the event, we found that the conquest of one set of evils was very largely counterbalanced by the creation of others. Since 1945, we have seen a succession of such things as the cold war, the nuclear arms race, and the upsurge of urban guerrillas and terrorism. Even if the casualty figures from these new evils are relatively small, they erode the quality of life almost as severely as did the two world wars. And it is the quality of life that counts, not just physical survival: after all, wars only occur when enough men say "I would rather die than live a life of such inferior quality".

How *do* we deal with what seems to us to be evil? The traditional answer, of course, is to separate ourselves from it. Until recently, it has always been possible to imagine that progress towards a better world would best be made by excluding what is evil or harmful from the world we know. Material waste or dirt could be channelled or dumped far enough away from human habitation for natural processes of decay to deal with them. Evil doers or troublers of the peace could be put away in prisons or asylums, or transported to distant convict settlements, or constrained in some other way to leave their country for their country's good. It was as if heaven on earth could be imagined as an island of ordered perfection lying in a sea of chaos.

But nowadays that kind of vision of the good life is not so convincing. Of recent years the world seems to have got smaller. The material rubbish of our technological society spoils not only our own but also our neighbours' physical environment. We don't know how to dispose of nuclear waste. Dumps of old cars disfigure the countryside. Rivers and streams are too poisonous for the fish that used to live in them. We are afflicted with butter mountains and wine lakes which we seem unable to dispose of. Not only can we no longer transport our convicts to far off lands, but our prisons and mental hospitals are both resisting the internal exile to which we formerly sent those whom society considered disorderly or disordered.

Whether we like it or not, we seem to be faced with the problem of having to *live with* what we find to be evil instead of being able to escape from it. Of course, the problem is not entirely new. Our views about what seems evil change with time. When we were children, we all had to put up with things that we found bad or unpleasant, at the behest of our elders and betters who insisted they would be good for us in the end. But I suspect that as children, however patiently we bore our afflictions, we cherished the belief that sooner or later we would be independent and able to escape from the things that troubled us. And as we grew up we went on believing that evil was certainly a problem, but that problems can in principle be solved. It is really only in the last few decades that it is being borne in upon us that there is no final escape from what seems evil in the world around us, and that we are going to have to find ways of living with it: we must learn the art of living with problems, to supplement the problem-solving skills of which we are so proud but which do not always work.

So far I have been speaking about evils that are external to us; but of course there are internal evils as well - those which we regard as sinfulness, the result of our own unregenerate impulses and feelings. To speak for a moment of my own field of work: it was a good deal earlier than the last half century that the pioneer psychoanalysts recognised our dilemma, of how to live with our internal evil instead of trying unsuccessfully to escape from it. It was Freud and Jung and their disciples who first showed in clinical work how evil experience could sometimes be lived with and turned to good account as a way of actually strengthening the personality. And, building on their foundations, their followers have shown how children need internal conflict as a stimulus to healthy development: to wrap children in cotton wool, as the saying goes, is to stunt or distort their development. And in studying families and small groups of people we have learnt to see how readily each person tries to escape felt evil by projecting it on to others: when God tackled Adam about eating the forbidden fruit, he was quick to say "it was the woman who tempted me". So the process of group psychotherapy can be seen as enabling people to find the strength and courage to withdraw their projections, and each to take responsibility for their own share of the evil experience of the group.

Although it is only in the last hundred years that we have realised the value of staying with evil instead of separating ourselves from it in the material and psychological spheres, its recognition in the spiritual sphere goes back at least to New Testament times. Before the life of Jesus, the model of deliverance from evil adopted by the people of Israel was the Exodus, when God freed them from slavery:

> "You have seen what I did to the Egyptians, and how I bore you on eagles' wings and brought you to myself. Now, therefore, if you will obey my voice and keep my covenant, you shall be my own possession among all peoples; for all the earth is mine, and you shall be to me a kingdom of priests and a holy nation".
> (Exodus 19, 4 – 6)

The interpretation which the people put on that experience was that deliverance from evil came from being separated from it. As a *"kingdom of priests and a holy nation"*, they sought purity from defilement not only by elaborate rituals but also, following their return from exile, even more painfully by separating themselves from their foreign-born wives and children. But the deliverance model offered us by Jesus is different. It is true that some of his sayings accord well enough with the old model, as when he said *"If your hand or your foot causes you to sin, cut it off and throw it from you"* (Mark 9, 43 – 6). So do some of his healing acts, as when he is reported as having cast out demons. But when we turn from the study of detail and survey his life and crucifixion as a whole, and in the context of its time, the message comes through loud and clear that a new and better way to deal with evil is to stay with it, to withstand it (in the sense of stand with it) and allow it to work itself out without inhibiting it or destroying it by force or power, accepting that this may involve suffering even unto death as a prelude to resurrection.

These two methods of dealing with evil, one from the Old Testament and the other from the New, seem to stand in sharp contrast to each other. The older model is fairly easy to comprehend: having defined what is evil, we seek either to destroy it or escape from it. In both models, of course, evil is seen as the enemy. But then Jesus tells us we should love our enemies. Does this mean we should love what is evil? Surely not. So it must mean that if we are patient with evil, and stay with it, there is at least a chance that what at first seems evil will later come to seem not evil, but good. But if we stay close to evil, do we not risk being corrupted? Well, perhaps so: there's nothing very Christian about avoiding risks. So I want to suggest that the risk can be lessened by our not paying too close attention to evil, even though we stay close by it. So often it seems to exercise a fascination - the paralysing attraction which the snake is supposed to exercise over his prey. The serpent is a very ancient symbol of evil. If his eyes can catch mine and hold them, then whether I will it or not my normal wide-ranging awareness of my surroundings seems to become narrowed to a single point. I become insensitive to other things and other people. This insensitivity is a risk inherent in the traditional model: it puts blinkers on people's vision and stops their ears. Compare this concentrated attention to evil with what St Paul said to the Philippians: *"Fill your minds with everything that is true, everything that is noble, everything that is good and pure, everything that we love and honour, and everything that can be thought virtuous or worthy of praise".* (Philippians 4, 8 – 10).

So the contrast seems to be a matter of how we focus our attention: whether on evil, to fight it or fly from it; or on good, to foster it and nurture it. I wonder if we could put it like this: that if you don't pay too much attention to evil, a lot of it will just go away - *provided* you pay a lot of attention to what is good. . . .

. . . The two ways of coping with evil as I have described them are not mutually exclusive. At times, the traditional Exodus model is appropriate, and at others the new way which we have associated with the Cross. So now I want to suggest that while the old model is always likely to appeal to us in situations of threat or danger, in order to appreciate the merits - and indeed the plausibility - of the newer one we need to have control of our fear and anxiety. There is a sort of parallel in the way our bodies work: at times of threat or danger, they are all tense and keyed up for fight or flight; while at other more normal times they are relaxed and can get on with the processes of digestion and growth and creative living. And if our bodies remain keyed up and tense when there is no need for it, we get ill, with stomach ulcers or high blood pressure or whatever.

So when Jesus wanted to show us by his attitude to life and death a new and better way to deal with evil, he had constantly to reassure us: do not be anxious, do not be afraid, have *faith*. He doesn't usually say "have faith in God" or "believe in me": mostly he just says "have faith". For him, faith seems to be less a matter of belief *in* something and more a matter of confidence. For him, faith is the opposite of fear: *"why are you so fearful?"* he would say, *"why is it that you have no faith?"* And at another time he said *"Fear not, only believe".*

So we are brought full circle to recognise once again the importance of the military virtue of courage. In fact, the new model of deliverance symbolised by the Cross demands an even greater level of courage than does the traditional one in its fighting stance against evil. And so to say "yes, well, perhaps that is a good model for saints, but it is too heroic, and not for ordinary folk like us". Well, no doubt that may be true for a man who tries to follow it on his own. Jesus was certainly alone at the end of his earthly life, and his courage was unique. But man is not intended to be alone in his encounter with evil: we can and ought to support one another. Where morale is high, quite ordinary men who are not heroes in their own eyes or in the eyes of their families or their mates can, like so many of those in the fighting services whom we remember today, lay down their lives for their fellowmen with a corporate heroism.

And what I have tried to suggest is that it is only when we recognise all other men as our fellows - our enemies and those who hate us as well as our friends; it will only be then that our corporate morale will be raised high enough for us to progress toward our ultimate deliverance from evil, our ultimate salvation, the salvation of the whole of humankind, the whole of God's creation. And this will be the work of the Spirit of wholeness, the Holy Spirit, who will guide us into all truth.

178 - 6 Sermon: Dealing with Evil.

CHAPTER NINE

LOSS

The classic human situation of loss is bereavement due to the death of a loved one. James saw the need to support a sufferer in facing the reality of their situation. He urged comforters also to avoid the soft options of denial and pretence. It is only through bearing the pain that resolution and resurrection to new life are given.

But losses are manifold - redundancy, retirement, children leaving the nest, broken marriages, menopause or loss of a limb. All require hard grief work in order to heal.

These 'little deaths' can be training grounds in preparation for our approach to final death. The pattern of life-through-death proves reliable. *Metanoia* (repentance or change of perspective) is also a pattern of loss because it demands our dying to old attitudes or beliefs, and internalising a new value with practical consequences. The realisation that we are wrong or have made a mistake requires a similar costly change of heart. Even the process of human growth and development involves loss of childishness as we struggle to become fully human. Like joy and woe, loss and gain are the heads and tails of the same penny.

At a meeting of doctors in the West Midlands the subject of depression was being discussed. The conference was groping with the possibility that depression is a normal part of grief. "How long" asked a family doctor "would you leave a bereaved patient in depression before you prescribed an anti-depressant drug?" "A week" suggested a consultant. "My God!" exclaimed James, "I hope you'd let me be depressed for more than a week if I lost my wife."

M.W.

MINISTRY TO THE BEREAVED

Birth and death are the only two experiences which are entirely inescapable for a human being. They occur only once in a lifetime, so each of them presents us with a crisis, a situation which is new to us, which involves a drastic change in our relation to the environment to which we have become accustomed, and the outcome of which we cannot foresee.

The loss of someone we love, bereavement, is another crisis which few of us escape. For most of us it will occur more than once; but, unlike death, we have to go on living after it; and, unlike birth, it is an experience which we are able to talk about with other people. It is only one of a large number of experiences of crisis which mark human progression from cradle to grave; and I want first to make some observations about crisis experience in general.

We face a crisis whenever we face a situation or life-problem which previous experience has not taught us how to solve. We perceive it as either a loss of something or some relationship we have depended on heretofore; or the threat of such loss; or as a challenge - to give up something we've depended on in the hope of gaining some greater good. Crisis is characterised by the disturbance of an existing stable relationship to our material and psycho-social environment, and the resultant instability means that we are more easily influenced by our surroundings, for better or worse. Subjectively, we feel upset, and show a rise in emotional tension. Often this tension leaks out in irritable behaviour which seems irrelevant and inappropriate. Sometimes we become obsessively preoccupied with one minor facet of the whole problem confronting us, and seem unable to pay attention to other aspects of it which it would be more profitable to tackle. Our distress makes us likely to behave in ways which may evoke helping responses from other people, like a baby crying, though such behaviour is not always consciously determined or acknowledged.

No organism likes to remain in an unstable state for very long, and throughout the crisis period the whole person - body and mind together - is actively, seeking ways of restoring stability, finding a new equilibrium. Optimally, the crisis-problem is solved by a newly-acquired understanding of what the situation needs. In such a case, crisis has been the occasion of learning, the person has achieved a greater maturity; and if the problem situation recurs, the repertory of possible responses is so enlarged that its solution is no longer perceived as a crisis of the same magnitude.

But all too often, the human organism finds the emotional tension rising to an intolerable degree, so that relief of this becomes too urgent to wait upon the understanding which would really solve the problem; and a sub-optimal or pathological 'solution' is found which, while easing tension for the time being, only serves to bind the person to their still unsolved problem. Such a sub-optimal solution is usually manifest as a physical or psychological symptom or neurotic character trait, while the person is likely to be more upset, rather than less, by a recurrence of the problem-situation. The cardinal practical point for anyone engaged in a ministry to those in crisis therefore, is the great importance of enabling the person to face the reality of his situation, rather than allowing or encouraging a way of escape from the tension involved which doesn't help solve the real problem.

Perhaps bereavement is more often a crisis than it ought to be. Although an unexpected death is bound to be a crisis, when death occurs in old age or after a long illness there has been time for those concerned to get used to the prospect. Mature people will no doubt often have done much of their grieving before the death of the loved one in such a case, and perhaps the dying member of a pair of lovers may be the best comforter for the survivor; but sometimes people aren't mature enough: they can't bear to think of it, and they go on pretending to themselves that it won't happen. When it does, the crisis is the more shattering. However, even the most mature of lovers is likely to find the actual death of the partner critical to some extent, for hope dies hard among those who love; and it is not surprising that there is a high death-rate and sickness-rate in the first year of widowhood.

There are many meanings hidden in our use of the word 'love', but there are two which are relevant here: the love of the small child for its mother is largely a passive-dependent affair; while the love of the mother for her infant is a caring, self-giving relationship. Adult love-relationships contain elements of both these in varying degrees, and so bereavement is likely to have an ambiguous meaning. Inasmuch as the survivor has been the dependable partner, who could care for the other without thought of self, the loss of the other will be painful and tragic. At his most mature, a man cannot give his heart to another without himself dying a little when the loved one dies. By contrast, inasmuch as the survivor has been dependent on the other, like the child who loses a parent, his feelings will be likely to contain an element of anger at his dereliction, and he will have doubts and fears about how he can survive without the other.

As I say, most love relationships contain elements of both sorts of love, so the experience of bereavement quite often contains feelings of anger against the departed. Because it conflicts with the sadness and resignation which seems more appropriate and is socially acceptable, such anger is often denied direct expression, and finds instead an outlet in projections of blame on to other people. You will often find grieving people blaming the hospital or the doctor or other relatives who didn't seem to care enough - or even blaming themselves - for what happened. This seeking for a scapegoat illustrates the kind of mechanism which the mind uses unconsciously to relieve feelings of tension, but which makes no useful contribution to the solution of the real problem - in this case becoming resigned to the fact of bereavement and seeking new relationships to replace the old.

Denial is another tension-relieving mechanism. It is of course more or less normal in the immediate catastrophic reaction to sudden death: our minds refuse to take it in at first, and we continue to act as if it hadn't happened. But once the immediate crisis period is over, denial can be seen to be increasingly abnormal and inappropriate. Many a bereaved wife has thought she heard her dead husband walking through the door, but only a few persist with hallucinations of this kind for long. However, some will persist, for shorter or longer periods, in keeping their husband's desk or wardrobe exactly as it was when he was alive. I recall a mother whose son had been killed in a motorcycle accident when he was nineteen. He had been dead a year when I visited her; and when I went into her house there on the sofa in the hall were his crash-helmet and motorcycling clothes still spread out ready for him to wear. His room and personal possessions were kept cleaned but unmoved. Such behaviour might be tolerably adaptive for an elderly widow with the house to herself. It was clearly not so for this woman, whose husband was embarrassed and whose thirteen-year-old daughter was emotionally neglected by her mother's concentration on the dead son's memory. This woman's prolonged mourning reaction was marked by considerable anger and resentment, which she directed at his companions on the night of the accident and the hospital which treated his injuries. Her relationship with her son seemed to have a large element of dependence on her part: she had been over-attached to him and felt she 'couldn't do without him'.

Another way in which people may express the anger, which comes from over-dependency on the dead person, is to blame God. "I can't go on believing in a god who would allow this to happen." They don't always say "who would allow this to happen *to me*", but this is what they mean. It is only the person who has achieved the maturity of a caring, self-giving relationship to the other, dependable rather than dependent, who can accept the situation with grief but without anger, and say, like Job, *"The Lord gave, and the Lord hath taken away. Blessed be the name of the Lord."*(Job 1, 21).

Perhaps we can now see some of the principles which should govern our ministry to the bereaved, at least those which have a relevance to preventive psychiatry, and the minimising of subsequent ill health. The death of a loved one presents a problem, which requires considerable effort and hard work to solve. Because the work of mourning is so arduous, it is a great help to have the moral support of understanding friends at such a time. There are the practical details of daily life to be carried on in a bereaved household, and during the initial stages of numbness and yearning the survivors are not well able to cope with these. People who need to express their grief outwardly should not be discouraged. Tears are a relief, especially when they can be shed in the presence of someone who understands but whose own involvement in the situation is controlled. At suitable moments, the bereaved should be encouraged to talk and reminisce about the dead. Part of the healing process of active resignation lies in recapitulating one's experience of the lost person - making a sort of inventory of memories, good and bad; and if the bad memories as well as the good can be outwardly acknowledged and shared the healing will be better. This kind of confession and affirmation of what the dead meant to the living can lead to forgiveness at a time when it may be critical for future mental health: the unforgiven dead can blight the life of the survivor quite as much as the unforgiven living.

Conversely, any tendency for the survivor to evade doing the work of grieving by projection or denial should be gently discouraged by directing attention back to the reality of the loss, perhaps by discussion of some practical problem involved - for instance in the change of role from wife to widow.

The business of caring for the bereaved is not easy. Few of us really enjoy entering a house of mourning. People who have suffered a severe loss are seldom at their most attractive. A gloomy mood is catching, particularly if we expose ourselves to it unthinkingly and without care. So are the tension and irritability which are evoked by the crisis. It is all too easy, and all too common, for well-meaning comforters to aid and abet the sufferer in escaping from the tension rather than facing the problem realistically. We tell them to "snap out of it" or we say "you mustn't brood" or "you must hide your feelings" or "you should take a holiday and get right away for a bit". And the reason we offer this cheap comfort is because we ourselves are unwilling or unable to face the reality of the experience of death and bereavement.

This leads us to realise that it is an essential part of our practical ministry to the bereaved that we should ourselves come to terms with our own fears and doubts about the matter. Some people, who have suffered bereavement in adult life and who have been able to accept such a crisis as a challenge to greater spiritual maturity rather than as a crippling loss, will have learnt the lesson through personal experience. But other people than these may be called upon to minister to the bereaved. How can they come to terms with it?

As a medical student, I was never taught how to help people deal with the fact of death. I suppose this is understandable, even if regrettable. A doctor's job is to help people live a full life, and if he were too constantly aware that death was the inevitable outcome of all his efforts, he might be a less welcome visitor in a sick room. But people in general, particularly the relatives of those who are sick, tend to take doctors seriously.

So if we adopt the attitude that death is at all times something to be fought against, evaded, not even to be thought about or spoken of, then folk will follow our example.

To illustrate: Many doctors still believe that it is unwise ever to tell a patient that he has a disease from which he is likely to die. Not only will they evade telling the patient, which may sometimes be wise, but also they will tell the truth to the relatives - and then instruct them to evade telling the patient too. This can cast a shadow over the last few weeks or months of a loving partnership between two who have never had any secrets from each other, and can leave the survivor with a sense of guilt to add to his grief. I don't think a doctor can ever be as good a judge of whether to tell or not as is someone who knows and loves the sufferer.

Five mothers in a maternity ward formed a happy and friendly group in the joy of their new babies. Tragically, one of them died suddenly from a pulmonary embolism. Naturally the others all asked questions about it - how would the baby get on, what would the husband do, and so on. But the nursing staff acting on the doctors' instructions refused to allow any discussion of it. Death was a subject that was taboo.

Such evasions of the reality of death are rather typical of doctors, especially if they work mainly from hospitals. It is an unsatisfactory attitude. All through human history the death of the individual has been recognised and faced up to as a real experience in rituals of burial or burning. A funeral traditionally was a solemn and public occasion, when the members of a community stopped what they were doing and gave themselves time to reflect on the inevitability of death, time to get adjusted to it, time to make real for themselves John Donne's thought that *"any man's death diminishes me because I am involved in mankind"*. It still is in rural districts, but with the coming of the internal combustion engine and the hurry and bustle of the modern city, the tendency is for the funeral to become a private affair for near relatives only. Someone has said that our attitude to death is becoming like the Victorian attitude to sex - it is necessary, but so long as the decencies are observed, the less said about it the better.

Much of our evasion of the subjective reality of death stems from our growing sensitivity to one another's feelings. One would like to think this was truly compassionate but it is often mere sentimentality. In more primitive ages and places it was - and is - impossible to evade the contemplation of death. Few households escaped the experience of having a child die in their midst; war involved face-to-face killing, the destitute died in the streets, executions were performed in public. In former days men were much more aware of the need to make a good death - if only because of the likelihood that it would be a public performance. But in the last few - very few - generations, we have cut down infant mortality, we abolished public executions only a hundred years ago and have hardly done away with capital punishment; while in war we only kill at a distance. Even on the roads our contact with those about to die is through a glass windscreen, darkly, rather than face-to-face.

Perhaps reflection upon our unconscious, absent-minded evasions of the thought of death may help us to become more objective and a little less fearful of discussing it with others. It may also help us to contemplate, with intelligent forethought and imaginative sympathy, what our own deaths will mean for those we leave behind, and, conversely, what their deaths will mean for us. Such thoughts do in fact occur to all of us one way or another; but don't we usually tend to keep them private, as if they were somehow indecent? And if they do enter conversation, the embarrassment they raise is dealt with by joking about them - which may be a healthy way of evading the embarrassment, but is an evasion just the same. If my son were to tell me that he had dreamed that I was killed in a car accident it would probably evoke some sardonic remark about wish-fulfilment dreams; but if he were to contemplate the same possibility in full consciousness he would really be showing intelligent anticipation; and would thereby doubtless be better able to cope with the bereavement crisis if and when it occurs.

Now I want to consider the possibility that some of our religious convictions may contain an element of evasion of the reality of death. Some people talk of the afterlife in a way which suggests that they assume a prolongation of time, as we understand it, into infinity. But how do we know that eternity is like this? I suppose that for many of us the essential thing about death is that it is "I", *my* ego, *my* self, or *my* soul, which we are reluctant to part from - that part or aspect of us which seems to endure through time in spite of all the changes and chances of this world. We are all nowadays ready to accept that the next world is not located in space, so we do not worry about our future shape or place. But if the time dimension doesn't exist in eternity either, what will a self or soul be then? We can't imagine it. This doesn't of course mean the next world doesn't exist; it only means that I am doubtful if any of us yet understand what our self or soul really is. Since the work of Freud we are slowly beginning to accept the fact that we don't really know ourselves: that most of our lives are governed by impulses of which we are unconscious. We dream, and find our dreams unrecognisable as productions of our own imaginations. Who is the dreamer who dreams my dreams? He is a stranger to me, outside my control. Am I responsible for his thoughts? Is he a part of myself? Am I going to be answerable for him on the day of judgement? Is he going to die with my mortal body, or is he part of my immortal soul?

The relevance of such considerations is that I suspect our anxiety about death and bereavement to be linked with a failure to transcend our egocentricity. Currently, theologians are striving to recover an understanding of the corporate or social aspects of the faith, in the light of modern work in the field of social psychology. We accept that - to quote S. de Dietrich – *"God does not call isolated individuals, he creates a community"*. But we still tend to think of death as an individual affair. To balance this, it may be profitable to contemplate the individual man as a cell in a social organism. We can then consider his death as analogous to the death of a cell in the biological organism. When we talk of the life of a man, we should remember that there is no life in him save that which is manifest in the life of his component cells. And that these cells reproduce, perform their special tasks, and die according to their kind. The brain loses 50,000 cells every day after a man is twenty-five years old, and none of them is replaced. His red blood cells perform no essential function until they are already degenerating, and then they only last four weeks.

Whether we look at the physical organism or at the social organism, the death of the individual component unit is an essential necessity to the continuing life of the whole. In social organisms where there is a high degree of mutual trust and understanding, where morale is high (as in Scott's expedition to the South Pole, or in an army in time of war), the individual does not find it impossible to value the success of the whole body above his own personal survival. Not every soldier who willingly goes forward into danger is exceptionally heroic, or has a firm belief in personal immortality, but his behaviour is admirable because - perhaps in spite of himself - he transcends egocentricity.

The vision of the social organism, however rarely it may be actualised in our own experience, does seem to take us one step away from that egocentricity which gives such a sting to our personal deaths and bereavements. It seems to lead in the direction which St Paul pointed out for us, in his vision of the spiritual organism, the resurrected body of Christ.

In summary then: at the practical level, a ministry to the bereaved should follow the general principles of a ministry to those in crisis. These include material aid and comfort and moral support while the sufferer does his hard work of grieving. The major task, to which the others are subsidiary, is that of enabling the mourner to face the reality of his situation; and, because this reality is something which he has to experience subjectively, the helper has to make an effort of imaginative sympathy; he has to try in some degree to enter into the other's experience while controlling his involvement. This is necessarily a painful process for the helper. To fit himself for it, I have suggested that he should reflect upon the phenomenon of death, and try to discern in advance the ways in which his own mind strives to avoid facing the issues of death and bereavement in his own life; whether by simply refusing to consider it, by a sentimental evasion of the unpleasant tension it arouses, or by fantasies rationalised under the guise of religious belief. Perhaps a full realisation of the daily Christian experience of dying to self is the best preparation for helping those who are bereaved.

76 - 2 Ministry to the Bereaved.

LEARNING TO BEAR LOSS

. . . To bring comfort to someone is to strengthen them. I am told that in the Bayeux tapestry there is a panel entitled 'King William comforts his troops'. The picture under this caption shows King William at the rear of a column of soldiers, prodding them in the back with a spear. While the kind of comfort which is appropriate for bereaved people is perhaps less physically crude than this the illustration may serve to remind you that by comfort I do not mean the kind of sentimental relief from a painful burden, or attempts at such relief, which are too often implied in our use of the word. If I lose my fountain pen, I will be comforted in the usual, easy sense of the word if you give me a replacement. But when I am faced with the death of someone I have loved, the kind of comfort I need is to be strengthened in order to come to terms with the reality of a dark and painful experience. I think that, in my use of the word comfort, I want to mean something that goes beyond merely restoring a person's soul to its state of previous equanimity. The care of the bereaved should always have as its aim to enable the bereaved person to grow through their experience; so that, after the pain, the survivor is more free, more mature, and more fully human than they were before. Perhaps the kind of comfort I am talking about is that which a good midwife can bring to a healthy mother bearing the pains of childbirth.

Faced with the death of a loved one, a man is likely to feel so much pain and distress that his main concern is to be relieved of the distress rather than to come to terms with the reality of the situation. So one of the most important functions of the caregiver is to help the sufferer, with whatever gentleness and compassion seems appropriate, to face reality rather than to escape from it - whether by pretending it hasn't happened, or by finding someone to blame for it, or by taking his mind off it by 'burying himself in his work', or by moving house, or by persuading a doctor to dispense tranquillisers and seek oblivion that way. All these are evasive manoeuvres, which simply delay the process of coming to terms with reality. Sometimes, for a short while, it may be wise for the sufferer to be helped to rest from his inevitable struggle by some kind of medical measure, but such measures ought only to be used with great circumspection. Dr Colin Parkes (1972) emphasises that grieving after bereavement is time-consuming. It is usual for it to take a year, sometimes longer. So we must be careful about anything which will delay the process, as evasive measures always do. . . .

. . . So, we can generalise and say that our ability to minister effectively to the bereaved depends in large part upon whether we ourselves can stand the pain of bereavement without flinching or running away from it.

This does not mean that no one can help a bereaved person unless he has experienced bereavement himself. Not everyone who has suffered a bereavement experience has become more mature as a result. After such an experience, some of us are left mistrustful, afraid of involvement. We may have emotional scars which seem to be reasonably well healed, but which are painful when touched. Some people are lucky enough to escape the experience of a major personal loss until after middle age. In their earlier years they may be diffident about offering support to a sufferer, but they are often very helpful in the way they can strengthen people; and I think it is possible to learn how to do this kind of ministry without necessarily waiting for someone you love to die.

We can, for instance, learn what it means to lose part of ourselves in all sorts of ways. All our lives are punctuated by a series of 'little deaths', as we grow up and have to give up childhood dependencies, toys and habits. We move from one school to another, and have to mourn the loss of playmates and familiar places. We have to relinquish treasured possessions which are so familiar that they have become extensions of ourselves. Some people have this kind of experience when they change their home, or their motor car. We don't usually pay much attention to these minor bereavements because the new situations give us adequate substitute satisfactions; but it does no harm to reflect upon such experiences at times, to survey the surprising amount of change that they bring in one's sense of identity, and. to recall to our minds the amount and kind of distress that such changes can cause us. The yearning of homesickness that a child experiences in his first long stay away from home is an important learning experience of what it means to withstand bereavement.

But we can go further than this. We can, for instance, teach ourselves humility by not running away from situations which threaten humiliation. One of the basic rules for mental health, I think, is to learn to withstand embarrassment. All adolescents, at least, know what this experience means, but only some of them will find the moral courage to expose themselves to embarrassing situations deliberately, so as to learn to cope with them without taking evasive action. But this is one way in which we can learn to do without our ego-props - by deliberate acts of sacrifice. Sacrifice is of course a rather frightening word, so perhaps I should hasten to point out that many kinds of sacrificial action are only temporary, not permanent. I am not here suggesting that a man should sell all that he has, and give to the poor (though even that degree of sacrifice might well prove only temporary, too). But here is what Jesus said: *"Do not set yourself against the man who wrongs you. If someone slaps you on the right cheek, turn and offer him your left. If a man wants to sue you for your shirt, let him have your coat as well. If a man in authority makes you go one mile, go with him two"* (Matthew 5, 39-42). Such things as these are only temporary embarrassments; and even if a young man is not yet constrained to do them through his love for God, he may nevertheless see some sense in doing them as exercises which will strengthen his emotional maturity.

As a further stage, we can seek for training courses, which involve the experience of being hungry, thirsty and physically tired - and still carrying on. The kind of training offered on Outward Bound courses, and some kinds of military training, are of this kind. We might designate them as 'wilderness' training. They can be designed to stretch young men and women to the limits of what they think they can stand - and a little way beyond. Experienced instructors know that most people can stand a good deal more than they think they can. The Gospel record says that Jesus was forty days in the wilderness, and it suggests that he was alone and solitary at that time. I do not suggest that we need training courses lasting as long as forty days; and I am quite decidedly not recommending that such training should be undertaken by one person alone. There is a risk of such training puffing up our ego without strengthening it; but the risks of this are slight if we are doing it in company with a group of our peers, and under the eyes of instructors who are more experienced than we are.

These, then, are some of the ways in which we can actively practice and exercise the kind of moral strength which will enable us to share the pain of another's bereavement, and perhaps our own, without running away from it. So far, I have spoken as if grief is an evil, to be faced boldly only since it can't be got rid of. But is grief always to be seen as an evil? . . .

. . . Grief is a price we have to pay for loving; and it seems to me that if we could abolish grief, we would be cheapening love to such an extent that it would lose its meaning. It is the possibility of grief that gives love its value; and grief is good since it guarantees the value of love. . . .

. . . There may be more wisdom in our little griefs than we commonly realise. Perhaps every grief contains within it the seeds of a higher order of love.

Reflections upon the meaning of the experience of loss seem to me to be an essential counterpart to our active concerns to develop techniques and strength to cope with such experience. When we come face to face with a problematic situation, our immediate response is so often 'what are we to do about it?' But often it is quite as important - or even more important - to ask ourselves 'what does it mean?' Viktor Frankl wrote: *"Suffering ceases to be suffering in some way at the moment it finds a meaning, such as the meaning of a sacrifice".*

Death is experienced as being most dreadful when it is seen in a context that is individuocentric; and in such a context it is also meaningless - a nothing - an absence. I was speaking with a group of funeral directors some years ago who were seeking advice about how best to structure their ritual activities when dealing with the funeral of an elderly person who had been living alone, in urban anonymity, and who had no-one to mourn their passing. What answer could one give? All I felt I could do was to express sympathy with them and with the priest on duty at the crematorium, at the terrible burden of meaninglessness, which our corrupt urban society imposed on them. And I recognise myself as an integral part of that corrupt society.

76 - 4 Ministry to the Bereaved III.

HEALTHY DEATH

. . . Our healthy society, then, is to embrace the whole of humanity. It is to foster the maximum possible variety and diversity of its members and will set a high value on the uniqueness of each one. It will be as free as possible from hard and fast boundaries between its various parts. It will develop a technology which respects and fosters the humanity of those it serves. It will discern a positive value in all that humanity has hitherto regarded as waste; or, to put it another way, it will become self-cleansing and self-regenerating. Death will be something to look forward to.

It is a society in which its component members will die. I think this unpalatable conclusion is inescapable. To ensure long-term adjustment to environmental change it will need continual replenishment of its reservoirs of variety, both genetically, by the recombination of patterns of genes, and culturally, by recombination of traditions and customs and ideas. This means that children must be born, which in turn means that older people must die.

What this teaches us about our present attitude to medical science is problematic. Somehow we have to persuade our doctors that they have to treat death not as an enemy, but as the person's end not in the sense of his end in time but as the end he has in view. In the healthy society, to make a good end or death will have to become something worth striving for: the reward for, and the fulfilment of, a job of living well done. This will be so important a life goal for everyone in the society - important because inevitable - that we will be at pains to instruct our children, from their earliest years, that death is something they should regard as a privilege, whenever it comes, rather than as something terrifying, to be denied and evaded or ignored. Death education will be as important as sex education is or ought to be now: both are basic facts of life. We will teach our children that the pain of bereavement is the price we have to pay for loving; and that, although it is costly, it is not too dear, since the experience of losing what you have loved, and grieving over it, is an opportunity for learning about yourself, of becoming more mature, more healthy, more truly human. . . .

113 - 1 A Healthy Society?

TO RELINQUISH AUTHORITY

. . . It is not sufficient for doctors merely to 'discuss' the question of admission with the nursing services. We should aim for it to become established practice for a nurse to see the patient before admission to a particular institution at a particular time as decided; and in my view it should be the nursing service which should have the power to veto an admission recommended by a doctor. The Guidelines do not face up to the present situation where it is doctors who can overcrowd institutions by too generous an admission policy; while it is nurses who get the blame for subsequent neglect of their duty for patient care.

The implicit problem of authority as exercised by doctors on the one hand and nurses on the other will not be an easy one to resolve.

I suggest that the medical man in a psychiatric hospital has two sources of authority: one is purely clinical - the needs of the individual patient in question. This stems directly from medical training. The other source of authority stems from his position of responsibility in an institution devoted to the care of sick people. This kind of authority assumes that he has management functions, which in many respects are those properly exercised by nurses. Thus, as a consultant, I may on the one hand judge that a disturbed patient requires in-patient care; but on the other hand may consider that because of inadequate nursing staff in the hospital he should not be admitted, as this would mean inadequate nursing not only for this patient but for many others. The latter judgement means that I am performing a *nursing* management function rather than a medical one.

It would do a great deal for the morale of nurses - and thus for their efficiency - if consultants (sic) insisted on acting as *advisors* to nursing staff rather than as *directors* of them. Many nurses would have initial difficulty in accepting this responsibility, of course, but they can only learn if given the opportunity.

Until our profession is prepared to relinquish its defensive fantasies of omnipotence in hospitals, the difficulties which lead to the present discussion of a code of nursing practice are likely to continue.

105 - Letter: The N.A.M.H.Guidelines.

FAILURE IS IMPORTANT

. . . At this point further discussion of morale usually leads me to talk about the fascinating question of leadership. But tonight instead of doing that I want to use what I have said about morale as a background or context to pursue a different topic: that of failure. Perhaps it is of more general interest: we may not all have experience of leadership but we certainly all experience failure. In fact we all *need* to experience it. If the road to maturity lies in increasing self-understanding, then we can say that we never learn anything new about ourselves from being successful. Success merely confirms us in staying in the same old rut of habits and complacency. Uninterrupted success would make for boredom; and it is important to remember in these days that boredom is even worse to experience than frustration! We need failure; which is just as well since we so often get it. We get it from infancy onwards. Often we don't recognise it, because it is masked by new opportunities. For the child, thumb sucking, that great pacifier sooner or later fails to satisfy. So do his toys, games, and early companions. Such failures are often unnoticed. But in adolescence, our early ambitions are so often thwarted or disapproved of by parents or others in authority, and we certainly notice those.

But then there are more important failures: when we set our sights on a specific objective and go bald-headed for it in a thoroughly committed way - a love affair, a higher educational qualification, acceptance in a particular career. Such failures can be very traumatic; they may induce feelings of uselessness and can lead to suicidal feelings or even suicide. They are the stuff of tragedy. Seen in an individual context, failure can be serious and very painful.

Like other painful experiences, failure tends to increase our egocentricity. Now it is difficult (at least I find it so) not to become abnormally egocentric even when we have a comparatively trivial pain like toothache. But this very fact indicates that self-centredness is not the normal condition for any of us. Most of the time, we are group-centered in greater or less degree. It is the normal condition of most people to be unselfish. It is important to recognise this: when we hear of industrial action, in hospitals or industry, or when we hear of violence such as is occurring in Northern Ireland, it is easy for us to blame the minority group for their self-centredness. But each individual within that minority group will justify his actions on the ground that he is acting for others, for his peers or his dependants. Our criticism should be not that he is selfish, but that he is identifying himself too exclusively with one group. And we are only justified in making such a criticism if we ourselves are sure that we ourselves identify with a more comprehensive group that is inclusive rather than exclusive.

Now perhaps the reason why I have tried to set our discussion of failure within the context of morale will become apparent: it is in an attempt to disengage or at least weaken the very strong and largely unconscious links we have developed between personal failure and egocentricity. If we can teach ourselves to see personal failures in a group or community context, their significance will be very different. The morale of whatever group a person is a member of will profoundly affect the severity and signifi-cance of a sense of personal failure. Where group bonds are strong and morale high, the one who fails will have the support of his peers; and the effect of such support, in whatever way it is conveyed to him, will have the effect of distracting attention from personal failure to reach a personal objective, and directing it to the greater importance of his contributing to the group's larger objective. Egocentricity or self-centredness will be replaced by that sort of group-centredness, which is, as we said earlier, *normal* for him.

The story of Elijah epitomises the situation for us (1Kings19). He was overcome by a sense of personal failure, went a day's journey into the wilderness, and prayed for death. What happened? First, the angel came and brought him food and water. Attention to such material needs is often the first step in the restoration of morale. Then, after a rest, came reconsideration of his personal objectives in the light of the group's objective - the demands of the Lord the God of Hosts. Elijah had called down fire on his offering on Carmel when the prophets of Baal had failed. But now the Lord appeared to him - not in the great and strong wind, not in the earthquake, not in the fire, but in a still, small voice. Then the Lord sends him off to do another task for the kingdom - pre-eminently not of an ego-boosting kind, since part of it was to anoint Elisha as his successor; and as an afterthought, points out to Elijah that, far from his being the lone survivor of the righteous, as he had claimed, there were still seven thousand left in Israel who had not bent the knee to Baal.

Partial failure of the individual member is often essential to the success of the group. The excellence of the group or community so often demands that the parts of it, whether they are individuals or component sub-groups, should be not excellent, but just good enough. Egocentric excellence is the enemy of the excellence of the group or community. Those of you who have attended meetings in hospital where next year's budget is being drawn up will understand this. One sees each special department striving by fair means or foul to get the resources they need for the excellence of their own department, too often refusing even to contemplate the possibility that by doing so they are forcing starvation on less forcefully represented but equally essential other departments. I suspect that it is this kind of relative egocentricity, this exclusiveness of specialised identity, which is responsible for much of the drop in hospital morale of which we hear so much. Every separate group wants to be perfect instead of accepting that if the whole is to approach perfection, its components should aim to be just good enough.

If partial failure of the individual is often essential to the success of the group, it is also true that total failure - death - of the individual is ultimately essential to the very survival of the community. Richard Lamerton tells of one of his patients in a hospice for the dying. She was blind, and had just been cuddling her baby grandson. "It's lovely when they're here," she said, "Some of us comes and some of us goes!" ...

153 - 5 Morale and Importance of Failure.

CRISIS: GAIN THROUGH LOSS

A crisis is experienced when a person (or a group of people) is faced with an obstacle to important life goals which their available previous experience (habits, education etc.) has not equipped them to overcome. All of us have certain basic require-ments for good health. They may be physical -we need food and shelter. They may be psychosocial - we need to be recognised by others, to have friends on whom we can depend; or they may be better categorised as sociocultural - we need to have some idea of what others may expect of us in the way of behaviour, and what we may expect of them. The environment commonly supplies these needs to us in regular and habitual ways. We are likely to experience crisis if some of these basic supplies are *lost,* or if their loss is *threatened,* or if we are *challenged* to give up some familiar supplies in order to have access to others, less familiar but more desirable.

Faced with a problem, which we can't solve immediately, we begin to experience increasing discomfort - anxiety or tension. For a short time we may seek to find a solution by trial-and-error; but if none is quickly forthcoming the tension becomes so oppressive that *we become more concerned to ease the tension than to find a solution to the problem.* We don't usually face crisis alone. We tend to seek someone to share the trouble with, perhaps family, or neighbours - or anyone who seems prepared to listen and sympathise. It is only in a minority of cases that we go to the family doctor or minister or someone who is a professional care-giver: most care for people in crisis is offered by untrained amateurs.

This is understandable when we realise that the experience of crisis is not something pathological - not confined to those whom we can justifiably label as sick. Crisis experience is common to all of us, and it contains quite as much potential for healthy growth as potential for sickness. But as the word implies, a crisis is a critical point, where events may turn out well or ill. The situation is an unstable one, and for just that reason, the effect of only minor intervention by a caregiver is likely to be extra powerful in determining the outcome.

Crisis experience is a part of normal human development. The processes of growth do not occur at an even rate. They are made up of phases each of which does show some measure of continuous progression, but between the phases there are transitional periods in which progress becomes unstable and uncertain; and the phase following such a transition is likely to show quite different characteristics from the phase that preceded it. It is during such transitional periods that we are likely to have crisis experience; though we must remember that experience is a subjective matter, and that it is always possible that someone may get through what is clearly a transitional period to the objective observer *without* suffering crisis experience - if he is lucky enough, or has had anticipatory training, for instance. Someone who falls out of an aircraft will only suffer a crisis experience if he is not a trained parachutist.

With this proviso in mind, we can conveniently categorise certain events in a person's life experience as likely to be critical. There are *developmental* crises, such as birth, puberty, childbearing and the menopause; and what we may call *accidental* crises, such as a first experience of going to school, or a new job, or getting married. These are *challenging* crises for most of us - offering new and better satisfactions in return for those which have to be relinquished. But for most of us there are other crises as well, such as physical injury, going to hospital, losing a job or livelihood, and - most important of all - bereavement, in which we are called upon to cope with the *loss* of something or someone on which or on whom we have depended, in situations which offer no apparent compensatory need satisfactions.

The outcome of a crisis experience is in practice unpredictable, because of the large number of variables which affect it. They include, for instance, the duration and intensity of the stress: no one is surprised when crisis follows a sudden and severe stress, but a less severe stress continued over a long period may result in a crisis unexpected by the onlooker - the 'last straw' phenomenon. The pre-crisis personality make-up is another variable: a man who has experienced a successful outcome to previous crises may be better equipped to cope with the present one - his repertoire of problem-solving techniques will be larger.

Another variable is the presence or absence of cultural aids or supports for people in crisis. It is one thing to break your leg in a city street where an ambulance and hospital is only minutes away, and quite another to break it when you walking alone on a mountain. It is one thing for the breadwinner to develop tuberculosis in a well-equipped welfare state; in a less developed country he and his family would experience crisis of a totally different severity.

Personal or group morale is another variable which may influence crisis outcome. So is the network of expectations of those around; a newcomer to a place, or an immigrant, may experience something more severely because his customary ways of behaving in crisis situations are not recognised, or not approved by those among whom he is now living.

All these variables interact with one another to make for unpredictability in the outcome of crisis in a particular instance. Of course it is possible to identify particular concentrations of hazardous circumstances and to take administrative steps - social action - to diminish their severity. You may provide special social worker services for immigrants, or special pensions for chronic invalids; or you can arrange 'anticipatory guidance' for those at special risk - sex education in schools, antenatal instruction for pregnant mothers, lectures on preparation for retirement from industry, and so on. But however effective they may be in general, their effect in the individual case will be uncertain.

How can you recognise that a person is in need of crisis help? As I said earlier, people in such a state are peculiarly sensitive to the intervention of others, and usually seek help, though not always directly. The small child will cry and run to mother. So will some adults, but many won't. The man who has a row with his wife may go to his familiar pub and after drinking more than his usual, may confide in the barmaid. The woman stunned by the death of her husband may remain isolated and silent in her room until the familiar visitor - the insurance agent, say, arrives to collect her weekly contribution or to pay out the benefit - and then she may pour out all her troubles in his sympathetic but unprepared ear. Perhaps she has presented a stoical facade to both doctor and minister when they called, and thus misled them both. She may even have been resentful and rejecting of their offers of sympathy and help.

More generally, here are some of the signs and symptoms to look for:

1. There is evidence of *confusion*. They say "I don't know how I feel". One moment they say "I'm all right, leave me alone", and the next they are behaving - whether quietly or noisily - in a way we would describe as 'distracted'.

2. They sometimes seem to suffer from *stereotyped perception* of the circumstances: the perception of a sudden catastrophe seems to burn in on the mind, and one's first - often inappropriate - response to it seems to go on repeating itself uselessly. The woman whose husband has had a stroke while out walking may wail "*I told* him not to go out

without his hat" - and go on saying it while neglecting to see other obvious implications which need thinking about.

3.   As tension rises, in less dramatic kinds of crisis, it tends to *leak out* over other irrelevant areas of life. So the wife who is anxious over whether her husband is going to lose his job will find herself unreasonably irritable with her children, her cooking or her dog.

4.   With this is linked a tendency to express *negative feelings* of hostility and anger. These are a natural enough result of the disturbance of homeostasis - stability - which the occurrence of crisis implies: no-one likes being disturbed; but their occurrence is noteworthy because they are in conflict with the need for help from others which crisis also implies. The unprepared neighbour is likely to respond to expressions of hostility with a shrug of the shoulders and withdrawal.

5.   And the last sign I want to draw attention to is the *fluctuating* nature of a person's awareness of crisis. This is not quite the same as the person's confusion which I mentioned above, though, it adds to the confusion in the observer's mind. Nature seems to step in to rest the mind which is in turmoil, so that the distress and confusion seems to wax and wane in intensity over the first few days; and the observer can be misled into believing that the crisis is over when a calm period supervenes after a storm - only to discover an hour or so later that another storm has blown up

Perhaps one of the most important features of a person's behaviour at times of crisis is that it tends to be *repellent* - it tends to repel the onlooker. The emotions associated with it - anxiety, grief, hostility, anger - are all infectious and none of them comfortable. This means that the unprepared onlooker who recognises, and is affected by, the sufferer's distress, is either going to pass by on the other side of the road, or if circumstances don't allow of this, is going to take steps to control the sufferer's *behaviour,* which is sending out the repellent signals, rather than to help the sufferer to digest the unpleasant emotional experience he is having or to take appropriate steps to solve the problem he is faced with. The most common attitude of the unskilled helper, whether verbalised or not, is "pull yourself together". This is usually unsuccessful, because the sufferer has already tried to pull himself together and failed. The next commonest attitude is "let us escape from this uncomfortable experience - have another drink, have a tranquilliser, have a holiday, go right away for a bit and think about something else". This attitude is much more acceptable to the sufferer, since he is usually only too anxious to ease the discomfort of his tension. But a crisis always implies a real situation, of loss, or threat of loss, or challenge, which gives an opportunity for learning about oneself, for gaining greater maturity of personality. And evasive techniques rob the situation of its potential value. Often, too, evasion of the reality is only maintained by the building up of defensive symptoms, which may be hard to alter later.

Here we come to a point where we can see that crisis theory is not just a part of preventive medicine, though it is certainly that; not just a matter of trying to ensure that people don't become ill; but that it has something to offer to a concept of *positive* health, to the idea of a fuller life, life of a better quality, rather than a mere return to the *status quo ante*. Crisis is always potentially a learning situation.

The particular case, which seems to illustrate this best in our present cultural situation, is that of bereavement, because so much of current practice fails to recognise it. Grief and mourning are so commonly regarded as inimical to health. Dr. Colin Parkes (1972) and others have demonstrated convincingly the increased rates of morbidity and mortality among husbands and wives in the two years after the death of a spouse. Are we therefore to conclude that grief and mourning are an evil to be got rid of? Many doctors would say so, as well as other people. And yet, isn't grief the price we have to pay for loving? If we could entirely prevent grief, would we continue to experience love with the same intensity and vividness as before? If humanity could thus get love on the cheap, would it be worth experiencing? Perhaps this is a question for metaphysicians.

In practical terms, what we should aim to do is not to try to get rid of grief, or anxiety or other uncomfortable experiences, but help people to make constructive use of them, to learn from them, to transcend them. What does this mean to the observer? What is needed to turn the onlooker into a caregiver? As I have said, crisis behaviour tends to be repellent. I think that some degree of prior commitment to the sufferer is needed to overcome this first hurdle. It may be that we already know and love the sufferer, as happens in families or among neighbours: our prior knowledge of him in health outweighs our reluctance to get involved. Or it may be a professionally or culturally learnt commitment, at least to go through the motions of being a good neighbour to those in trouble.

Whatever the motivation, the result is that the caregiver responds to the situation by staying in it, and helping him to face the reality of his problem - staying with the sufferer instead of passing by. This imposes on him the necessity of sharing the sufferer's discomfort - he inevitably becomes involved to some extent. But if he is to avoid the collusive evasions of which we spoke earlier, he has also to retain some degree of detachment - he has to control his involvement. This is the hardest part of becoming skilful as a caregiver - learning how to control one's emotional involvement in another's troubles. It is the essential skill of the psychotherapist, and one which can go on increasing throughout life. Fortunately, even those with only moderate control over their emotional involvement can be of help to those in crisis; it is a skill, which increases with experience, and even a little is better than none at all.

The mother, whose two-year old falls and grazes his knee, like the doctor faced with the man with a broken arm, can deal with the crisis and the crisis experience of the sufferer with only a trivial amount of involvement. But at some time in a child's life, he will run to mother in a state of distress, and instead of taking unilateral action to put things right she will say to him "Oh dear, we are in trouble, aren't we?" And she will go on to say "What shall we do to solve the problem?" By using the first person plural she will show the child that she shares his problem, and enables him to share in the solution of it. The lesson for the caregiver is clear: he tries to demonstrate his willingness to share the burden of the person in crisis, but is well advised not to 'take over' the attempts at solving the problem from the sufferer too readily. This is the besetting sin of doctors, of course; the message their behaviour too often conveys is 'put yourself entirely in my hands, do nothing for yourself, leave it all to me'. Of course, doctors - particularly psy-chiatrists - only see a minority of people in crisis. Nowadays, most professional caregivers tend to have appointment systems, and often waiting lists. By the time your appointment comes the crisis is over - for better or worse. The lesson here is to avoid this defensive trick of the professional: the time to intervene is during the crisis, when sensitivity and vulnerability is greatest, not after.

One of the signs of a person being in crisis, as I said, is his tendency to stereotyped perception or 'tunnel vision'. He can only see his situation in one way, which offers no solution to the problem. This often happens during the initial period of confusion, even when the sufferer is quite intelligent enough normally to think of other possibilities. The caregiver is usually detached enough to make quite simple suggestions as to how the problem can be further investigated. "Why don't you consult your relatives, or solicitor, or employer, or the social security office?" Surprisingly often some such simple feeding in of different ways of perceiving the situation is all that is needed to set the sufferer on the way to a constructive solution. Sometimes more factual information needs to be sought for; and here again is a chance to ask questions which can get the sufferer to think more constructively.

Often the caregiver is tempted to give false reassurance. When the schizophrenic is being carried off to the mental hospital he is told he is just going to a nursing home for a week or two or some similar improbable euphemism. This kind of sentimental deception is fatal to a caring relationship not only with the immediate caregiver, but also with others - in the hospital, for instance.

Sometimes, particularly when the person in crisis is showing negative or hostile feelings, he may need a good deal of persuasion to accept perfectly reasonable help, from neighbours or relatives, for instance. And a major principle of crisis intervention is to try to diminish the tendency for the sufferer to blame other people for the trouble - or to blame themselves. This is a common way of evading thinking about the reality of the situation: 'if only - the doctor had come sooner; if only his employer had been more considerate; if only I had not spoken so harshly to him'.

Part of the reality of most crisis situations is that they involve not just the immediate sufferer, but also those with whom he is naturally in relationship - his family or work group. It is often the case that the caregiver can suggest ways in which the family group can re-organise itself so as to ease the total burden: when father breaks his leg, the children can take on some of his household tasks while mother can take on others. Measures, which help to maintain the integrity of the sufferer's natural group, will of course play a big part in helping him as well as them.

You will see that crisis theory, as I have outlined it, has somewhat different emphases from the counselling approach modelled on traditional psychotherapy.
1.   The crisis caregiver is taught to pay much less attention to the historical background of the crisis or the sufferer's previous personality. Both these are seen to be red herrings in this context, tending to distract attention from the real task of coming to terms with the perplexing current situation. Crisis theory focuses on present and future rather than on present and past. However, the chronically unstable person is likely to be in crisis more often than a previously stable person; and if he can have a succession of good crisis experiences, with successful outcomes, his changed expectations may enable him not only to face the future more boldly, but also the previously repressed traumatic

experiences in his past. Thus the application of crisis theory may be as effective a treatment for neurosis itself as is a traditional psychotherapeutic approach.

2.   At times of crisis, there is less need to worry about the client becoming dependent or 'clinging'. Crisis experience is (by definition) of limited duration, because of the organism's tendency to return to a steady state after a disturbance; and during crisis a high degree of dependence is natural enough and is less of a danger signal.

3.   The crisis caregiver can afford to be a good deal more directive than the psychotherapist aims to be - at least in the way of seeking constructive solutions to the current crisis problem.

4.   Crisis care giving invites more immediate concern with the involvement of the group of 'participant onlookers' - family or neighbours or work group - than is common in psychotherapy. . . .

. . . There are of course other respects in which psychotherapy and crisis care are alike: both depend on the establishment of a good relationship, both encourage frank emotional expression and the facing of reality, and both are concerned to discourage projective mechanisms for dealing with badness.

Dr. Lambourne has described healing as *'a satisfactory response to a crisis, made by a group of people, both individually and corporately'* (ed. J.M.Wilson, 1995, p.15) This description says a number of things of pastoral significance. It says that healing is a response not only on the part of a sick man, but applies also to the rest of us - the not yet sick - if only because we are so often onlookers and therefore involved in the sickness of others. Crisis theory is not only concerned with those in trouble, but in building up the strength of the community or group of which the man in trouble is a member. It says also that crisis experience is not something to be borne alone. At the very least, caregiver and sufferer have to share in it if either are to remain human, or become more human, as a result. And nearly always the onlooker, the third person, is an essential participant in the crisis, who also has a chance to learn, to participate in the grace of healing, through his perception of what is happening.

One last thought. The satisfactory outcome of a crisis experience often, if not always, implies that those involved as sufferers or onlookers have undergone a change in their attitude, to themselves and to the events and to one another, as a result of the experience. Their sense of identity is altered and enlarged. This 'change of mind' seems to me precisely what is implied in the Greek word *metanoia*, which we translate as repentance. My dictionary tells me that repentance means a 'change from past evil'. I suggest therefore that true healing - the satisfactory response to a crisis - requires repentance, not in the limited sense of having one's transgressions blotted out, or the limited sense of having one's pain and suffering relieved; for such expressions imply only a return to a presumed previous state of well-being or innocence; but in the sense that repentance, the change of mind induced by learning from crisis, leads forward, in the words of the prayer book confession, to *'newness* of life'.

104 - 1 Crisis Theory.

BIRTH AND DEATH

Human beings, and the communities or societies in which they live are, like all living things, subject to evolutionary law. Environments constantly change, however slowly, and species need as constantly to adapt to the changes or be extinguished. So to survive, it is imperative for a species to maintain and replenish itself within a reservoir of variety. Since no single individual can possess more than a fraction of the variety required, individuals must vary among themselves: we must cherish our differences from one another for the species' sake. The replenishment of such variation depends upon either the occurrence of viable genetic mutations, which are rare, or upon the recombination of genetic material which occurs in sexual reproduction. It follows that when there is an increase in the rate and diversity of environmental change, a species needs *more births* to maintain variety; and this, both logically and empirically, requires that it needs *more deaths.* In non-human species, the latter requirement is, of course, met by natural selection itself: those less well adapted to the changing situation die off. In the human species, we are now in a situation where the environment is indeed changing rapidly, because of the activities of man himself. All species modify their environment to suit themselves, but none does it so drastically as man. But however the rapid change has come about, our response (in western civilisation at least) has so far been to seek ways of *decreasing* the number of births, and of *reducing* the number of deaths – which appears to be precisely the wrong strategy for species survival! . . .

162 - Evolution and Human Values.

CHAPTER TEN
BECOMING

I hesitate to head this chapter 'Education' because the word has been so impoverished in English society that its meaning is now near to 'training for work' - a 'good investment'.

By running his Diploma in Pastoral Studies seminar on therapeutic community lines (see Introduction p.7) James was making a public statement about the nature of knowledge. He supported the high priority given to establishing the student group as a community of trust, in the belief that love enables knowledge to happen. It is a view more akin to the monastic understanding of knowledge which involves the whole person, head and heart, not merely rationality. The modern University subscribes to the scholastic tradition, and given the present value system of Western culture which gives top priority to economics, knowledge has become an achievement, a commodity to be bought and sold in the market place.

For James, knowledge was something to be shared - a very controversial view in today's university. Likewise, James' realisation of the limits of conscious thought, and of the vast hidden agenda which influences university decisions on curricula, research, and budget allocations, was alien to the institution.

Consequently James was completely free of any concern for academic recognition by publication of his papers. Rather he recognised in himself a very human passion for communication (a two-way activity). He saw many things, such as death, counselling, mental health, suffering and loss, marriage etc. in the context of human growth - both of an individual and evolution-wise of humanity in general. He did not see development in a linear way, but rather proceeding in a spiral of surprises through one explosive insight after another: with a great deal of silent gestation in between, like the seed growing secretly. We tend to emphasise the drama of the Exodus, but forget that Israel endured the previous four hundred years in slavery.

Education kindles the inner being of a learner because it is in a community of love that knowledge - in the meaning of both the French words *connaitre* and *savoir* - unfolds. We all help or hinder one another in becoming the person we were born to be. Human growth and development of mind and emotions enable people of any age to enjoy the delights of life-together in work for the common good.

M.W.

EDUCATION FOR LIVING

It occurs to me that there are only two essential aims in life: the Search after Truth, and the Expression of Truth. Most of mankind seems to have but a hazy idea of what it is looking for, or trying to do. I fancy that few men find, until life is nearly over, the real aim of all their effort. The better half of civilised mankind often express a philanthropic aim, to make the world a better place for this or that section of the community, or race, or generation. But to what end does the philanthropist desire to improve the world? How can a man tell what *is* improvement? Alteration, certainly, but isn't he rather bold who classes his work as improvement? There appears to be but one factor in life today that renders us more able than our progenitors: that we *know* more, that more truth has been made apparent to us; and by virtue of this new knowledge we have more control over our environment. We have, in fact, more responsibility for our environment. . . .

. . . What is the place of this knowledge in our scheme of things? To what purpose is it employed? Knowledge, of itself, is dead. Only as it is transmitted into action is it a force of value to us. Inevitably, no one man can know all that there is to know. We have therefore taken the obvious step, and we divide knowledge amongst ourselves, and develop the process we call specialisation. We failed to realise that, in time specialisation might overpower us, that the servant would become the master. Already, we feel the burden of knowledge so great in our minds that we yearn to be rid of it. We insist, we philanthropists, on passing our burden, (as much of it as possible), on to everyone else. We spend astronomical sums on 'education' in a desperate endeavour to ease the strain on ourselves. The process gets us nowhere. We are becoming increasingly specialised. Our vital energy is directed more and more to the upkeep of this dead-weight of knowledge, and less and less to its original function of living.

In a vain endeavour to get some order from the chaotic mass of facts, we have evolved that soulless and sinister figure, the bureaucrat. I see a close spiritual analogy between the bureaucrat and the child of tender years put to work in a mine, or a 'dark, satanic mill' - a hundred years ago. Contemplate for a moment the amount of unclassified knowledge coming daily to the administrative offices of a modern industrial or scientific institution. Could any man really perceive this vast bulk of knowledge - and live? He is bound to crush out of his life any tendency to appreciation, to perception, to *feeling.* Again, we cast upon the world a never-ending stream of books and periodicals, all crammed with knowledge, with facts; and we make illiteracy a crime, lest someone escape their share of the burden. Is it not time that we awoke to the fact that to know, without perceiving, is an expense of spirit - a sin we might say? The soul's vitality is too precious to be wasted on that which yields no return. All knowledge must be made a part of life, if we are to claim an improvement in civilisation. . . .

. . . Education, in the past few decades particularly, has been very largely a matter of instilling knowledge into the young. This seems to me to be a totally wrong conception. What use have the young for knowledge? Our aim must be, rather, to instil the *desire* to know. The emphasis of our lessons should not be on the facts, but on discipline, self-reliance, or some other facet of the art of living. . . .

. . . Our education must draw the children's attention to the fundamental aims: the search after truth, or the expression thereof. They must have free choice of the two - (I conceive it to be no part of a teacher's duty to make the choice) - and for balanced character they must have a sound grounding in both methods of life, the scientific, and the artistic. The one requires rigid self-discipline, the other, free self-expression. Music (which here includes literature), and gymnastic were the two points of Plato's scheme of education: fundamentals have not changed. . . .

. . . The hallmark of our system must be balance. There must be no undue emphasis on this or that phase of life. And there must be no confusion from the introduction of non-essentials. Twenty years is not too long a time to build up a character, and until a man has a formed character, he is incapable of deciding his destiny.

What of our teachers? Here, I think, is the crux of the matter. The usual requirements of a teacher are that he knows well the subjects he is to teach, and that he knows a certain amount of child psychology. But I demand quite other standards. If our children are to be well-balanced in mind and soul, so must the teachers be. If the latter are to instil self-discipline, they must have self-discipline. If they are to teach at all, they must have the ability to express themselves. If they are to instil a love of truth, they must love truth. And, since they are concerned with fundamentals, they need not, should not, shew too profound a specialised knowledge. They must, in fact, *vilify* specialisation. It is not important to children. A child prefers a good man to a good scientist; and this is the expression of nature, of instinct. The teaching profession must be the highest calling. It is more important and more vital than the church, or the profession of medicine. It should be the calling from which statesmen are chosen. The child must be given an absolute ideal to live for. He must be taught how to serve this ideal with his mind and with his body. He must know how to use his head, and his hands, and his eyes, and his voice, and his limbs; and he must be shown to what purpose he is to use them. He must be taught that a fact is of no value, is not *true,* unless it is perceived, appreciated, as well as known. He must be taught to use his own facts, his experience, and not other people's; for only thus will he learn to grasp their real significance. A fact should be savoured, like music, or poetry, or a picture, and thus become a part of life.

In some such manner, then, let us rearrange our ideas. I deem it immoral – worse - for the individual to allow into his life facts which he cannot spiritually digest and absorb. Our news bulletins, newspapers, cinemas, and professional journals, all pander to our unfortunate tendency to factual gluttony. It is as important to keep our minds clear and clean as our bowels; and in so civilised, and therefore artificial a world, this can only be done by a person with self-respect and self-control, and a taste continually schooled to discrimination.. . .

0 - 2 Truth and Knowledge (1941).

LEARNING TO COMMUNICATE

Peter Scott tells how he followed up his childhood interest in birds and animals by going to a university to study zoology. He was dissatisfied and disillusioned. He was looking for explanations of the way animals behaved - and found himself put to the dissection of creatures who, because they were dead, could not be said to be behaving at all. No doubt, if he had persisted, he would have learned a great deal about the bodily mechanisms which underlie the behaviour of the living animal, but this wasn't what he really wanted. He wanted to know the meaning of behaviour - the reasons *why* a creature did certain things - and all he was being taught was *how* it did them.

Since the time when he was an undergraduate, the study of animal behaviour has achieved the status of a distinct discipline under the name of *Ethology*, and perhaps the most interesting part of ethology is the study of the way animals behave in *social encounters* with one another. In this field we can begin to see how behaviour can be studied, not as a matter of mechanism, but as a matter of communication between animals. The posture adopted by one animal evokes a behavioural response in another, which in turn releases a fresh posture or behavioural sequence in the first. In the higher mammals, at least, it seems justifiable to say that the behaviour of one animal means something to the other - that the behaviour *communicates* meaning to the other.

Perhaps we can see more clearly in the human being, that much behaviour has a significance as a means of communication. Facial expression changes with emotion: we laugh if we are happy and shed tears when we are sad. We thrust our heads forward in anger or aggressiveness, and scratch our heads when perplexed or the back of our necks when embarrassed.

With this for introduction, we can see that sexual behaviour can be studied either as mechanism, or as communication.

Sex as mechanism has presumably been explored by previous speakers in this series of lectures. Such problems as contraception and the avoidance of venereal disease have this as their frame of reference, and so do discussions about such things as the relief of sexual tension, autoeroticism, and the normal physiology of coitus. It is when we come to think of sex as an aspect of human personality that its significance as communication becomes clear. For personality is a function of human relationships, and the definition of a human relationship is that it is a continuing channel of communication between people.

Whatever the genetic and constitutional endowment a baby may have at birth, it is only by virtue of the relationships he forms with other people that he will develop a personality at all. The relationship with mother is of course the fundamental one. Studies of maternal deprivation, and clinical experience, have established this in considerable detail. As I have said, this relationship is a channel of communication. Of course, not only verbal communication. Communication, as I am using the word, is something two people have in common - a shared meaning. It is not just a message sent out, not just self-expression; but a message received and understood, self-expression by one person perceived with sympathy by another, who in turn expresses their sympathetic under-standing to the first. It may be expressed by any form of behaviour, and may be perceived by any of the senses - eyes and touch, as well as hearing. The poet Rupert Brooke, recalling his earliest memory of communication, talks of "*the comfortable smell of friendly fingers*".

Psychologically, this relationship is not as one-sided as it appears to be objectively. The dependence of the baby on the mother for food and warmth is no doubt one-sided. But its dependence on her for continuous presence, and for solace, is more nearly matched by her dependence on her baby for these same things. Which is more grieved by the loss of the other, mother or child? Although they are physically separated at birth, psychological separation comes only slowly over a period of months and years.

Within the security of this relationship, the baby feels free to explore the surrounding universe, to learn about it, to adventure into it, and gradually to differentiate himself from it. He discovers his own body, as an object distinct from other objects. More gradually still, he becomes aware of himself as a person, who can communicate and have relationships with other persons.

All this he can do if his relationship with mother or mother-substitute is a healthy one. But if this basic relationship is distorted or damaged in any way, all his subsequent relationships are likely to carry evidence of it. As the twig is bent, so will the tree grow.

So there is an important sense in which sex education begins at mother's breast; because it is there that one first learns, or fails to learn, how to have a full and satisfying relationship with another person.

The mother-child relationship is one of love. The arch-enemy of all relationships is fear. Fear is the true opposite of love, not hate. Love connotes attraction, a coming together or staying together. Fear connotes repulsion, separation. Love implies a channel of communication, through which meanings can be shared; fear implies barriers to communication. Common speech confirms this: my face was frozen with fear, we say, or, I was paralysed with fright, or, I was dumb with terror. Behaviour, which expresses fear, is behaviour which denies communication. So, if a child is not constantly assured and reassured of its mother's presence, it feels first fear, then panic - and the channel of communication is stopped. The baby's capacity for exploration and for learning - its span of attention, is narrowed to a fascinated focus on this one overwhelming need - for mother's return. And, after such a separation (whatever the reason - for the infant doesn't understand reasons), it takes much time and patience for the relationship to be re-established. Since such separations are almost inevitable, I suppose the vast majority of us carry forward some elements of this primitive anxiety into our later relationships - especially the deep and intimate ones which characterise our sexual lives as adults.

In so far as the primal relationship is a secure one, temporary separation from mother can occur without anxiety, and further relationships become possible, with other members of the family, and then schoolfellows, teachers, and people in general. All are characterised by a willingness to communicate, by some degree of mutual trust so that each is prepared to 'give himself away' to the other, even if only a little, and by some degree of mutual understanding. And all these later, differentiated relationships are likely to be limited, in each of these respects, by an element of fear which has been learned in earlier, more basic ones.

At some time before the age of five, there occurs in each of us a differentiation of mental functioning which arises as a result of mental conflict. We are born not only with an instinctive need to have a continuing relationship with mother, but with other instinctive tendencies - to get angry when frustrated, to take what we want without realising that others may have a claim to things, to 'show off', and perhaps to explore and play with parts of our bodies which we will later discover to be our genital organs. And since mother is likely to disapprove of these activities, and to threaten, however obliquely, to withdraw her love if we indulge them, we have a conflict of interest.

The need for mother's continued approval usually emerges victorious from this conflict sooner or later, however strongwilled the child may be. Or, at least, apparently victorious. For we solve the situation by a pretence. We deny the antisocial impulse. We pretend we didn't have it. In technical language, we repress it. It becomes unconscious. We don't know it is there. But because these impulses - on both sides of the conflict - are biologically rooted in our nature, they remain active even when repressed. They continue to seek expression in some disguised form, and account for much that is irrational or neurotic in our behaviour. Note that there is always some element of fear in this process of repression: a fear of the loss of social approval; and this fear must be overcome before the repressed impulses can be allowed into conscious awareness again.

So it is easy to see how anxieties in early childhood interfere with later sexual behaviour and attitudes. When parents are unwilling or unable to satisfy a growing child's natural curiosity about sexual matters in an understanding way, or where their own behaviour toward each other is of a kind which the child perceives as frightening, it is predictable that the child will come to regard his perfectly natural interest in sex as too dangerous to be dealt with by the conscious ego. If this is the case, as it often is, it is not surprising that formal sex education in the classroom or elsewhere in later years is often as unassimilable, and seems as irrelevant, as the conjugation of irregular Latin verbs. And when we come to courtship and marriage, we find that sexual behaviour, far from being the delicate and tender means of joyous communication which it can be at its best, tends to be compulsive, clumsy, and a source of embarrassment until these childish fears have been transmuted by the generosities of love.

The unconscious part of our minds does not only consist of repressed impulses and ideas. What Freud called the Id is really a vast reservoir of impulses and experiences of which we have never become aware, which have never been scrutinised or become incorporated into the conscious ego. The primitive identification with mother which precedes self-awareness, for instance, remains part of our experience though we are not conscious of it, and clinical work with patients regularly demonstrates how this experience can continue to affect our behaviour into adult life. We do not know who we are. We are certainly not limited to that part of ourselves of which we are conscious. So it is important to remember that a person who is loved is not what he thinks he is. Your mother loved *you* - not merely your self-conscious ego, you as you remember yourself, but you as you really were, ego and id together. . . .

. . . In fact the development of personality seems to lie in a progressive series of discoveries about who one really is, mediated through the succession of relationships - the channels of communication with other people - which alone can make such discoveries possible.

So far I have given you an outline of how personality develops in early life, and how distortion, by fear, at this infantile stage can affect later behaviour. During the 6 to 12 year old stage - the gang age, or what Freud called the latency period, children seem to take the relationships they have established pretty well for granted; and to turn their attention to learning techniques and skills for manipulating and exploiting the objective world around them. They learn to play team games, to build dens and forts, to make things and to be concerned with mechanical or constructional activities. At this stage they admire adults who show an ability to control power - power over things, like engine drivers or ships' captains or soldiers - or power over people like generals or kings. They are more interested in what you can do than in what you are.

But with the emergence of sexual interests at puberty, psychological development enters another stage, concurrently with the physical changes which signal the arrival of adulthood. There is an upsurge of sympathy and feeling for other people, rather than the detached interest which characterised the latency period. The intensity of emotion which may be aroused is often a major source of embarrassment to the individual concerned. In infancy, strong emotions were aroused but were freely expressed. But in the latency period it is 'not done' to express your personal feelings or even to admit that you have any. So the intensity of feeling in early adolescence makes this a rather critical period, and difficult to manage.

From the age of about 13 onwards, we find ourselves moved to make spontaneous, if furtive, contributions to the War on Want fund; or we begin to read poetry, or perhaps develop hero-worship for a schoolmaster or the games captain. Or - more commonly but by no means always - we develop an interest in girls or boys. But I want to make the point that this interest in the opposite sex is not necessarily because they offer the so-called 'normal' outlet for the physical tensions of sex. At this stage, masturbation is probably just as 'normal', and homosexual activity very nearly so, at least among boys. This dissociation between the physical expression of sex - what I have called sex as mechanism - and the urge to establish personal relationships - channels of communication - with people of the opposite sex is, I think, a normal stage of development.

As we have seen, during the latency period, the years before puberty, we develop the skills by which we manipulate and exploit the world of objects. At this time, other people were also just objects to be manipulated - as when we learned the technique of wheedling an extra 10/- pocket money out of father, or how best to annoy the form master at school. At puberty, we find ourselves endowed with a new technique by which to express ourselves - that of sexual activity. As with other techniques we have learned, its exercise is pleasurable. But once we enter adulthood, we have entered a world wherein we discover that people are not just objects to be exploited, but like ourselves, subjects, not only objects, with whom we can have relationships based on mutual respect, wherein the greatest degree of satisfaction can only be obtained for either if it satisfies both. And our various techniques, including sex, can be used not only for their own sake, for exercise or for fun, but for a social purpose, for the benefit of other people whom we want to satisfy because their satisfaction brings satisfaction to us.

I hope it is becoming clear to you that maturity of personality is not just a matter of achieving, at any given moment, a balanced relief of emotional tension, a return of the human machine to a condition of homeostasis. Human behaviour only appears to reach an endpoint of minimal tension when it is studied in isolated fragments.

(Even the ultimate homeostasis of death is only an endpoint if the individual is considered in isolation from his social context. The death of one member of a family can enable other members to become more mature through the experience of bereavement.)

If you look at the mother-baby situation as if it were a 'closed system', as scientists say, you would not be able to predict how the baby would grow and develop and differentiate as a personality, nor in what ways the mother would become more mature for the experience. You could indeed see that when the baby cried, mother would become equally distressed unless she were able to reduce the emotional tension of both baby and herself by taking appropriate action, such as changing the wet nappy. This could certainly be interpreted as a homeostatic mechanism. But it would shed no light on the process of emotional growth. However, if we survey the situation in its natural setting, which is an 'open system', with expanding and variable boundaries, we can observe that the channel of communication between mother and child is a *necessary condition* for emotional growth to occur. Growth, the creation of life, cannot be caused to happen in a mechanical sense. It is a potentiality which emerges, given the necessary conditions. And it does seem that what we call creative activity in any sphere, difficult and painful and unsuccessful as it often is, is best understood as the effort to establish or maintain channels of communication with other human beings.

As I say, it is often unsuccessful. To try to establish a relationship with someone is to be adventurous, to take a chance. It is of the essence of a love relationship that you are prepared to 'give yourself away'; and in so doing you are running a risk - of losing your heart or your self. But this, of course, is what creation is about; this is what you must seek if you are to achieve a mature and fruitful personality. There can be no creation without in some way transcending yourself.

Of course, no-one on this earth is ever likely to achieve *complete* maturity of personality. It is a direction for us to follow, if we are so minded, rather than an end result which we can expect to attain by the age of thirty. Our personalities, even at their best and most mature, carry in them the vestiges of our preceding immaturities. If we get ill or frustrated, or when we meet a crisis in our lives, we are likely to regress to less mature patterns of behaviour (including sex behaviour) - a sort of '*reculer pour mieux sauter*'. I suppose for most of our lives we fluctuate between automatic behaviour - a predictable sequence of activities aimed at maintaining homeostasis and personal comfort, eating and sleeping and earning our living - and creative behaviour, when we make an unpredictable and often strenuous effort to grow, to seek something better, to get out of the rut. The important thing is not to mistake achievements of the former kind for those of the latter.

To sum up: There is a distinction to be drawn between knowing how your car engine works, and knowing how to drive your car from A to B. No doubt you will be wise, if you wish to have a trouble-free journey, to know enough about the way the engine works not to abuse it by bad driving. But cars are made for going places.

So it is with sex. A knowledge of sexual mechanisms and techniques is worth having, but the exercise of technique for its own sake, however momentarily enjoyable, does not get you anywhere. It is only when the sexual act is recognised as the most precious, self-affirmative and self-committing communication which two people can make to each other, in love, that its meaning and value for human personality can be fully understood. . . .

56 - 1 Fact and Meaning of Sex: sex and personality.

BECOMING WHOLE

... Some time between four and twelve months, most babies - perhaps all - seem to interpose some thing, some buffer, between the inner self and the world of concrete objects. From birth, most infants suck thumbs or fingers as a substitute satisfaction; but within a few months, this kind of natural comforter has got itself associated with a bit of blanket, or a teddy-bear, or something else which is usually soft and cuddly. Winnicott[1] has shown us how very important this 'buffer zone' is for healthy development. He talks of the cuddly toy - the first thing a child truly 'possesses' - as a transitional object, and points out that such transitional objects are, *for the child*, neither inner reality nor are they part of his world of objects. They are somewhere in between. He can make of them what he will. For him, they may represent, at any moment, what he subjectively conceives of, or what he objectively perceives.. ...

... Under mother's protection, then, a healthy child can make for himself this buffer zone, this intermediate area between his inner world of dreams and illusion and the outer world of true objects, in which he can experiment with fantasy and fact and create new ways of matching them. The 'good enough' mother respects this intermediate area as being the child's own, as the space he needs, free from interference, to smooth his transition from dependence to autonomy; and the healthy child vigorously resists any encroachment upon it - as any mother will testify who has tried to replace, or even wash, the insanitary doll or rag which the child has so firmly adopted.

It is in this intermediate area, between fantasy and actuality, that a child can find room to *play*. Another observer of children, Erik Erikson, describes the purpose of play as being *"to hallucinate ego-mastery and yet also to practice it in an intermediate reality between phantasy and actuality."*[2] There is a continuous line of development from the transitional object, peculiar to each child, through the whole gamut of children's shared imaginative play and story telling. Games like 'I'm the king of the castle' and stories like 'Winnie the Pooh' will serve as examples. In all such situations, the child is taking something - a toy, a story - which to adults seems definable and objective, but uses it for his own purposes as something 'not real'; so that wood blocks can transiently become a house or a train or a fort - and can as easily be forgotten and again become wood blocks. And it is easy to see how the experiences of such imaginative play in childhood can develop and continue into the adult field of cultural experience in art, drama, literature and so on.[3]

So to return to our theme, I want to suggest that the primitive experience or illusion of wholeness, the early omnipotent fantasy, can be remembered and developed and differentiated and (in greater or lesser degree) matched with the objective world precisely in this intermediate area, this play space, which we can now see to be a major element in the healthy human personality. But we must take it further. The adult search for wholeness, for an answer to the question as to how men can become whole, is a religious search. Wholeness is not an objective matter. Except in its origins, it may not always be wholly an illusion or hallucination; but its manifestation, whenever we glimpse it, is iridescent, perpetually changing. It has a dynamic quality. The notion of wholeness must include the notion of constant change of perspective and understanding, constant change from what yesterday appeared to be evil or inadequate or irrelevant, of constant conceptual repentance. Theology, the queen of the sciences, should be seen as a game - to be taken seriously but not too seriously. The unbroken thread which links infantile omnipotent but hopeful fantasy, made possible by 'good enough' mothering, and the sublimity of religious thought, can be seen in St. Paul's exclamation *"I can do all things through Christ which strengtheneth me."* [4]

Winnicott speaks of this buffer zone, this intermediate area between inner self and outer world as a *potential* space. The infant who is deprived of satisfaction for his instinctual needs - for food, for warmth, and for what Rupert Brooke called the *"comfortable smell of friendly fingers"* - will not easily develop it. *"Hope deferred maketh the heart sick,"* [5] and if the frustration of inner needs is prolonged and becomes overwhelming, the child experiences his need as something bad; and when eventually the objective world does provide a breast or bottle or whatever to meet the need, this object is felt to be bad also. Such a heartsick child no longer *likes* the breast or the bottle which have proved so untrustworthy - he just has to have it, to grab it. For such a child, there is no *fun* in feeding or snuggling into the warm; from the beginning, life and survival are real and earnest, an anxiety-ridden battle to be rid of feeling (which is for him so regularly associated with something bad) - by immediate, compulsive gratification and subsequent oblivion or hopeless apathy. The outside world comes to be perceived as largely an array of hostile objects to be destroyed or devoured or avoided.

Erikson contrasts the 'wholeness' of normal, healthy experience with what he calls the 'total' restructuring of experience in anxious people. He says,

> . . . *"wholeness seems to connote an assembly of parts, even quite diversified parts, that enter into fruitful association and organisation. This concept is most strikingly expressed in such terms as wholeheartedness, wholemindedness, wholesomeness and the like. . . . Wholeness emphasises a sound, organic, progressive mutuality between diversified functions and parts within an entirety, the boundaries of which are open and fluid. Totality, on the contrary, evokes a Gestalt in which an absolute boundary is emphasised; given a certain arbitrary delineation, nothing that belongs inside must be left outside, nothing that must be outside can be tolerated inside. A totality is as absolutely inclusive as it is utterly exclusive. . . ."* [6]

Thus in the total mode, between whatever we choose to label as good and bad, there is no room for give and take, for play, for experiment. Totality interprets the world as if it were sharply black and white, with no grey shading from one to the other. It allows for no development of the potential space, which Winnicott describes.

Characteristically, we associate play with childhood and immaturity. We see that children and young animals play, alone and together, seriously but not too seriously; but that as adults they seem to know the realities of their environment and no longer need this moratorium in which to learn about it. Perhaps because I myself am not yet mature, I am unwilling to accept all the implications of this. The mature animal is one who has reached an end-point of development. An adult ape is an ape is an ape. But a young ape of one species is very like a young primate of several other species. As organisms mature, they specialise in both form and behaviour, in both structure and function; and we recall Teilhard de Chardin's words, that *"specialisation paralyses, ultraspecialsation kills."* [7] Alone among species, mankind and his ancestors have avoided this trap of specialisation at the biological level; and as we survey the history of evolution we see how the prolongation of immaturity goes hand in hand with greater adaptability to the environment and greater autonomy within it. From this perspective, maturity begins to look like something to avoid. . . .

. . . We can interpret the cosmos as if it were a meaningless accident resulting from the operation of impersonal scientific laws, or - perhaps more comprehensively - as if it were the creation of a benevolent super-personal deity.

We are free to choose among a variety of visions of what it is or might be to be fully human. Indeed, we each of us can create, and go on re-creating, our own particular vision, perhaps sharing it with others; but this freedom depends, I think, upon our cherishing and cultivating this intermediate area, this play-space between subjectivity and objectivity, between concept and percept, between illusion and final disillusionment. And, having achieved such a freedom, perhaps we assume a moral obligation to use it, to actively experiment with changes of perspective; Donald Winnicott is only able to give us his fruitful insights about 'good enough' mothers and transitional objects because, instead of looking at children from the perspective of a doctor or psychiatrist, he changed perspective and looked at their situation through the eyes of a child.

What would happen if we were to experiment theologically with the idea of a 'good enough' God? We are familiar with the distinction between the God of wrath and the God of grace. From our perspective here, the idea of a God of wrath suggests that we are interpreting Him in a 'total' rather than a 'whole' way, with a sharp distinction between right and wrong, and a stress on obedience, commandments, servanthood, justice - concepts which have a judicial or legalistic connotation. The God of grace, on the other hand, leads us to stress love, mercy, unconditional acceptance, forgiveness, childlike dependency. Perhaps these two images, superficially so paradoxical, are best seen as the two ends of a continuum; and between the two something may be gained if we (acknowledging our child-like status in relation to Him) were to play with an image of God as just 'good enough'. A God who frustrates us for our own good - but never to excess. A God whose grace is sufficient for us; just sufficient for today - we are not to be anxious about tomorrow. From a perspective as children within God's family, we can see that it is neither His perfection in relation to ourselves, nor is it our own perfection in relation to other men that we have to seek; it is the perfection of the whole Body, in which each part can only be seen by the others as just 'good enough'. It is only from God's perspective, not ours, that true perfection, true wholeness, might conceivably be discerned.

Such a perspective, organic rather than judicial on the one hand, and emphasising responsibility rather than infantile dependency on the other, could have important practical implications.

1. Men in community might be more ready to forego the obsessive search for excellence in their own particular, partial, localised field of endeavour within the whole body politic, and might thus avoid the mutually destructive competition for resources which afflicts us in so many different fields now. The pursuit of excellence in any field which uses resources is dangerous; it nearly always goes along with scarcity or starvation in other fields which are just as important. It is only in the purely creative arts such as poetry, music, drama and painting - and perhaps worship? - that we can safely pursue excellence without penalising other people.

2. If men were to give up this kind of idolatry (for that is what it is) and were content to accept a share of resources which enabled them to be just 'good enough', they might find it easier to focus attention on the common good - the *common excellence* - which of course means more than just the greatest good of the greatest number. They might seek more widely to do what was best for everybody, even when this involved accepting temporary or minor injustice, for themselves.[8]

3. And lastly, they could begin to see themselves, and the jobs or professions or vocations with which they identified themselves, as being *partly* responsible for the *whole* good of society, instead of - as too often now - wholly responsible for just their own small part of it.[9]

Finally, to summarise what I have said:

1. Our individual ideas of wholeness take their significance and colouring from the primitive experience of at-one-ness which we have as babies in our mother's arms.

2. As babies we create for ourselves a buffer zone between inner and outer worlds in which we can experiment with ways of matching inner fantasy with outer fact.

3. This buffer zone or play area allows us to test out, alter and develop our ideas of wholeness so that they may more nearly fit the world we know and our hope for its future

4. Just as mother seeks to make herself appear to her child as 'good enough' in order that he may build on his infantile experience and develop autonomy and responsible interdependence, it may be that the Incarnation is God's way of presenting Himself to us as 'good enough', to encourage us to build on our experience of childlike dependency as 'infants in Christ'[10] and develop responsible autonomy as God's 'sons and heirs.'[11]

References

1.	D.W.Winnicott,	**Playing and Reality,** (Penguin), 1974.
2.	E.H.Erikson,	**Childhood and Society,** (Penguin), 1965, p.204.
3.	D.W.Winnicott,	**Op. Cit.,** p.60.
4.	New Testament,	**Philippians,** chap. 4, v. 13.
5.	Old Testament,	**Proverbs,** chap.13, v. 12.
6.	E.H.Erikson,	**Identity: Youth and Crisis,** (Faber), 1971, pp.80-81.
7.	P. Teilhard de Chardin,	**The Phenomenon of Man,** (Collins), 1959, p.159.
8.	P. Baelz,	*'Ethics of Strikes in the Caring Professions'*, paper given to the I.R.M. Conference, London, Jan.1975.
9.	P. Teilhard de Chardin,	**Science and Christ,** (Collins), 1968, p.13.
10.	New Testament	**1 Corinthians,** chap. 3, v.2.
11.	New Testament	**Romans,** chap.8, vv. 14 - 17.

121 - 6 The Experience of Wholeness.

GROWTH OF CONSCIENCE

. . . I shall be speaking as a biologist: that is to say I shall be dealing with living processes. If I speak of sin, guilt or illness, I shall be meaning to talk of sinning men, guilty men or ill men. I shall speak of love, but I shall not usually mean *Love* in the comprehensive, absolute way in which, for instance, we believe that 'God is Love'. I shall only mean to talk of love in the partial and relative way in which it is manifest in human beings. This point is important. Any theologian will tell you that the Love of God is the fundamental source of all love, from which man's love for his neighbour is derived. It is the first commandment that *"Thou shalt love the Lord thy God"*, and only the second that *"Thou shalt love thy neighbour as thyself"*.

Similarly, the physicist will tell you that Einstein's formulation of the laws of physics is more comprehensive and fundamental than was Newton's. But Newton's first approximation to the truth had to come before Einstein's, and as a biologist, my experience leads me to believe that a human being in infancy must learn and discover the significance of love as displayed by human beings, before he can become capable of appreciating the significance of the love of God. *"If a man say I love God, and hateth his brother, he is a liar; for he that loveth not his brother whom he hath seen, how can he love God whom he hath not seen?"* Of course, whether or not anyone appreciates God's love may make no difference to its reality, but St. John's statement that the love of one's neighbour is a necessary preliminary to love of one's God, may well have implications for Christian teaching and practice beyond those which are currently accepted as adequate by many of us.

Another warning of the limitations of my approach is this: when you are dealing with living individuals and their development you are bound to use words which are static for processes which are functional and dynamic. Fertilised ovum, embryo, baby, child, youth, man, are all stages of one continuous living process, with every gradation between them. The ovum, however, is quite undifferentiated: it shows no limbs, or hands or feet; and even a young embryo only shows limb-buds, not recognisable fingers and toes. Similarly, mental characteristics such as self-consciousness, loving kindness or self-respect, while they can become quite clear and demonstrable aspects of our adult make-up, are quite unidentifiable and undifferentiated in the infant, and only gradually emerge with any clarity. A potentiality for human relationships and for love is no doubt inherent in every baby at birth. So is a potentiality for walking. But in the same way as the ability to walk can only become actual when normal development has proceeded for some distance, so the ability to love does not become a reality for some time after birth. One has to try to understand the evolution of such concepts as love and conscience, not only by studying their objective and visible results in behaviour, but also by an effort of sympathetic imagination, by trying to see things from the viewpoint of the child or baby. People tend to have difficulty in appreciating the psychoanalytic accounts of psychosexual development in young children for this reason. Such ideas as the Oedipus complex, or anal eroticism in children, for instance, are repugnant to many people at first acquaintance. On second thoughts, they are reluctantly accepted, because they do so often fit in with the objective facts of childhood behaviour. But it is only when one contemplates the significance of certain kinds of behaviour to the innocent mind of the child that one can reach a real understanding of what such ideas mean.

A final *caveat* I would like to enter before committing myself to my thesis is also concerned with the use of words. When I talk of "mother" and her relations with the infant, I don't mean to limit the concept to that of the natural mother. I rather mean in a general sense the person who fulfils a mother's functions towards the child; it may be a foster-mother, or a father, or even on occasion a nursemaid or schoolteacher, and it may possibly be a combination of these.

Conscience, in its beginnings, is 'what mother tells you'. The newborn child, equipped with a highly developed sensory system, and a much less developed motor capacity, is only able to take a 'selfish' view of its experience. Some sensations it likes, and others it doesn't. It likes warmth, it likes its mother's milk, and it likes the kind of gentle touch which it gets from her hands. It doesn't like loud noises, and it doesn't like being left alone for long when awake. Within a few months of birth it will show that it likes to see the smile on the face of its mother, and dislikes the frown of a stranger. As the baby grows, it finds it can control its limbs, and when its teeth come through it can bite. Along with this greater motor capacity comes the discovery that certain kinds of things that it can do evoke smiles and comfort from mother, while other kinds of behaviour evoke no such pleasurable response. Mother, in fact, has begun to tell baby things. Not in words, but in gestures and attitudes - in what she doesn't do as much as what she does. She has begun to *communicate* with the child. Or should we say that the child has begun to communicate with her? The child has, of course, been sending out signals to which she responded from the moment of its birth; but the child cannot deliberately intend to communicate until it is able to become aware of what it is doing, and able to control what it is doing to some degree. Communication, in the sense in which I am using the word, is a two-way process between people; it is the process by which each gets to know what the other means. As Newcomb says, *"It is meanings, not the words and gestures which are their vehicles, which are the essence of communication"*.

It is, I think, clear that this kind of continuous meaningful communication between the child and its mother implies a loving relationship between them. Love is the emotion of relationship: it keeps people together. If there is no love, there can be no continuity in the sympathetic transfer of 'meanings' from one to the other, and thus no growth of mutual understanding. And, conversely, if there is no development of mutual understanding, love will tend to wither away.

If conscience, then, starts off as something that mother tells us, it is something which depends upon there being a loving relationship between mother and child, and in order to maintain such a relationship there must be a capacity for meaningful communication between them.

As I have said, the newborn baby is so constituted that it cannot help being self-centred. But when it develops its capacity to act deliberately, and thus can gain definition of its self-awareness, it can exercise some choice between actions, or between doing something or refraining from doing it. Every action it takes in its mother's presence is, of course, a communication of some kind - it conveys some sort of a meaning to her; and some she will approve of and some she will disapprove of. Thus it is that the child can begin to learn the difference between right and wrong. 'Right' is what mother likes me to do, and 'wrong' is that which she doesn't like me to do. Quite often, I *want* to do what she doesn't approve of. Sometimes, it almost seems that 'everything I want to do is wrong'. And then she is likely to tell me I am being selfish!

Here, it seems, we are up against the fundamental penalty of being human: our inborn equipment of likes and dislikes is not a sufficient guide to behaviour if we are to keep the approval of mother, at least, as an essential if we are to survive. So our 'selfish desires' have to be controlled, and we very gradually learn that in order to maintain our loving relationship with mother we have to behave unselfishly. At first, we behave this way only reluctantly: the 'meaning' which our first attempt at unselfish behaviour conveys to mother is: "I am not doing this because I want to, but because I love you and want you to go on loving me". But as time goes on, we eventually find that we have accepted mother's teaching wholly - it has become our own; and 'right' behaviour has become second nature to us. We have, in fact, learned sufficient self-control to behave unselfishly as if we liked it.

However, every now and then, for one reason or another - when we are tired, or ill, or faced with a new situation, we find ourselves doing 'wrong' - something which mother would disapprove of if she were there. It makes us uneasy and perhaps a little ashamed. We feel guilty. We are aware of the operation of conscience.

Conscience, as something recognisable, only emerges slowly. The kind of moral decision we make shows a progression, from "I must do what mother likes me to do", through "I must do what mother would like me to do if she were here", to "I must do what I think mother would like me to do even though there is no likelihood of her ever finding out what I do". Authorities on child development agree in saying that conscience - the ability to make some simple moral decisions independently of mother - begins to manifest itself in the child's behaviour round about the age of five, though, of course, this may vary quite widely from one child to another. No doubt the child's subjective awareness of conscience emerges at about the same age; though this cannot be proved. We only feel *guilty* if we act wrongly, or at least feel a strong impulse to act wrongly. We won't feel anything we can recognise as guilt so long as we are lucky enough to make right decisions without too much effort.

I hope it will have become clear to you how much the development of a conscience - and the quality of conscience - depend upon the love relationship between mother (or mother-substitute) and child. Conscience is not something you are born with, but is something that is *learned*, and it can only be learned with difficulty, from a person who is constantly at hand and with whom one can communicate readily. If mother is not constantly at hand - if she or the child is ill in hospital, or if she neglects the child through ignorance, or through a preference for someone or something else; or if she is so unpredictable that she fails to communicate her meanings consistently to the child, then conscience will be undeveloped or distorted,

Separation from the mother is thus one cause of failure in the development of conscience. Fear is another. What can be more frightening for a baby than to feel alone? *'Perfect love casteth out fear',* and even a little love will keep fear at bay; but mother must be available to give that little love. Fear creates barriers to communication. The frightened animal stands still and hopes it won't be seen. We talk of being paralysed by fear. If we see someone we are frightened of, we run away and hide. Lack of under-standing can be a cause of failure too. I know of a girl, adopted at the age of a few weeks, who developed a disease of the stomach which made her unable to digest her food, even milk, and she was therefore constantly sick and hungry. The mother and the doctors made every effort to find some suitable nourishment for her. She was almost skin and bone when they succeeded, after many weeks, and after that she made a good recovery physically. But she never developed a normal conscience in spite of her foster-parents' love for her. From the baby girl's point of view, the foster-mother had apparently 'failed to understand' her efforts to communicate her distress, and so she never learned to love her in a normal way.

Now let us consider what happens to us when we feel guilty - when our conscience is pricked. It is an unpleasant feeling, and we have to try to get rid of it. I want to speak of three methods:

1.   *Denial.* We can pretend to ourselves that we are not guilty: what we did was not really wrong. But our conscience derives from what mother used to tell us. Could we have pretended to mother that what we had done was not really wrong? To have done so would have been to do something 'meaningless'. If mother said that something was wrong, then it *was* wrong: at the beginning, she was the sole arbiter of right and wrong. So to deny wrongdoing to her would have done nothing, except to have interfered with the process of communication - to have spoiled the original love relationship in some way. So to deny our own guilt implies a split in the personality - a sort of internal barrier to communication - between the self and the conscience. Of course, there are degrees of denial. Much more common, and therefore in the long run more important, is our partial denial: "Well, all right, we'll admit we were wrong, but it wasn't very serious, and didn't hurt anybody else since nobody knew about it". But *we* knew about it.

2.   *Projection.* We can't bear to accept responsibility for the wrong our conscience convicts us of, so we blame it on someone else, "It wasn't me, it was him". This is a very common way of dealing with feelings of guilt, and can be applied with great ease to any convenient scapegoat, or group of people we don't know well enough to love. Projection is always easiest when you don't know your scapegoat too well. You can always attribute qualities of wickedness and nastiness to it, woven out of your own fantasies, which would not stand up to a really close acquaintance. That is why totalitarian governments find it convenient to erect iron curtains. But there are two sides to an iron curtain, and the projection isn't only to be found on one side.

Projection is a mechanism which is not only turned on to those we don't know well; sometimes we project on to those we love, or at any rate on to those who love us. Under such circumstances, it is obviously inappropriate and pathological, and draws attention to itself as a clinical problem. Although this kind of projection is much more striking, it is probably less important to humanity at large than the less obvious projection on to strangers - less obvious because so often we share it with other members of our own group.

3.   *Repentance.* We can contrast these two common ways of dealing with our guilty feelings with a much less common, but much healthier one. We can be like the prodigal son. We can feel sorry, because we come to realise how sorry father (or mother) feels. We can come to our senses, admit we have done wrong, and be prepared to make restitution. If we do this, communication is restored between conscience and self, and we regain our self-respect.

I say self-respect instead of self-love, because this latter term is usually used to mean something quite 'selfish'. It will be clear, however, that a healthy conscience is not selfish; it is, as Freud called it, part of the 'super-ego', derived from another person, and from another person who is loved. So that it is obviously right to love and respect one's conscience. The existence of conscience obviously implies the existence of evil. As Stephen Neill (1959) says:

"Evil comes into existence only as a function of human freedom. It can be recognised as such only in relation to a <u>commandment</u>, a standard external to ourselves which we accept as valid".

Once the child's conscience has become real to it, once it has really incorporated into its own mind the system of values which it has learned from its mother, its conscience is able to go on developing and differentiating in its own way. It can make moral judgements on new issues, in areas of experience in which, perhaps, mother could never participate - in school, in work, even in war. So the image of mother's personality, which underlies the immature conscience, will gradually become less clear. Throughout our years of development, we all have a tendency to 'identify' ourselves with certain people, to hero-worship them, and each of our heroes will leave a trace of their personality on conscience. By the time we come to deal with moral issues affecting the whole of our society, or humanity at large, the personal basis of conscience may well be lost sight of as the problems seem so abstract. It is one of the strongest points of the Christian religion that it insists on the personal nature of God who judges, and on the personal nature of the Holy Spirit who comforts and strengthens the righteous. There is a practical difficulty here for the adult mind: the progression in a child's mind from the image of a loving, intimately known person like mother, to the image of an all-powerful, all-seeing God cannot be telescoped into too short a space of time. A schoolteacher told me recently of a small child who burst into tears when she talked about God. She said, "I like stories about Jesus, but God hasn't got a face".

* * * * *

So far, I have talked about conscience, and about our *feelings* of guilt, but have made no contribution toward the moral problem itself. 'What mother tells us' is, I agree, a quite inadequate standard for an adult conscience, however fundamental it may be biologically. As with mother's milk, we have to be weaned to stronger fare.

Parental prohibitions and encouragement are carried forward in the child's conscience as more or less definite ideas of right and wrong. But these ideas of right and wrong are in no objective way absolute, and what was right for one generation may easily be quite wrong for the next. The work of social anthropologists in the last half-century has, perhaps above all things, shown the relative nature of most of the moral judgements which lie so firmly in our consciences. All kinds of behaviour are only to be understood in their proper social and cultural contexts, and the scientific investigator of today can tell you nothing of absolute evil or absolute good. Professionally at least, he sees no black or white, but only a succession of shades of grey. We may, as individuals, be convinced that certain things are absolutely right or wrong, but these are subjective convictions, beyond the reach of science.

Stability of moral standards demands as a *sine qua non* a stability of social background from one generation to another. It requires that 'what mother said' shall still have some relevance when the child is adult. One cannot expect the moral judgements of nomadic tribesmen to be entirely appropriate to a settled urban society; and in a techno-logical revolution such as Britain has been through in the last hundred and fifty years, it is inevitable that a majority of us should be morally 'displaced persons'.

In fact, we live in a society that has become 'demoralised' to a considerable extent. Our judgements are confused, and our feelings of guilt considerable; but we find ourselves unable to relate the feelings of guilt to any clear conviction of personal sin. The psychiatrist is sometimes blamed by the moralist for 'making excuses' for the sins of individuals. I myself am quite prepared to accept such a criticism. I will always try to make excuses for my patient, at least to a third party. The moralist who feels impelled to judge his fellow man is rarely the person who has made a sincere and sympathetic effort to study the motives underlying any particular pattern of sinful behaviour, and the deeper one goes into such a clinical study, the more one replaces an attitude of judgement by one of compassion. Too often the judging moralist is applying a code of judgements applicable to his own childhood, which is no longer entirely appropriate either to his present self, or certainly to any other person outside his family. There is no answer to the problem of sin in the ossified conscience. Although we speak of conscience as if it had a definite structure, it is in fact a process: it is one kind of activity of the living mind, and if it operates only in a stereotyped and rigid way, it is either sick or senile.

If I have to examine a sinner who has broken his marriage promises and left his wife and children, I may find that his love relationships in early life were such as to make it exceedingly hard for him to develop a healthy conscience. It is very common in such a case to find that the sinner's own parents were themselves separated at some time during their marriage. I may also know from external evidence that he has moved in a part of society, which holds the marriage tie as being much less binding than Christians should. In addition it is likely that his wife has given him a great deal of provocation. The analysis thus shows that the sinful action which we start with is actually a more or less inevitable outcome of a large number of sinful actions by all sorts of people, some quite distant from the sinner in time and space. And it is quite unlikely that any of the people who performed those sinful actions had the slightest idea of how they would lead up to this particular sin: they can have had no feeling of guilt in relation to it. The attempt to deal with the specific overt sin by way of judging the sinner is too often, in fact, a matter of locking the stable door after the horse has bolted.

Although I think that the more I know of the social and individual background of any sinful action, the less ready will I be to blame the sinner, I do still believe in individual responsibility for sin. But the sins we should be concerned to stop are those minor actions and thoughts and evasions, which we are all prepared to forgive ourselves on the grounds that 'they won't do anyone else any harm'.

Thus we see the need for each of us to have a highly sensitive and vigorous conscience, which is not only prepared to refer each questionable impulse back to the standards of 'what mother tells us', but is also able, by the use of prospective imagination to visualise what may be the outcome of our actions on future generations, or on people far removed from us. There is, any of us may think, no possible sin in taking a car on the road, and no possible sin in failing to ask our local MP what his attitude is to the over-crowding on antiquated British roads. And yet our society, which means you and me, is responsible for allowing or causing hundreds of deaths on the roads each year. Will future generations hold us guiltless of sin in this respect?

What, after all, is the ultimate purpose of conscience? Biologically speaking, it is I suppose the means whereby a man can choose that course of personal action which will most benefit his group or community, however much the group or community may resent the disturbance such personal action will cause. In the primary religious sense, the purpose of conscience is to help a man avoid sinful action - whatever the sinful people around him may think or say about it. But in the truly Christian sense it is surely to help us to see how best we can love our fellow men, and thus how we can best love God. This, no doubt, is likely to prove the most upsetting value of all to established society.

I know that *"The fear of the Lord is the beginning of wisdom",* and that the healthy conscience does contain an element of fear and awe. Developmentally, that fear is 'fear of loss of love' - the child is afraid of doing things which cause mother to 'turn her face from him'. But as a biologist I believe that fear is the great enemy of love; that fear is almost always damaging to human relationships; and that good behaviour obtained through fear involves in the long run a denial of human dignity. This world is a fearful place for the child and adult alike: it has been so since Adam and Eve left the Garden of Eden, and no doubt it always will be. But a fear-ridden conscience is a bad conscience in every sense of the term, and I believe that the moralists will do better to preach a gospel of love, and righteousness through love, rather than by trying to drive people to repentance through fear of the wrath of God.

Every one of us, and every one of our enemies, likes to be loved. Love is always acceptable as a keynote of doctrine for the other chap. But when we ourselves are invited to do the loving, we find it makes impossibly strenuous demands on us. How many of us can say that we really love our enemies? Psychiatrists may or may not be right if they say that their patients become ill because they have been insufficiently loved, but there is no doubt at all that every sufferer from a neurosis - whether he ever visits a psychiatrist or not - suffers from some inability to love his fellow man. And in this sense it may be justifiable for us to say that a large majority of us are neurotic. To love someone is to live dangerously. It is to risk losing a part of one's self. It is to cast one's bread upon the waters, to give a hostage to fortune. It is no activity for those who lack courage. And the kind of courage that is needed - moral courage - is only to be found in the man with a well-developed conscience, founded on love and a sense of security, and fostered with understanding. . . .

9 - A Psychiatrist's Approach to Sin and Guilt.

BECOMING LIKE CHILDREN

Matt 18 3: *"Truly, I say to you, unless you turn and become like children, you will never enter the kingdom of heaven. Whoever humbles himself like this child, he is the greatest in the kingdom of heaven".*

. . . Children protect themselves from too much information by having only a limited span of attention. Adults often regard this as a childish weakness, whereas it is really a strength - a virtue appropriate to their stage of development. I remember how one of my small children (when I was a rather inexperienced parent, no doubt) resisted my earnest attempt to explain a somewhat complicated machine by saying firmly "Tell me *one thing* about it". In fact children try to stop their minds being cluttered with information they can't use - while the adult world expects school teachers to overcome this healthy resistance, and to fill their minds with what we, rather than the children themselves, feel to be relevant. When we criticise them for inattention, it is because they aren't paying attention *to us* -but they are always attending to someone, or something. Children are always *learning,* though it is often something other than what we are trying to teach.

Another feature of childhood, which Jesus may have had in mind, is the child's capacity for *play*. When he wanted to criticise the people of his time he said *"we piped to you and you did not dance, we wailed and you did not mourn"* - in fact, whatever game we offered you refused to play. Play has two elements: one is that it allows the players to experiment, to try things out, in a protected context where nothing critical will happen if the trial is unsuccessful. And the other is precisely that - that it doesn't have to be taken too seriously. Do not be anxious about tomorrow: your heavenly Father knows what your needs are. You can afford to relax, because ultimately it is God who takes the responsibility. Perhaps the game of life can best be played light-heartedly.

Children learn through playing; and their games can be picked up or left off on the spur of the moment if something more interesting invites attention. For them the world is always new, and perhaps it is their own *newness* which Jesus wanted to emphasise. In his encounter with Nicodemus he made the point even more strongly: *"unless a man be born anew, he cannot see the kingdom of God."* To be sure, the world can only continue if it contains the old as well as the new, the stable as well as the disturbers of stability; but God has so made the world that what is old, and stable, and established, and mature - can be largely left to look after itself. The next stage after maturity is decay and death. Which of us really wants to be mature? Jesus said, *"let the dead bury their own dead".* It is the new to which he points our attention: we should watch for the new and unique elements even in well-known and established situations and in the ordinary routines of life.

The distinction between becoming child-like and behaving childishly is no doubt a hard one to make. When David and his men recaptured the ark from the Philistines, he danced before the Lord as part of the general rejoicing (2 Sam.6), and his wife ticked him off for what she felt was his unseemly behaviour. No one likes to lose face, to be put out of countenance. When we are caught in an embarrassing situation, we often wish the floor would open and swallow us up. But, you know, it never does; and life goes on after the embarrassment much as it did before. So I have come to believe that one of the rules of mental health is to train oneself to *withstand* embarrassment - to put up with it, to treat it as you treat a shower of rain when you are caught in the open without an umbrella - by gritting your teeth and waiting for the discomfort to go away. So don't allow the thought of embarrassment to stop you behaving like a child when it seems a good idea; and if your husband or wife disapproves - just remember David. . . .

246 Sermon: St. Mary's Church, Hay-on-Wye, July 1983.

MARRIAGE RELATIONSHIP

Nature has certainly written in to our bodily structure one particular specialisation: that of the two sexes, for reproductive purposes. Otherwise, she has allowed humankind to avoid the trap of structural specialisation, and instead has given human beings a brain that is so enormously versatile that all the other functions which the family needs can be done or left undone by individuals so long as they are done by somebody. So to speak, it does not matter who does the cooking or collects the food or defends the territory or cares for the babies so long as the jobs get done. Perhaps this is an oversimplification: in fact, as individuals, each of us does have an inborn need to exercise the emotional equipment appropriate to these various functions. Children have to be given opportunities to explore, to feel frightened, to defend themselves, to get used to change - even though the family as a whole does not depend directly on their doing so. Taking care of such individual biological needs has now become part of the sustaining-healing-growth complex, the restorative function of the whole family group, and is seen particularly in the recreative element which we call *play*. For adults, playful recreation is obviously restorative; for children it is essential for growth as well. . . .

. . . Rudyard Kipling (1936) wrote a story called *The Miracle of Purun Bhagat*. In it he speaks of an old Indian 'law of life': *"twenty years a youth, twenty years a fighter (though a man may never carry a weapon), and twenty years head of a household"*. And then, at the age of about sixty, the man settles his affairs, leaves his home dressed as an anonymous beggar, and goes forth to seek enlightenment. To paraphrase the story in terms of psychological development: a child or youth's development is egocentric for the first two decades. In early adult life he falls in love and mates and rears children, and in so doing loses his *ego*centricity to some degree and becomes *family*-centred. By the time he is approaching forty, his children are coming up to adolescence and no longer needing physical care, his life is half way through, and his ability to provide home and livelihood are reasonably foreseeable if not entirely to his liking. His family-centred orientation has brought him more or less in sight of its objective and has outworn its usefulness. He needs a new compass bearing for his life, and he finds it in some sort of service to his community, however he may define this. He becomes *sociocentric.* This carries him on to retiring age, and thereafter - what?

The psychoanalyst E.H. Erikson describes eight stages of development. The first five are all connected with the young; but in adult life he lists three strengths or virtues, each building on and incorporating those that preceded them. In young adulthood, the internal conflict between the desires for intimacy and isolation is resolved with the emergence of love: *"Love is mutuality of devotion forever subduing the antagonisms inherent in divided function"*. In full adulthood, the conflict is felt to be between generativity and stagnation, and from it springs care: *"Care is the widening concern for what has been generated by love, necessity or accident; it overcomes the ambivalence adhering to irreversible obligation."* And finally, in maturity, the conflict is that between ego-integrity and despair, from which emerges wisdom; and wisdom, he says, is *"detached concern with life itself, in the face of death itself"*.

So here we have the outline of a psychological context in which to set the marriage relationship. It is a part, and only a part, of an ongoing life story. Its health depends upon a satisfactory succession of stages of growth toward maturity in each partner before they meet (Erikson characterises them as hope, will, purpose, competence and fidelity) and then on the further succession of mutual love, developing into care, and loving care for others developing into wisdom. The move from one stage to the next is often marked by a period of crisis, in which existing habits of thought and attitude are challenged and revised. Failure to grow through a critical phase handicaps and 'fixes' development to some extent, though the recurrent shaking up at the time of subsequent crises offers fresh opportunities for change and growth.

The picture I have drawn is one in which a man is continually challenged to 'leave self behind so that he can find his true self'. He will make a satisfactory marriage, and become 'one flesh' with his partner, only if he brings with him an adequately developed self to commit to that 'one flesh'. But the developmental process goes on. The 'one flesh' will only mature if together the couple become able to leave the exclusivity of that 'one flesh' behind and centre their joint life in a larger grouping, first in their family and then in successively wider social fields, until finally their caring concern is with so wide a humanity, spreading over past, present and future generations, that they have difficulty in distinguishing their love for their fellows from their love for God. . . .

. . . Growth within the marriage relationship will not be improved if it is too closely watched. It must be allowed to happen at its own speed, and that is bound to vary. At times, for years perhaps, nothing much will be seen to change - and then a lot will alter quite quickly. Growth is more likely to happen as a result of discomfort and disturbance, if it is confronted and resolved in a realistic way, than as a result of long periods of freedom from stress. But where, as in most healthy marriages, there are frequent occasions of upset or conflict, generated either from within or without, the partners are usually too busy to notice whether the relationship is developing well or not - and I do not think it matters.

Healing is a larger topic. Few of us come to marriage fully individuated and without hang-ups. Even if we do, or think we do, the new relationship itself is a challenge to the separately established selves, and demands fresh adjustments, trial and error learning; and some bruising, at least, is likely to occur. Marriage provides each of us with an identity crisis, at the same time as it provides us with a psychotherapist or counsellor to help us through it. It is my belief that to work through such identity crises takes about eighteen months, and for at least the first twelve of them we are less stable than usual, more in need of moral support, and indeed more susceptible to the influence of others. Murray Cox says that the work of a psychotherapist or counsellor is *"always that of enabling the patient to do for himself what he cannot do on his own"*. So within marriage each partner has to help the other towards a more complete individuation - to be more completely himself or herself. Only so can each contribute a full share to the relationship. There is much good in each partner being ready to sacrifice himself for the other - but each, with the help of the other, should strive to develop a self worth sacrificing. Healing thus described may seem to focus on the individual, and we must remember that our concern is with the individual only in the context of the marriage. So such external resources as are called upon to aid in the care of a threatened marriage must be deployed not only to help the one who presents the difficulty, but also the partner who has the task of helping him or her through it. Therapeutic interventions should so to speak strengthen both partners in their complementary roles of client and counsellor. Wounds to the marriage may come from external sources as we have seen - from poverty, say, or the interference of other people. If so, healing is not *best* achieved by an intervention which removes the poverty or the tiresome parents-in-law, though this may help at times. Preferably, the partners are enabled to do *for themselves* what they cannot do on their own.

Many marriages fail to be sustained in our current society. We are in a period of rapid cultural change, and the winds of natural selection, winnowing out cherished and long established traditions, seem to be rising to gale force. But there can be no value in trying to preserve marriages which fail to serve the wellbeing of the partners (except perhaps temporarily for the sake of young children); and no merit in trying to preserve them for outworn moral reasons only. Morality is always related to culture, and is concerned with social control. It values conformity above diversity. But at times of change, diversity may be more important for the survival of the human race - even though many of the variants are doomed to fail. It may be that the failure of the many is a condition for the success of the few. . . .

. . . The lifelong monogamous marriage which the Christian holds as an ideal norm meant something very different in New Testament times from what it does today in the West. The expectation of life was much shorter. Women were subordinated in a way that we no longer find tolerable; and the family was understood as an extended household, and not as the nuclear family for which we have built housing estates in recent decades. The spiritual significance of a marriage lies not only in itself but equally in the social context which shapes it. How do we assess those social forces which continue to separate children from the parents and home-makers whose historical biological task it has always been to nurture them? Our systems of maternity care, our schools, our welfare system, all seem designed to weaken these nurturing links despite the lip-service we periodically remember to pay to their importance. And our pattern of industrial employment, encouraging not only men but also women to leave home in order to work, comes under the same judgement. Perhaps it is the shortcomings of industrial society on which we should focus attention, rather than the marriage breakdowns and difficulties which are symptomatic of them.

207 - 2 Reflections on the Marriage Relationship.

ON NOT SOLVING PROBLEMS

The family does not have a good press in modern western society. Originally the word meant the 'household'. It included not only parents and children, but all those who lived together under one roof, in daily face-to-face communication with one another, whether they were biologically related or not. In their dealings with society at large, all the members were represented by one man whom they knew personally and even intimately - the householder, the head of the family. In pre-industrial communities, although there were many individuals who did not live in families or have a roof over their heads, it was essentially the family that was the unit of society rather than the individual. So in 1611 the translators of Psalm 68 thought it an appropriate expression of praise to say that *"God setteth the solitary in families"*, and the revisers in 1884 saw no reason to alter the expression. But it has disappeared from all more recent translations. In 1897, Emile Durkheim characterised society as a *"disordered dust of individuals"*, and 80 years later the corollary of this was expressed by Dr Edmund Leach when he said that *"far from being the basis of the good society, the family, with its narrow privacy and tawdry secrets, is the source of all our discontents."*[1] In fact, I suspect that the *"monogamous, neo-local nuclear family"* of which he spoke originated as a sociologist's observation – a tidy generalisation which ignored many of the apparently random and idiosyncratic ways in which each family actually related itself to the wider society. In my experience, the boundaries of any particular family are rarely so precisely drawn as he suggested; and it is those statistically unmanageable, often only temporary relationships with the outside world, unique to each family, which express its vitality and capacity for survival as a human institution despite all the destructive pressures which assail it.

A family, of its very nature, cannot for long remain exclusive and 'narrowly private'. If it tries to, its members either die, or else they become sick or mad, and get taken off to a doctor, whose questions or interventions quickly breach the walls of privacy on which they had relied. We do not always seem to realise that whenever we ask questions of people about their behaviour, they are very liable to start behaving somewhat differently; and this either makes scientific observations of behavioural norms out-of-date almost before they appear in print, or else they act as self-fulfilling prophecies. It is dangerous to take sociological generalisations in this area as if they are facts of life which persist from past to future. Their significance is more reliably historical than predictive. But this conference is about curing and caring - words which refer to the present and future rather than present and past; and so I propose to talk about the family, not necessarily as it is, but as an institution which can become 'healthy, normal and ordinary,'[2] and to which therefore curing and caring may reasonably be directed. This may sound unscientific, but actually it is much the same as the attitude of a doctor with a patient: the man *is* sick but his treatment is aimed to achieve what in his and his doctor's view would be healthy, normal and ordinary for him.

From this perspective, I envisage the family as a group of two or more people who relate to one another as persons, in regular, face-to-face contact, communicating not only in words but in nonverbal ways as well; and who provide a nurturing environment for the immature and dependent young who arrive among them as a result of (in Erikson's phrase) 'love, necessity or accident.'[3] Please note that this does not pretend to be a *definition* of the family. To define something is to set it within certain bounds or limits. My description does not try to set limits: rather it is meant to imply that the boundaries of a family are uncertain, fluid and fluctuating, and that individuals who at one time seem clearly inside it are at other times outside it, and *vice versa*. The family is a nexus of intimate social relationships which is alive and dynamic and has creative power. It has all the essential characteristics of other living organisms save one - that it is not confined within a visible skin.

What are some of the stresses, which impinge on the family? Some of them appear to originate externally. They may stem from the material environment, as for instance shortage of nourishment or shelter; or they may come from the social environment, as for instance hostility, or perhaps lack of recognition, directed at family members either individually or collectively. But in either case it is important to recognise that the external agent is always only half the problem, and that the other half lies in the family's response to the external agent. Any living organism, and particularly the human organism, has a capacity to adapt; so the therapeutic task of relieving stress always offers two possibilities: either trying to diminish the external pressure, or to foster the strength and adaptability of the family to cope with the pressure - or of course a combination of both. In dealing with individual sickness, doctors often appear only to be concerned to relieve the external stress, though in fact I suspect that they do more things which are strengthening of the sick person than they often realise (and they usually confuse the issue by talking of treatment without saying whether they mean treatment of the sickness or treatment of the person who has it). In caring for families in stress, both possibilities need to be considered; and while good interventions often require a mixture of them both, I suggest that an intervention which *only* eases the external pressure and ignores the building up of family strength is nearly always suspect. To give a starving man a fish may save his life for a day or two, but unless you also ensure that he has fishing tackle and knows how to use it, he will probably starve next week. We divorce therapy from education at our peril.

Let me make a cartoon sketch of some of the external stresses which have so grievously damaged family life in Britain over the past two hundred years or so. The invention of the static steam engine, a powerful prime mover for machinery, meant that men had to leave their homes all day to work close to it in factories. This soon led to industrial slums, and urban migration from the land led to a more damaging kind of poverty than rural poverty had been, bad as that was. Poverty led to industrial child labour and that led to the introduction of publicly provided schools, which robbed the family of its children for several hours a day; and also to social security measures which robbed poor families of their self-respect as well. With both their menfolk and their children away from home, the women who remained suffered from increasing boredom until they found excuse and opportunity to get out and go to work themselves. The family home became little more than a dormitory; and that has been reflected in the kind of housing which public authorities provide. Nowadays, women are even discouraged from having their babies at home.

These changes - provision of factory work, of schools, of welfare benefits, housing and maternity hospitals, were all originally offered as a means of reducing external stress on families. But there has been no parallel attention to strengthening families to deal with the stresses themselves. Almost any measure which might be thought of as nurturing strength rather than eradicating causes of weakness has been directed not at families, but at individuals - as for instance in educational facilities. A visitor from outer space might indeed assume that our society was deliberately seeking to destroy the family by creating a dust of individuals. . . .

. . .The family, then, can be seen as an arena, perhaps the most important arena, in which the conflicts and challenges inherent in human biological, social and spiritual development can be constructively worked at. Activity within it tends to be at least as noisy as harmonious, constantly straining our adaptability, a barely manageable mixture of pain and pleasure, of frustration and fulfillment. It is not the institution anyone would choose in which to do the intellectual work necessary for the solution of difficult problems; but it is the institution *par excellence* in which one can learn, not to solve problems but to live constructively with unsolved problems. Problem-solving and the technology of problem-solving have their place, but it is secondary and subordinate. To solve any problem inevitably reveals fresh and more difficult ones, and these always have to be lived with for a time at least. . . .

References
1. E.Leach, The Listener, Nov.1967, vol.78 No. 2018.
2. R.Dingwall, **Aspects of Illness,** (Martin Robertson), 1976.
3. E.H.Erikson, **Insight and Responsibility,** (Faber), 1964.

216 - 1 Families: On Not Solving Problems.

LEARNING

Dr Wilson's book starts with an essay called 'The Primary Task of the Hospital.'[1] After surveying the various tasks which a hospital does - of curing, caring and teaching, he concludes: *"The primary task of the hospital is to enable patients, their families and staff, to learn from the experience of illness and death how to build a healthy society"*. The primary task of everyone in a hospital is learning. Yes, of course. Curing, caring and teaching are tasks which involve doing things to or for other people. We can do them or not do them. But we are always learning. A surgeon said *"We can cure people these days without even knowing their names"*(p 5). But what is he learning when he does this? And what is his anonymous patient learning? Ward sisters can provide care for sick people by allocating tasks to be done by each nurse in a routine and impersonal way, instead of by allocating to each nurse certain people to be looked after. What do nurses and their patients - and the relatives and friends who watch them when they visit - learn from this? In this twentieth century, we teach people what we think they ought to know - and they either absorb our teaching or they don't. But some educationists are aware that, when little Johnny fails to absorb the arithmetic his teacher has been showing, the relevant question may be not 'why didn't he learn this arithmetic?' so much as 'what was he actually learning while teacher tried unsuccessfully to teach him arithmetic?' In the primitive tribe, the initiative for education doesn't come from teachers who know what the uninstructed need to know; but from the uninstructed themselves, who have to persuade or bribe the knowledgeable ones before they will part with their knowledge. So the chaplain should pay deliberate attention to enabling people to learn - himself as well as other staff and patients. He won't be able to avoid teaching, at certain times and seasons; but learning goes on all the time: it is the context in which teaching has to find its place. Learning comprehends teaching, and teaching which doesn't arise out of the desire of people to learn is nothing.

Reference
1.   M.Wilson,   **The Hospital - A Place of Truth**, (University of Birmingham), 1971.

135 - 1 The Role of the Hospital Chaplain.

WAITING

. . . Students of animal behaviour are also showing a growing awareness of the importance of waiting. Animal intelligence, like that of humans, is the mental capacity which varies with ability to solve problems of different degrees of complexity. Recent theorists have distinguished four factors in it: a factor of motor skill, one of memory, a third which involves seeing similarities and differences, and a fourth which I would emphasise here. It is called the P factor - where P stands for *postponement*. This is the ability *not* to respond automatically or instinctively or impulsively, but to pause and explore the situation more carefully. The more intelligent the animal, the longer he is prepared to wait before acting. Part of the value of this is that it often reduces the need for action, and thus the expense of energy and resources. Impulsive action, taken without enough thought, tends to be crude, insensitive and extravagant.

Or childish. If we think in terms of child development, it is clear that the young spend much unnecessary energy in action - at least, it is unnecessary by adult standards. Actually, action by the young is often justifiable as learning *how* to do things. Between the ages of 6 and 14 years this learning and practising of bodily and mental techniques is a child's proper business. These are the years in which a child is most amenable to instruction (which is not to say education). But after puberty, progress toward maturity depends increasingly on learning when, why and whether to do the things one knows how to do (perhaps such learning is the business of education rather than instruction) - and so in maturity one expects to find a decrease in impulsive activity, an increase in reflective thought, and thus a greater capacity for constructive waiting.

One other biological observation is worth noting. It is reported that in some flatworms, which have the beginnings of a true central nervous system and brain, it is possible to cut off all the incoming nerve impulses from the sensory cells, and yet the rhythmic motor activity typical of these creatures persists. What this seems to mean is that motor activity is more fundamentally characteristic of life than is sensory activity: the two do not appear to be necessary to each other in the sense that each implies the other, as for instance light implies darkness or height implies depth. (This seems to me to be a radical departure from the whole behaviourist, reflex, stimulus-response, Pavlovian explanation of nervous activity and behaviour which was the received wisdom throughout my medical career - and which I was never happy with because it seemed unduly mechanistic. The assumption underlying the theory seemed to be that the organism is a machine that needs to be set going by an outside stimulus, as if an unstim-ulated organism were equivalent to a dead one; whereas I have now come to understand that the living machine is going already: the engine is running, and the stimuli from outside actually function as governors or regulators - accelerators, brakes or steering wheels. It is the *signal* value of the stimulus, and not its energy value, which is important. The model is still mechanistic, but somewhat more credible than the old one.)

So both from a phylogenetic and an ontogenetic viewpoint (that is, whether we take the perspective of species development or that of the individual), it seems that we are faced with a similar pattern of successive phenomena to that which Canon Vanstone discerns from a theological stance: that while activity may be the fundamental character-istic of God, and of man, and of most if not all living organisms, the process of life develops in such a way as to refine activity by developing ways of taking in and processing wider and wider amounts and varieties of information - a way which both allows and requires a delay in action.

Let me emphasise that this waiting, this passivity, is not a negative phenomenon, not a mere absence of activity. Whether from a theological or a secular standpoint, waiting has a purpose: it is to prepare oneself to make an appropriate response at the right moment. One waits *for* someone or something. In the garden of Gethsemane, you will remember, Jesus asked his disciples to *"tarry here and watch";* and perhaps the word 'watch' carries some of the meaning we are after. Perhaps the injunction to *"watch and pray"* can be paraphrased as "pray (that is, wait upon God) with your eyes open". "Wait upon God with your eyes open". . . .

237 - 2 Waiting and Reality.

CHANGE OF IDENTITY

The object of this paper is to consider the proposition that some kinds of critical change in a person's life experience bring about a change in his sense of identity which is not subjectively recognised and acknowledged until between one and two years after the critical event or initiation of the critical change.

I first formed this impression when as an army psychiatrist I was interviewing expatriate soldiers in India in 1943. Those whose complaints appeared to be mainly referable to a failure to adapt to the stress of expatriation had usually left the United Kingdom between 12 and 15 months before their low morale had led to clinical referral. At some time during the second year of expatriation it seemed that there was a change in many men's subjective response to mail from home, linked with a memory change. Whereas in the first year letters were valued for their detailed content, and gossip about the neighbours and acquaintances provoked the same kind of interest as it would have at home, there came a point when this interest in casual detail faded, while letters themselves became more intensely valued as symbols that loved ones still cared. At about the same time interval, I noticed that soldiers' accounts of their home circumstances tended to become idealised: for example, a man whose home was in fact a poverty-ridden slum marred by parental strife would give an account of an Arcadian cottage inhabited by a serene old couple who had no greater interest in life than to await his return. It was of course only rarely that this kind of discrepancy could be confirmed by external evidence. At the time I regarded this as an example of the Gestalt principle of 'closure' applied to memories, but did not appreciate the possible significance of the time interval of 12 to 18 months.

At the end of the war, particular efforts were made by the authorities to find suitable employment for ex-servicemen (especially ex-prisoners of war) whose jobs had disappeared during hostilities. In the first few post-war years I was surprised to meet with a number of men who had apparently been satisfactorily 'resettled' with help from the authorities, but who after about 18 months had given up quite good occupational prospects and sought fresh jobs of their own choosing. It seemed that subjectively, even when the experience of resettlement went smoothly, this amount of time had to elapse before some men had regained enough self-confidence to reassert their autonomy as individuals.

During the last eight years I have been attending weekly psychodynamically oriented group sessions with students taking one-year courses, some in pastoral studies and some in residential child care. In both settings one has the impression that at the end of a year many students are still in the process of struggling with the novelty of an altered perception of themselves and feel dissatisfied; but among those one meets a year or more later it seems as if the psychodynamic experience has been emotionally digested and, in retrospect, realistically valued.

An even more idiosyncratic observation may be made. Having retired after 12 years as a mental hospital superintendent in June 1971, it was not until February 1973 that a casual recollection of this item of personal history struck me with astonishment: 'how on earth did I ever come to be playing a role which (now) seems so foreign to me?' I take this to mean that my sense of personal identity has altered, in a decisive if unspecifiable way, in something not greatly less than the 20-month interval.

These personal impressions have lately been reinforced by evidence from other sources. In one of his papers Parkes (1970) reviews the symptoms of grief which occur particularly in the first twelve months after bereavement, and then goes on to say:

'Among widows whom I talked to, most seemed to feel that the watershed occurs round about the second year of bereavement. By the end of the second year, they're on course. At the end of the first year, they're past the peak of their grieving, but they still haven't found a new course.'

In other words, a widow tends to accept her changed sense of identity only after a lapse of appreciably more than twelve months.

The evidence points in a similar direction in the case of offenders. Follow-up studies now in progress of patients in a psychiatric prison are beginning to suggest that (measured by rates of reconviction within two years) the optimum length of stay in the institution is not less than 13 to 15 months and not more than 3 years (Jillett, 1973).

There are other indications, which suggest the possible importance of a 1 to 2 year interval. The typical degree course at a university, which might be described as enabling an identity-change from 'late adolescent' to 'professional person' for many students, lasts three years. It seems to be widely recognised that it is during the first two terms of the second year of such a course that students show most evidence of subjective discomfort and dissatisfaction with themselves. If indeed the first 18 months of this kind of experience is taken up mainly with achieving and consolidating a personality change, then the third year of the degree course may be required for the learning-in-context of the technical equipment proper to the holder of the degree. This interpretation suggests that the first four terms of a university course might be more appropriately structured to enable the desired personality reorientation to occur, allowing elements of technical indoctrination to play only a secondary part in the curriculum.

Medical men coming to Britain for postgraduate study from non-Western countries tend to be reluctant to return to their home countries (which often can ill spare them), if they stay here more than a certain length of time. I know of no published study showing how long this time is, but have the impression from talking with postgraduate teachers that it is something under two years.

In the industrial field, the promotion of a young married man in a big organisation may mean his uprooting home and family as well as taking on unfamiliar responsibilities at the same time. Senior executives are only slowly becoming aware, through bitter experience, of the bad effect on health and stability this sudden change can sometimes have on the man and his family during his first year. If it were recognised that most men need about 18 months to become familiar with their new identities, industry might be able to temper the demands it makes on such men to accept heavy responsibilities immediately after transfer.

The achievement of a new sense of identity following a critical change in life circumstances is, of course, a sign of health and growing maturity, not of pathology or illness. In the field of pathology it is profitable to search for a particular cause which may account for multiple effects, but in the field of healthy development the reverse seems to be true: that a particular achievement (in this case an adaptive personality change) can only result from a multiplicity of antecedent 'causes'; and prediction is impossible in practice because of the excessive number of variables which would have to be taken into account. And if indeed there is 18 months delay between the crisis experience and its final resolution, shorter-acting variables arising during this 18-month period may also bear on the outcome and complicate the aetiology still further. Experimental verification of the hypothesis would thus seem very difficult. In any case, a man's sense of identity, though crucial to his effective functioning, is a matter of inner experience with no easily definable objective signs. But even if the hypothesis remains unverifiable (or unfalsifiable) as a cause-and-effect sequence it may still be a useful interpretation if it leads to more effective action. One possible consequence would be to suggest a need for longer-term follow-up of people exposed to crises when these are known to disturb a man's sense of identity. The follow-up period of the series reported by Parkes (1972) is limited to 14 months, for instance, since he is mainly concerned with the bereavement experience as a cause of ill-health rather than as a life crisis which can lead to greater emotional health and maturity. Another consequence might be that young professionals from the 'third world' coming to this country for postgraduate study should be encouraged to stay for no longer than a year at a time.

Caplan (1964) elaborated a theory of crisis experience, which emphasised the organism's tendency to regain homeostasis, either in a healthy or pathological direction, within a fairly short period of time. The more obvious kinds of behaviour disturbance often seem to settle within a few weeks; but there is a good deal of evidence (e.g. from the bereavement studies) that some degree of psychosomatic disturbance commonly persists for about 12 months. So it is logical to expect that evidence of complete resolution of the disturbance would not be manifest until some time in the second year.

What is not clear from any of the evidence presented here is the relative importance, in determining the final outcome, of the initial 'shock' period of the crisis (which can be postulated as lasting not more than 12 weeks), as compared with the total 18-months' exposure to a new psychological environment. In the case of bereavement, expatriation, promotion at work, or admission to a psychiatric prison, the change which initiates the process continues throughout the period. But in psychotherapeutic situations significant personality change sometimes occurs as a result of a relatively sudden flash of new insight or understanding of oneself. The question then arises as to whether or not the important activity in psychotherapy is the establishment of rapport and the sowing of a seed of new insight, which is likely to occur in the first 12 weeks and is similar to Caplan's concept of 'crisis intervention'; while the healthy outcome of this change in the client's way of viewing himself is not accessible to assessment until about 18 months later. (It is not necessary that the client should consciously acknowledge his new insight: an unwelcome interpretation may be consciously resisted but may still be effective.) If this is so, it suggests that the therapist's relationship with his client, necessarily exploratory and intense in the initial stages, could be continued at a less intense and more simply supportive level for some months thereafter. To use a biological analogy: insemination and conception has to be followed by a period of gestation; and, while the success or failure of insemination remains hidden for a considerable time, prolonged or repeated insemination over the gestation period will not lead to the birth of healthier offspring.

There are two basic attitudes, which can be adopted by those in the caring professions to sufferers from emotional disturbance. One is that of the problem-solver, seeking to elucidate cause and effect and to use technical means to interfere with a process which it is feared may lead in an unsatisfactory direction. The other attitude is that of nurturing and sustaining someone who is going through a developmental process which is inevitably stressful, easing only unnecessary pain and offering moral support in a non-specific way, with a minimum of technical interference. If the hypothesis here proposed is accepted, it suggests that the nurturing attitude has a much larger field of relevance than is commonly recognised in the treatment or care of people who are suffering the effects of environmental change; and that at certain stages of treatment it might often be appropriately substituted for a problem-solving attitude which is temporarily irrelevant if not harmful.

SUMMARY

Observations and arguments are adduced for the hypothesis that critical experiences which initiate change in a man's sense of identity are not usually emotionally digested until about 18 months have elapsed. If accepted, the hypothesis has significant implications for those programmes in education and therapy from which personality change commonly results; and suggests that the effectiveness of such programmes cannot be adequately assessed in less than 18 months from their initiation.

Bibliography

G. Caplan,   **Principles of Preventive Psychiatry**, *(*London), 1964.
R. L.Jillet,   'Personal communication', 1973.
C.M. Parkes,   *The nature of grief and the reaction to bereavement in adult life*, in
                Good Grief,   (Institute of Religion and Medicine), London, Report of a Conference.
        "   **Bereavement**, (London), 1972.

134 - 4 The Gestation Period of Identity Change.

TOWARDS A HEALTHY DEATH

. . . We must avoid running away from death, as so many of our medical institutions do. Since it comes to us all, we should teach ourselves to see it as part of the privilege of being human. It is something we should look forward to, not with pleasure perhaps, but with the kind of tension and anticipation felt by a runner before a race, or an actor before the opening of a play. Death challenges us to see it as the end we have in view, not as an overwhelming enemy from whom we should try to escape. With many other critical life situations, we try to provide anticipatory guidance. We provide sex education for the young, premarital instruction for those who are courting, antenatal classes for mothers-to-be, and even pre-retirement courses for those past their working prime. Such guidance is, or should be, aimed at strengthening people to face crisis without panic and with flexibility. It should not be offered as providing a blueprint for behaviour during or after the crisis, since (by definition) the outcome of crisis is, for the individual, unpredictable. Such guidance has often been seen as a pastoral responsibility of the clergy, as has death education. Is it not time for death education, too, to be reconsidered in a more secular context? It should start at school age or even before. It is quite as important as sex education. I do not propose to outline a syllabus for death education here, but will offer two propositions for consideration.

In health, man explores the limits of his environment, both as an individual and as a species. This means that those most properly involved in dangerous adventures are young, healthy adults - those whose faculties are at their best. And it is on them therefore that the greatest risk of death and injury will fall. They are the cutting edge of the species in its struggle with the environment, and the cutting edge is that part of the blade which gets damaged. This is equally true whether the exploration is a physical matter or whether we think of adventures of the mind. We are wrong to disapprove of risk-taking by the young, whether they climb mountains or seek mind-widening experiences through drugs; though we may well worry about them and seek to ensure that the risks are minimised. The deaths of a young mountaineer and a young drug-taker, however grievous, deserve as proud a tribute as does the death of a young soldier in his country's war.

And the second proposition is best illustrated by a physiological parable. Conception results from the meeting of a single spermatozoon with an ovum, and the spermatozoon dies. But millions of spermatozoa are needed to enable this one to penetrate the wall of the ovum, because it needs the death of the millions to provide enough of the enzyme, which softens the ovum wall to allow the one to penetrate it. The one can achieve nothing without the many, and which of the many becomes the one is a circumstance beyond the control of any of them. All of them die, and it is the strenuous effort of them all, which achieves the result. Death is the final and fundamental contribution, which the individual makes to the renewal of the species; and this is true whatever role he happens to have played in his life or may be playing at the time of his death.

An evolutionary perspective upon human problems thus seems to call for almost an inversion of our day-to-day values. To deny that suffering should always be relieved; to suggest that delinquency and drug-taking by healthy young men may not be wholly evil; to say that our search for security and stability is of no more than transient importance; and to affirm that death should be something to look forward to: these are the things I am saying and they seem perhaps not only absurd, but perverse and even morbid. But am I wrong in believing that the values they imply are precisely those exemplified in the life and death of Jesus?

162 - Evolution and Human Values.

CREATIVE SUFFERING

"The Spirit of the Lord is upon me, because he hath anointed me to preach the gospel to the poor; he hath sent me to heal the broken-hearted, to preach deliverance to the captives, and recovering of sight to the blind, to set at liberty them that are bruised, To preach the acceptable year of the Lord" (Luke 4 v. 18-19)

I suppose a doctor feels at his most successful when he can say to himself that his ministrations have enabled someone who has been bound with the chains of illness to 'go free'. My most exalted moments as a psychotherapist come when I can point out, to a person who comes to me, something about himself which he has been blind to, so that there is a dawning hope in his eyes as he says 'I never thought of that - I *see*'. At its best, the service that a doctor gives to those who come to see him is a liberating one - freedom from suffering, from disability, from ignorance, from blindness, from fear. My profession can sometimes enable people to be free *from* evils. But we are not so good at knowing what people want to be free *for*. Perhaps it isn't a doctor's business. It sounds a funny question, doesn't it? - what do you want to get better *for*? But it isn't always a silly question. I have met plenty of patients who *need* their illness, at least for the time being. Active life has proved too much for them, and becoming ill gives them a respite from their difficulties.

Some eighteen years ago I had an illness which took me out of circulation for twelve months. It was an infection and the doctors seemed to think I caught it from my patients. But that doesn't explain why I got it just at a time when I *needed* a good long break from my job. It gave me a chance to take a good long look at myself and revise many of my ideas. I have always been grateful for that illness.

When Jesus saw the man who had been crippled for thirty-eight years by the pool of Bethesda, he asked him '*Do you want to recover?*' (John 5, v. 2ff.) After all that time, I expect the man had got well used to his disability; and he would quite probably find that the process of rehabilitation to normal life would be strenuous and demand a lot of courage and adaptability: in fact it would be a challenge before which many people might tremble. Even though Jesus was able to cure his disease instantly, he could not relieve him of the pain of readjustment.

There are quite a variety of situations in which pain and suffering are part of normal life. Judging by the way in which newborn infants cry, I think being born must be painful. Bearing a child is certainly painful for the mother. Growing up is full of minor suffering - learning that we can't get our own way, suffering the pangs of homesickness, putting up with the kicks and bumps and general misery of playing compulsory football on a wet winter's afternoon, suffering the terrible embarrassments that are an inevitable accompaniment of adolescence - these are all an essential part of life, and (except for a mother having a baby) they aren't the kinds of suffering that we usually go to the doctor for. Learning a new job can be painful; and to do something really well usually requires us to 'take pains' with it.

No normal person really likes suffering for its own sake; but most healthy people will put up with some pain if they can see that it has a purpose. As life goes on, we come to realise that taking pains, strenuous endeavour in pursuit of a worthwhile goal, however unpleasant it is at the time, can be a valuable experience from which we learn a lot about ourselves. Unpleasant experience can be character-building. Take embarrassment for instance. We all know what it is to wish that the floor would open and swallow us up, though we all try to forget such occasions as soon as we can. They are times when our self-esteem or self-respect suffers damage. How can you help anyone who is embarrassed? It is a difficult social skill to enable someone to 'save face'. I often think that one of the most useful rules of mental health is to learn how to *withstand* embarrassment, at least for the adolescent. I said *withstand* embarrassment, not avoid it. When you are young, your self-respect is fragile and sensitive. But it will only become strong if it is exposed to the elements, not if it is protected from the cold winds of criticism and the withering comments of those who feel superior. In psychiatric practice these days we are developing what we call 'group therapy', where we sit around and discuss personal feelings in as free a way as possible. It's a wonderful training ground for learning how to withstand embarrassment - for the doctors as well as the patients. But embarrassment is a kind of suffering for which few people seek a doctor's aid. Most of us have to cope with it with what little sympathy - usually unspoken sympathy - we can get from our mates or colleagues.

Another kind of suffering which is very common is grief. Probably all of us know what it is to lose something or someone we love. Apart from bereavements, there are broken love affairs, or having to move from a familiar neighbourhood to a strange place, or perhaps having to change jobs away from people you know and have grown fond of. When such things happen, we may get depressed and sad. Perhaps we feel like weeping, we lose sleep and appetite, or we get moody - irritable and silent. We may lose weight and get thin. Nowadays people suffering in these ways often go to the doctor and ask for sleeping tablets or a tonic, and perhaps they get antidepressant pills. I wonder if we doctors are always right to prescribe such things? I know that when I was younger, if someone came to me with depression, I would think it my immediate task to get him out of his depression and back to being his normal cheerful self again as quickly as I could. But now I'm getting more experienced, I wonder.

Certainly, I find myself much slower to prescribe such evasive measures. I have come to feel that if someone is grieving, it usually means that he has lost someone or something of value to him, and that the experience of loss is part of the price he pays for his love. If he evades the experience of loss, isn't this cheapening the experience of love which preceded it? Let me quote a story recorded by the psychotherapist Viktor Frankl:

'Once, an elderly man consulted me because of his severe depression. He could not overcome the loss of his wife who had died two years before and whom he had loved above all else.Now how could I help him? What should I tell him? Well, I refrained from telling him anything but instead confronted him with the question, "What would have happened if you had died first, and your wife would have had to survive you?" "Oh," he said, "for her this would have been terrible; how she would have suffered!" Whereupon I replied, "You see, such a suffering has been spared her, and it was you who have spared her this suffering; but now, you have to pay for it by surviving and mourning her." He said no word but shook my hand and calmly left my office. Suffering ceases to be suffering in some way at the moment it finds a meaning, such as the meaning of a sacrifice.'

This example will show you why I am becoming a little less ready to rob someone of suffering when I feel it may be a learning experience which may be of value to him. To love someone is to die a little - to be ready to give yourself away. It is an important experience, to learn a little of what Jesus meant when he said that anyone who wishes to be a follower of mine must leave self behind. (Mark 8, v. 34-35)

So nowadays when I'm faced with someone who is depressed, I set myself to the task of finding out what it is that they have loved and lost; but after we have discovered that, what can I do? I can perhaps share their sense of loss in some small measure. I can perhaps provide a shoulder for them to weep on. The word comfort originally meant to strengthen, rather than to relieve. It didn't mean to take a burden off someone, but to enable him to bear it. So perhaps in this sense I can comfort someone. This is certainly a work of healing, but I don't think it is one which a doctor is specially equipped to do.

It seems to me that there are two elements in a doctor's work. One is that he is specially trained to know about ways of getting rid of disease and disorder and suffering. This part of his work is highly technical and no one but a trained man can do it. The other element in his day-to-day work is not a matter of getting rid of anything: it is this matter of strengthening or comforting a person so that he can cope with his disease or pain more effectively. This kind of healing work can be done by people without medical training - it is something I find myself doing for people in trouble not because I'm a doctor, but because I'm a human being. And any of you may be better at it than I am.

To put it another way: doctors have to treat diseases, and to treat people. These are very different kinds of activity. The first is a specialised task; the second isn't specialised at all. Someone once described the doctor's job as 'to cure sometimes, to relieve often, to comfort always'. I'm sure we'd all agree with that. The point I would want to add to it is that we cannot leave the job of comforting or strengthening to the doctor or professional caring agency alone. It isn't specialised, and it is needed not only by the sick but by people who have the kinds of suffering we mentioned earlier, which don't need medical attention. We have to learn to *withstand* embarrassment or grief, not to avoid them. And the same is true of the pain of growing up, the pain of being misunderstood, the pain of frustration and failure. We have to find from somewhere the strength and courage to face the evils of life instead of running away from them.

And where can we find such strength - except from our fellow men? We may pray for God's grace and love in the privacy of our own hearts; but the answer so often comes to us by the hands of our fellow-men; not only from the hands of those we love, but from others too. We often get an accession of strength from those who seem angry with us, or who act aggressively towards us. The man whom I identify as my enemy is often the man who makes me strong. You remember what Jesus told us, "*Do not set yourself against the man who wrongs you. If someone slaps you on the right cheek, turn and offer him your left ... Love your enemies and pray for your persecutors.*"(Matt. 5, vv. 39 and 44)

We are all in this business of helping one another to bear the world's suffering together, whether we like it or not. Those of us who aren't attending the doctor and aren't in pain like to believe that we are healthy. We would do better to call ourselves those who are not yet sick. In this world, each individual one of us has to die, and the law demands that a cause of death, be it sickness or accident, has to be written on the death certificate. Separately, everyone of us has his periods of weakness and pain, and that is as true for the nurse and doctor as for everyone else. It isn't something to be avoided: each of us has to bear a part of the world's suffering as part of the price humanity has to pay for its creative achievements, its loves and its joys. It is in this shared understanding of suffering that we can find its meaning, and it is by sharing our joint strength that we are able to cope with it.

> *'For I reckon that the sufferings we now endure bear no comparison with the splendour, as yet unrevealed, which is in store for us. For the created universe waits with eager expectation for God's sons to be revealed. It was made the victim of frustration, not by its own choice, but because of him who made it so; yet always there was hope, because the universe itself is to be freed from the shackles of mortality and enter upon the liberty and splendour of the children of God. Up to the present, we know, the whole created universe groans in all its parts as if in the pangs of childbirth. Not only so, but even we, to whom the Spirit is given as first fruits of the harvest to come, are groaning inwardly while we wait for God to make us his sons and set our whole body free.'* (Romans 8, vv.18ff.)
> *'We are God's heirs and Christ's fellow heirs if we share his sufferings now in order to share his splendour hereafter.'* (Romans, 8, 17.)

95 - Sermon: St. Luke's Day, 1970.

TEXTUAL BIBLIOGRAPHY

(ALPHABETICALLY BY AUTHOR)

Abercrombie M.L.J., **The Anatomy of Judgement**, (Pelican), 1969.

Adamson J., **Born Free**, (Collins & Harvill Press), 1960.

Appell G.N., *'The Plight of Indigenous Peoples: Issues and Dilemmas'*, Survival International, 1977.

Appiah-Kubi K., *'The Church's Healing Ministry in Africa'*, Contact, (Geneva), 1975, No.29.

Baelz P., *'Ethics of Strikes in the Caring Professions'*, paper given to the I.R.M. Conference, London, Jan. 1975.

Balint M., **The Doctor, His patient and the Illness,** (Pitman Medical), 2nd Edition, 1964.

Barnett L., **Homosexuality: Time to Tell the Truth,** (Gollancz), 1975.

Bateson G., **Steps to an Ecology of Mind,** (Paladin), 1973.

B.C.C.Working Party, **Pastoral Care and the Training of Ministers**, (British Council of Churches), London, 1968.

Berger P.L. & Luckman T.,**The Social Construction of Reality,** (Allen Lane), 1967.

Bernstein B., **Class, Codes and Control,** Vol.1, (Routledge & Kegan Paul), London, 1971.

Bion W.R., **Experiences in Groups,** (Tavistock Publications), 1961.

Brown W., **Exploration in Management,** (London), 1965.

Buckley W., **Sociology and Modern Systems Theory,** (Prentice-Hall International), London, 1967.

Caplan G., **Principles of Preventive Psychiatry**, (Tavistock Publications), 1964.

Carpendale B., *'Thoughts on the Possibility of Community'*, The Teilhard Review, 1975, Vol.X, No:1, p.2.

Chance M.R.A., **Social Groups of Markings, Apes and Man,** (Cape), London, 1970.

Church Information Office,

Exorcism, Statement on Behalf of 65 signatories, 1975.

The Community Mental Hospital, (W.H.O. Technical Report), 1953.

Cox M., 1)**Structuring the Therapeutic Process: Compromise with Chaos, The Therapist's Response to the Individual and the Group,**

2)**Coding the Therapeutic Process: Emblems of Encounter - a Manual for Counsellors and Therapists,** (Pergamon Press) - Oxford, 1978.

Crocker L.H. and Pearse I.H.,

The Peckham Experiment, (Sir Halley Stewart Trust

Publication, Allen & Unwin), 1943.

Davis D. Russell,	American Journal of Psychiatry, September 1967, 124.3, p.98.
Dingwall R.,	**Aspects of Illness,** (Martin Robertson), 1976.
Dominian J.,	**Depression: What is it? How do we cope?** (D.L.T.), 1976.
	The Capacity to Love, (D.L.T.), London, 1985.
Durkheim E.,	**Le Suicide,** (Étude de Sociologie), Paris, 1897.
Erikson E.H.,	**Childhood and Society,** (Penguin), 1965.
Erikson E.H.,	**Identity, Youth and Crisis,** (Faber), 1968.
Erikson E.H.,	**Insight and Responsibility,** (W.W.Norton), New York, 1964.
Exeter Commission,	**Exorcism,** (S.P.C.K.), 1972.
Foulkes S.H.,	**Introduction to Group-Analytic Psychotherapy,** (Heinemann), 1948.
Freud S.,	**The Psychopathology of Everyday Life,** (Hogarth Press), 1901.
Freud S.,	**Introductory Lectures on Psychoanalysis,** (Allen & Unwin), Revised Second Edition, 1929.
Goffman Erving,	**Two Studies in the Sociology of Interaction,** (Allen Lane), London, 1972.
Hick J.,	**Evil and the God of Love,** (Macmillan), 1966.
	Hospital Trends and Developments 1940-1946, (Commonwealth Fund).
Irenaeus,	**Against Heresies, IV, XXXVIII, 3.**
Jay A.,	**Corporation Man,** (Jonathan Cape), 1972.
King M.,	**Medical Care in Developing Countries,** (O.U.P.), 1966.
Kipling R.,	*'The Miracle of Purun Bhagat'* in **The Two Jungle Books,** (Macmillan), 1936.
Kitson F.,	**Low Intensity Operations,** (Faber), London, 1971.
Kuhn T.S.,	**The Structure of Scientific Revolutions,** (University of Chicago), 1970.
Laing R.D.,	**The Politics of Experience,** (Penguin), 1977.
Laing R.D. & Esterson A.,	**Sanity, Madness and the Family,** (London), 1964.
Laing R.D.,	New Society, 1 Oct.1964, No.105, p.12. Vol.1, *'Families of Schizophrenics'.*
Lambourne R.A.,	*'Authority and Acceptance in Pastoral Counselling',* Expository Times, 8 May, 1970,Vol. 81, No.8.
Lambourne R.A.,	*'Authority, Personal Knowledge and the Therapeutic*

	Relationship', <u>Contact</u>, (Edinburgh), Nov.1968, No.25, pp.22-40.
Lambourne R.A.,	**Community, Church and Healing,** (D.L.T.), 1963: Reprinted (Arthur James), London, 1987.
Lambourne R.A.,	*'Models of Health and Salvation'*, <u>Study Encounter</u>, (World Council of Churches), 1971,Vol.VII, No.1.
Lambourne R.A.,	*'Objections to a National Pastoral Organisation'*, <u>Contact</u>, (Edinburgh), June 1971, No.35, pp.24 - 31.
Lambourne R.A.,	*'Personal Reformation and Political Formation in Pastoral Care'*, <u>Contact</u>, (Edinburgh), Spring 1974, No.44, pp.30-40.
Langsley D.G.,	et al., **Treatment of Families in Crisis**, (Grune & Stratton), 1968.
Leach E.,	<u>The Listener</u>, November 1967, Vol. 78, No. 2018.
	<u>The Observer</u>, 31st. December, 1967, p.10.
Lorenz K.,	**Studies in Animal and Human Behaviour,** (Methuen), Vol.II, 1971.
Lorenz K.,	**King Solomon's Ring,** (Methuen), 1952.
McGilvray J.C.,	**The Quest for Health and Wholeness**, (German Institute for Medical Missions, Tübingen), 1981.
McLuhan M.,	*'The Gadget Lover: Narcissus as Narcosis'*, in **Understanding Media: The Extensions of Man**, (Routledge and Kegan Paul), 1964.
Macmurray J.,	**Persons in Relation**, (Faber), 1961.
Macmurray J.,	**The Self as Agent**, (Faber), 1957.
Main T.F.,	**The Hospital as a Therapeutic Institution**, (Bull. Men. Clin.), 1946, 10, 66.
Martin D.V.,	**Adventure in Psychiatry,** (Bruno Cassirer), Oxford, 1962.
Maslow A.H.,	**Motivation and Human Personality,** (Harper Row), 1970.
Masters J.,	**To the Coral Strand**, (Michael Joseph), 1962.
Mathers J.M.,	See *'Complete Bibliography of Collected Papers'*: Numbers 88 (1969) & 79 (1968), et.al.
Maxwell Jones,	**Beyond the Therapeutic Community**, (Yale U.P.), 1968.
Mead M.,	**Male and Female,** (Pelican Books), 1962.
Melinsky M.A.H.,	in **Religion and Medicine,** (S.C.M.), London, 1970. See for instance: '88 *'Two Approaches to Healing'* (<u>Guild of Health pamphlet no. 28</u>); and '79 *'Psychiatry and Religion'.*
Morris D.,	**The Naked Ape**, (Jonathan Cape), 1967.
Neill S.,	**A Genuinely Human Existence**, (Constable), 1969.
Newcomb T.M.,	*'Autistic Hostility and Social Reality'*, <u>Human Relations</u>,1947, Vol.1, No.1, p.73.

Parkes C.M.,	**Bereavement**, (London), 1972.
Parkes C.M.,	*'The Nature of Grief and the Reaction to Bereavement in Adult Life'*, in **Good Grief**, (Institute of Religion and Medicine, London), Report of a Conference.
Price F.W.,	**A Textbook of the Practice of Medicine,** (Oxford Medical), 7th Edition, 1946.
Rapoport R.N.,	**Community as Doctor**, (Tavistock Publications), 1960.
Revans R.W.,	**Standards for Morale: Cause and Effect in Hospitals**, (O.U.P.), 1964.
Righton P.,	Journal of the Association of Workers for Maladjusted Children, 1975, Spring, Vol.3, No.1.
Russell Davis,	American Journal of Psychiatry, Sept.1967, Vol.124, No.3, p.98.
Rycroft C.,	**Psychoanalysis Observed**, (Constable), London, 1966.
Sargant W.,	**Battle for the Mind,** (Heinemann) 1957.
Schumacher E.F.,	**Small is Beautiful**, (Blond and Briggs), 1973.
Seabrook J.,	*'Poverty as Metaphor'*, New Society, 28 Feb.1980.
Shore P.,	speaking at Heathrow Airport, (London), 21 Jan.1976.
Simpson G.G.,	et al., **Life: an Introduction to Biology,** (London), 1957.
Szasz T.S.,	**The Myth of Mental Illness**, (Paladin), 1972.
Teilhard de Chardin P.,	**Science and Christ**, (Collins), 1968.
Teilhard de Chardin P.,	**The Future of Man**, (Collins), 1964.
Teilhard de Chardin P.,	**The Phenomenon of Man,** (Fontana, Collins), 1965.
Van der Post L.,	**Jung and the Story of our Time**, (Penguin), 1978.
Vanstone W.H.,	**The Stature of Waiting**, (D.L.T.), 1982.
Ward B. and Dubos R.,	**Only One Earth,** (Penguin), 1972.
ed.Wilson J.M.,	**Explorations in Health and Salvation** - a Selection of Papers by R.A.Lambourne, (Dept. of Theology, University of Birmingham), Re-issued 1995.
Wilson J.M.,	*'Exorcism'*, Expository Times, July 1975, Vol.LXXXVI, No.10.
Wilson J.M.,	**Health is for People**, (D.L.T.), 1975.
Wilson J.M.,	**The Hospital - a Place of Truth**, (Institute for the Study of Worship and Religious Architecture, University of Birmingham), 1971.
Winnicott D.,	**Playing and Reality,** (Penguin), 1974.
Working Party,	**Homosexual Relationships - a Contribution to Discussion**, Report to the General Synod of the Church of England, (Board of Social Responsibility), 1979.

THE WISDOM OF JAMES

After a working lifetime in psychiatry I still feel a sense of wonder at the incredibly small place which our rational consciousness plays in our mental lives.

We must always recognise that any truth we find ourselves uttering is provisional, an approximation, a tentative question rather than a dogmatic statement.

We only dare to utter what we - usually mistakenly - believe to be the truth because we are assured of God's forgiveness in advance.

Our pilgrim road through life can be described as one of progressive disillusionment; each morning we need to be ready to break the image of God which seemed so clear and certain the previous day.

People will only learn to behave as responsible human beings if they are treated as responsible human beings.

This seems to be a rule of mental health, that the more healthy a person is, the more responsibility they will be prepared to take on.

People will not make sense of God without Christ.

It is often more helpful to be imaginative than right.

It is meanings, not the words and gestures which are their vehicles, that are the essence of communication.

The psychotherapist sees mental illness as an indication that the patient has difficulty in communicating his meanings.

Nowadays it is probably just as dehumanising or alienating for someone to feel that they cannot make their voice heard as it has been in the past for a person to be lacking a job.

Leadership is a function of social situations rather than a functional characteristic of particular individuals.

Suffering in other people raises anxiety in those who try to care for them.

A community consists of individuals each of whom not only lives but also communicates: so the brain and nervous system may in some ways be a more useful model for community than the body as a whole.

The way we listen to others may bear witness to the Christian message as powerfully as the way we speak to them.

We all need to experience failure. If the road to maturity lies in increasing self-understanding, then we can say that we never learn anything new about ourselves by being successful.

Can Medicine ever do more than move people from one risk category to another? We must know about the 'within' as well as the 'without' of things.

My interest in psychiatry was always that of wanting to understand my patients, and not at all in controlling them.

The reward of a psychiatrist comes when a patient responds to his/her comments by saying "I see!" A psychiatrist's guiding vision is to proclaim release to the captives, recovery of sight to the blind, and to set at liberty those who are oppressed.

All people share in the responsibility for all the evil experience of humankind. We share the responsibility; but that doesn't mean that we are called upon to apportion blame.

We will not attempt to draw conclusions: all we are trying to do is to seek for different viewpoints from which to survey the problems that will certainly remain.

The achievement of true personhood is always the achievement (for better or for worse) of all those people with whom we are or have been in relationship. Personality is a social or corporate achievement.

A human being can only be understood in a social context.

Only in relationship with others can we become truly human.

Mental health is something which has no meaning for the human individual considered alone. It is by definition a social phenomenon.

The establishment of human relationships and their continuous development is the basis of mental health.

Perhaps self-control is more likely to result from the effort of a caring person to understand, than from the effort of a caring person to control.

To ignore someone is the most potent way of threatening their sense of identity.

A plea that hospital planners should be concerned to do what is good for patients, rather than what is bad for diseases.

The therapist or observer in the clinical situation is inevitably participating in the very life-stream that s-he is trying to study or manipulate.

The therapeutic community and the body of Christ are there already, if only we believe that they are.

We should recognise that tomorrow's greater good is more likely to emerge from the reconciliation of today's good with today's evil, than from the elimination of today's evil.

The person who is never prepared to make a mistake never makes anything.

How can we enable these people, even though they are crippled, to share with us a responsibility for the common task of improving the society in which we both have to live?

No one can be healthy in isolation: and institutions isolated from the community can't be healthy either.

We will certainly discover that an intolerable emotion can become tolerable when it is shared.

What we call disease is always an interaction between an organism trying to stay healthy, and a pattern of pathogenic factors: it is not a thing but a relationship.

If people have an innate compulsion to express their feelings one way or another, they have an equally innate need to be satisfied only by the receipt of a response which indicates 'your signals received and understood'.

Communication of emotion is a biological imperative among social animals.

If our emotions are not expressed in an appropriate way, because we suppress or inhibit them, consciously or unconsciously, then they will find ways of expression that are inappropriate and unhealthy.

Jesus did not distinguish between healing and preaching: love worked both ways.

It is one of the penalties of an academic education that we tend to give undue importance to verbal communication, and to forget that while words are the most delicate and precise means of communication, they are also the most likely to be misused and misunderstood.

Maladjustment to a sick society may after all be more healthy than a supine acceptance of it.

Genes are like the keys of a piano: they determine what possibilities are available, but leave pianists free to make their own music.

It would seem to me almost possible to define the good life as the search for wider and deeper relationships with more and more people.

The mother/child relationship sets a basic pattern upon which all subsequent relationships tend to be modelled.

From a biologist's point of view can a child who has been starved of a good mother-relationship have any conception of the love of God?

Good mental health is largely a matter of good morale.

I use the word 'morale' rather than 'spirit' because the latter carries theological overtones, which might make for misunderstanding, though the French expression 'esprit de corps' indicates its equivalence.

Wisdom is not good at advertising itself.

We don't really 'grow' plants or 'heal' wounds: plants just grow, and wounds heal.

In a technological revolution such as Britain has been through in the last 150years, it is inevitable that a majority of us should be morally 'displaced persons.'

If you give your heart to someone, you risk being heart-broken if you lose them.

Grief is the price we pay for loving, and love would be cheapened if grief were less.

To love someone is to live dangerously. It is to risk losing a part of one's self. It is to cast one's bread upon the waters, to give a hostage to fortune. It is no activity for those who lack courage.

Clarity of outline is a luxury in thought for which the gods exact a price.

Marriage is a sacrament, and for this sacrament to bear fruit we must give our marriage away to others in a life of service.

Love is a quality of experience without boundaries: ready to respond. A quality of staying in relationship.

One's ego identity grows stronger as one widens the scope of one's we-identities, so that at one's best an individual can be prepared to lay down his life for his friends because his personal identity has become co-terminous with theirs.

Science and technology in Medicine and elsewhere aim at predictability - at reducing uncertainty.

A difficult situation is often one which may solve itself if only we make and keep ourselves (and one another) strong enough to live through it and, hopefully, learn from it.

Emotion certainly needs control: but an attempt to appreciate the ideal with the intellect alone is to deny the verity of our emotional nature and is doomed to failure.

What is a human being but a knot in a network of human relationships?

A human relationship is a continuing channel of communication between two people.

Mental health requires free channels of communication between one person and another.

Sex education must begin at mother's breast.

A therapeutic situation in which there is no third person involved is always dangerous, and needs to be kept as brief as possible.

It is, of course, impossible to visualise a world where all people are equal. The most anyone has ever suggested seriously is that everyone should have an equality of chance.

My top priority, as medical superintendent of a psychiatric hospital, is to prevent patients - already damaged on admission - from being further damaged by the life of the hospital.

Mental health depends very largely upon our ability to face facts, particularly when we dont like the look of them.

There is no answer to the problem of sin in the ossified conscience.

There is no such thing as sin - there are only sinful thoughts and feelings and actions.

There is no such thing as grief: there are only grieving people.

Prejudice is a killing disease.

The discovery of truth by scientific method is a gift of God.

The study of a patient's mental illness by traditional methods of scientific medicine focusses attention on him in a way which in itself is deleterious to his recovery of mental health.

Exclusiveness is a denial of an essential activity of love and therefore of love itself.

There is nothing static about mental health. It is always either improving or falling back.

Ultimately all anxiety is the fear of separation; of separation from our fellows, of isolation.

The sense of guilt tends to arise in the individual when he fails to share a sense of common purpose with his fellows.

In an important sense the human 'self' is a person's relationships - there's nothing left of a person without them.

You cant be a good group leader unless you are first of all a good member of the group.

There may be more wisdom in our little griefs than we commonly realise. Perhaps every grief contains within it the seeds of a higher order of love.

Action which follows upon understanding is usually more effective than action which precedes it.

Only in an increasing sympathy and sense of community can an individual find the key to the completion of their personality.

Sharing one another's burdens of evil experience is no longer just a pious fantasy but a conscious and realistic social objective.

If mother reads about unpleasant crimes in the Sunday paper with obvious interest and fascination, the child's evaluation of such matters will be similar - irrespective of her mother's bald statement that such crimes are wicked and wrong.

Psychiatry is more a point of view - a way of looking at things - than a matter of imparting instruction.

A clear vision of God is the culmination of personality.

Advances in understanding (even in science) come not only from the acquisition of new facts, but also from alterations of emphasis as to which facts are important - rather like what happens when you shake a kaleidoscope.

Wholeness is inclusive: it includes both the sick and the well.

At cost to whom am I healthy?

Power exists whether it is recognised or not (i.e. it has an 'objective reality'): authority only exists when it is recognised.

The success of a marriage depends almost as much upon the society in which it occurs as upon the partners themselves.

In the perspective of the therapeutic community, we are all in it together, therapist and client alike, all helping to remove the beams and motes from one another's eyes.

We divorce therapy from education at our peril.

COMPLETE BIBLIOGRAPHY
OF
JAMES MATHERS' COLLECTED PAPERS

This bibliography of his papers (letters, notes, addresses, articles, sermons, reviews and broadcasts) has been arranged as follows: basically the papers are numbered in the order in which he wrote them (he usually dated what he wrote). Any revised texts are placed with the first draft, together with any magazine or journal in which the paper was published (even if much later).

In a few instances there are a number of papers, articles or sermons on the same major subject, such as Health, Participation and Objectivity, Community, or Guilt Feeling which I have numbered together in a batch with the first paper, regardless of the dates of later papers.

WAR-TIME PAPERS, 1941 - 1943

0-1 **Truth**, Tidworth, 1941 (probably): revised Aden 1942.
0-2 **Truth and Knowledge**, Tidworth, 1941.
0-3 **Communism**, Malabar Coast, Jan., 1942.
0-4 **Dynamic Psychology**, Bombay, Feb., 1942.
0-5 **Vital Energy**, Bombay, March, 1942.
0-6 **Elizabethans and Civilisation**, on a troopship, Bombay, March, 1942.
0-7 **Science, Psychology and Philosophy: the Search for Light**, Bombay, May, 1942.
0-8 **Philosophy of Life**, Massawa, June, 1942.
0-9 **The Battle Against Chaos**, undated, unplaced.
0-10 **Philosophy of Life**, Ranchi, July, 1943.

WAR-TIME PAPERS, *The Arakan Front, Burma*, 1944 - 1945

1-0 Letter: 27th. Feb., 1974, from Dr R.Tredgold to J.R.M. enclosing 1/1.
1-1 Psychiatric Report by J.R.M. (Psychiatrist, 36th Indian Division) on **Diagnosis and Treatment of Psychiatric Casualties on the Arakan Front**, Feb.- April, 1944.
1-2 Letter: 17th. May, 1949, from Dr Rodger to J.R.M. enclosing 1/3 and 1/4.
1-3 Letter: 30th. Jan., 1945 from J.R.M. (Capt.R.A.M.C., H.Q., 36 Division, S.E.A.C.) to Brigadier Rodger (Consultant Psychiatrist, Advance H.Q., S.E.A.C.).
1-4 Letter: 4th. March, 1945 from J.R.M. (In transit, 51 Indian Reception Camp, S.E.A.C.) enclosing 1/5 and 1/6.
1-5 Report: 25th. Feb., 1945: to A.D.M.S., 36th Division, from J.R.M. (Psychiatrist, 36 Indian Division) on high incidence of psychiatric casualties in the 10th Glosters due to exhaustion.

1-6 Report: 26th. Feb., 1945: to D.A.A.G., 36th Division, from J.R.M. (Psychiatrist, 36 Indian Division) on causes of poor morale in 10th Glosters and recommendations.

WAR-TIME PAPERS, *Undated (probably 1945). Mostly unplaced*

2-1 Unfinished article on Post-war Plans, North Burma, Undated.
2-2 **The Psychological Basis of Morale**, unplaced. ? 26th., December.
2-3 **Fear, Anxiety and Group Morale**, unplaced, undated.
2-4 **On Being Human**, unplaced, undated.
2-5 **The Healing Effect of Groups**, unplaced, undated.

POST-WAR PAPERS, 1948 - 1986

1948

3 Review: S.H.Foulkes, '*Introduction to Group-Analytic Psychotherapy*', <u>N.A.M.H. Journal</u>, November 1948.

3-1 Psychiatry)
) Post-war Papers,
3-2 Definitions of Neurotic Illness) probably 1948,
) unplaced.
3-3 Education through Art)

1958

4-1 **The Man-man Relationship**, address to Guild of Health conference, handwritten notes, August, 1958.
4-2 Published script from tape recording, for <u>Health and Healing</u>, (Guild of Health), London, November, 1958, pp. 166-170.
5 **Courtship, Marriage and Family**, handwritten notes for address at Wadderton, Birmingham Diocesan Retreat House, Sept., 1958.
6 **Suicide**, address to National Council of Women, Friends Meeting House, (unplaced), 17th. Oct., 1958.
7 **Mental Health in Old Age**, address at Warwick, 17th. Oct., 1958.
8 Address: Edgbaston Old Church, Hospital Sunday, 19th. Oct., 1958.
9 **A Psychiatrist's Approach to Sin and Guilt**, Unplaced, 24th./25th. Oct., 1958.
10 **The Art of Medicine**, unplaced, 26th. Nov., 1958.
11. **Mental Health and Mental Illness**, address to 'Med. Women,' 10th. Dec., 1958.

1959

12 **Mental Health in Old Age**, handwritten, unplaced, 1959.

13 **Antithesis between Science and Religion**, handwritten notes for address to S.C.M., unplaced, 22nd. Jan., 1959.

14 Sermon: Matthew 18,3 *'Except ye be converted...'* King's Norton, 15th. Feb., 1959.

15 **Sex Education**, address at Uffculme Clinic, Birmingham, 14th. March, 1959.

16 Sermon: *'Human Love'*, St John's, 18th. Oct., 1959.

16-1 **Human Love as a Doctor sees it**, published in Contact, (Monthly paper of the Church of England in Longbridge), Nov., 1959.

17 Address: to Women's Voluntary Service, unplaced, 9th. Nov., 1959.

18 Address: at Midland Nerve Hospital, Birmingham, 2nd. Dec., 1959.

1960

19 **Therapeutic Community**, address to the Royal College of Nursing, unplaced, 23rd. March, 1960.

20 Handwritten notes on **Therapeutic Community**, unplaced, undated.

21 **The Search for Mental Health**, unplaced, 1960.

22 **The Application of Co-ordinated Preventive Activities to Social Problems: Mental Health**, Arthur Thomson Hall, Birmingham, July, 1960.

23 **Courage,** St George's Edgbaston, 16th. Oct.,1960. Repeated in St John's, 19th. Oct., 1960.

24 **Mental Health and Personal Relationships**, handwritten, partly notes, for address to Convention of Ministers of the Church of Christ, Barnes Close, 8th. Nov., 1960.

25 **The Art of Marriage**, Students' Union, University of Birmingham, Dec., 1960.

25-1 Published in Moment, (St Francis Hall, University of Birmingham), Christmas, 1960, pp.8-22.

1961

26 **Responsibility and Mental Health in relationship to congregational participation in the life of St John's**, Longbridge, Feb., 1961.

27 **Group Therapy**, handwritten notes for addresses on 8th. and 15th. March, 1961: 23rd. May and 13th. July, 1962.

28 **Relationships and Communication**, handwritten notes for address, Hodge Hill, 23rd. April, 1961.

29 **Mental Health**, Diocesan Readers' Board, 20 June, 1961.

30 **'No Man is an Island'**, Conference of the Churches' Council of Healing, Blackheath, 24th. Oct., 1961.

1962

31 **Healing,** St Mary the Virgin, Acock's Green, 13th. May, 1962.

32 **Songs of Praise**, introduced by J.R.M. for a congregation of doctors and nurses, at St Martins-in-the-Bullring, Hospital Sunday, 1962. B.B.C., recording on Wednesday 12th. Sep., 1962.

33 **The Christian Outlook on Mental Health**, lecture at the Town Hall, Dudley, 2nd. Oct., 1962.

1963

34-1 **Mental Healing and the Community**, first draft 30th. March, 1963.

34-2 Revised draft, 23rd. April, 1963.

34-3 Published in <u>Frontier</u>, Summer 1963, Vol 6, II, pp. 127-130.

34-4 Same paper read at the University of Birmingham Extra-mural Course (Dept. of Theology), at The Queen's College, 23rd. April,1965.

34-5 **Pastoralia and Positive Concepts of Mental Health**, the Extra-mural Course at Queen's, an outline of the proposed General Thesis.

34-6 A copy of the programme. J.R.M.'s paper 34/2 was read in place of David Jenkin's opening address on Friday evening.

34-7 List of Conference attenders.

34-8 J.R.M.'s handwritten notes of papers by John Eaton, W.Curr, and other sessions.

34-9 Map of Conference venue, Queen's College, Edgbaston, for attenders.

35 **Morale in the Community**, unpublished, unplaced, 9 April, 1963. Similarities in content to 34.

36 **Vandalism**, unplaced, 1963. Published in <u>Contact</u>, (Edinburgh), 1988, No:97, 3, p.8.

37 **A General Psychiatric Hospital and its Relationship with General Medical Practice**, handwritten, Shelton Hospital, Shrewsbury, 28th. April, 1963.

37-1 Invitation (dated 19th. April, 1963) to Dr Mathers from Medical Superintendent of Shelton Hospital to attend a *Symposium on Mental Health* on 28th April 1963.

38 Notes for a slide show to visitors at Rubery Hill Psychiatric Hospital, 1963.

39 **Introducing your local hospital: New approaches to an age-old problem**, Rubery Hill Psychiatric Hospital, 1963.

40 Address: to doctors and nurses at Selly Oak Hospital, 20th. Oct., 1963.

41-1 **The Gospel and Man's Self-Understanding**, St Francis Hall, University of Birmingham, 27th. Oct., 1963.

41-2 A second text with alterations.

42 **What is Man?,** Statements designed to introduce a discussion at The Rectory, 12 Sir Harry's Road, B 15, (The Rev B. Dolman), 25th. Nov., 1963.

43 *A Plan for a Hospital Community*, news item for <u>Birmingham Christian News</u>, Nov., 1963.

44 J.M.'s Index Sheet on Fly-leaf of Folder labelled 1958 - 1968.

1964

45 **The Therapeutic Community**, Uffculme Clinic, Birmingham, May, 1964.

45-1 Carbon copy of 45.

46 Sermon: *'Hospitals'*, St Luke's Day (Hospital Sunday), Quinton Parish Church, 18th. Oct.,1964.

47 **Sex and Personality**, University of Birmingham, 19th. Oct., 1964. (See also 56).

48 Sermon: *'Unity and Separateness in the Communion of Saints'*, Patronal Festival at All Saints, Sanderstead, 1st. Nov., 1964.

48-1 Loose sheet of handwritten sentences for inclusion in Sermon 48.

49 Report: to the Birmingham Diocesan Conference on a meeting of the Church Assembly (of which J.M. was a member), 18th. Nov., 1964.

50-1 **Discovering Other People**, B.B.C. Silver Lining Programme, 1st. Dec., 1964, pre-recorded 27th. Nov., 1964.

50-2 **Discovering Ourselves**, Ditto, 8th. Dec., 1964, pre-recorded 27th. Nov., 1964.

50-3 **On Having Something to Look Forward To**, Ditto, 29th. Dec., 1964. pre-recorded 21st. Dec., 1964.

1965

51-1 **Putting Gangs Into Perspective**, original M.S. typed for the <u>Birmingham Post</u>, 4th. Feb., 1965.

51-2 Newspaper cutting of 51/1, <u>Birmingham Post</u>, 11th. Feb., 1965.

52-1 **Functions of a hospital Medical Staff Committee, and duties/qualities of its Chairperson**, Rubery Hill Hospital, April, 1965.

52-2 Handwritten notes headed: *SOWRY, Medical Administration*. Filed by J.R.M. attached to 52/1, 11th. May, 1965.

53 Friends of Rubery Hospitals, Broadsheet No: 1, May, 1965.

54 Sermon: *'Rubery special service, Philippians 4, v.8'*, handwritten, 11th. June, 1965 or 1966.

55-1 Review: Sidney Cohen, Richard Blum et al., *'Drugs of Hallucination: Utopiates'*, 7th. Oct., 1965.

55-2 Review: printed in <u>New Christian</u>, pp. 24-25, 7th. Oct., 1965.

56-1 **Fact and Meaning of Sex: sex and personality**, C.A.T., Gosta Green, Birmingham, 8th. Nov., 1965.

56-2 A second text with alterations.

57-1 **Two Ways of Treatment in Mental Hospitals**, Selly Oak Colleges' open meeting at Rubery Hill Hospital, first draft, 25th. Nov., 1965.

57-2 Same text, second draft has an addition of two handwritten pages 9 and 10.

58 **Mental Illness and the Community**, introduction to discussion in Seminar 1 of a *'Wholeness Conference'* organised by the S.C.M. (Theological College Department), at Saltley College, 29th.-31st. Dec., 1965. Cyclostyled programme with handwritten notes for a discussion starter on Seminar 1's topic.

59 Review: Gerda Cohen, *'What's Wrong with Hospitals?'* 14th. Oct., 1965. Published in

Contact (Edinburgh), No.16, Jan., 1966.

1966

6o An account of a prayer group for members of St John's, Longbridge, meeting in one another's homes, written for Contact, (Longbridge Parish), 14th. April, 1966.

61 **Phenomenon**, a paper on Teilhard de Chardin's thought given to the local branch of the Institute of Religion and Medicine in Birmingham, 2nd. May, 1966. Repeated at Harris College Preston, Blackpool, 4th. March, 1971.

62-1 Reviews:

1)M.Serrano, '*C.G.Jung & H.Hesse, A Record of Two Friendships*', (Routledge and Kegan Paul).

2)G.Cruchon, '*A Psychology of the Person*', (Darton, Longman and Todd).

3)Erik H. Erikson, '*Insight and Responsibility*', (Faber).

62-2 Published in New Christian, 5th. May, 1966, p.19.

63 **Healthy Death**, address to local branch of the Guild of Health, Birmingham, 19th. May, 1966.

64 Sermon: St John's, Longbridge, 12th. June, 1966.

65 **Friends of Hospitals**, address given in St Martins-in-the-Bullring, 16th. Oct., 1966. Repeated to the Local Council of Churches at St Agnes, 28th. May, 1968.

66-1 **The Participant Observer**, address to New Society, University of Aston in Birmingham, Oct., 1966. (See also 101/1).

66-2 Revised draft.

66-3 An older draft without bibliography.

66-4 **Participation and Objectivity**, address to Association of Residential Group Workers Spring Conference, Birmingham, 9th. March, 1971.

66-5/0 **Becoming a Participant Observer**, first draft of address given at the Teilhard Centre, Nov., 1984.

66-5/1 **The Activation of Energy**, Evolution and Society Forum No.3, at the Teilhard Centre. Programme within which paper 66-5/0 was given.

66-6 Revised draft.

66-7 Final text plus bibliography.

67-1 Sermon: in handwritten notes, for a United Service organised by the All Saints (Birmingham) Hospital Management Committee, All Saints Day, 1 Nov.1966.

67-2 Order of Service at which above sermon was preached.

68 **Guilt**, article in News and Views, (a local duplicated sheet, Falkirk – Scotland), 10th. Dec., 1966.

1967

69 **Faith and Neurosis**, address at St Francis Hall, University of Birmingham, 16th. Jan., 1967.

70-1 **Crisis**, an outline for an address/discussion in a training course for counsellors entitled 'Mental Health and Mental Disorder', at Carr's Lane Counselling Centre, 20th.

April, 1967.

70-2 Outline for discussion on a case history.

70-3 Notes for an address on **personality development, mental health and mental disorder**.

71 **The Context of Anxiety**, address to the Institute of Religion and Medicine, Sheffield, 12th. July, 1967. Published in ed. M.A.H.Melinsky, **Religion and Medicine,** (S.C.M.), London, 1970, pp.16-24.

72 **Church Leadership and Health**, address to Churches' Council of Healing, Friends Meeting House, London, July, 1967.

73 Intercessions: St John's, Longbridge, 22nd. Oct., 1967.

1968

74 **The Family of the Mentally Afflicted Patient,** address to London Medical Group, Westminster Hospital Medical School, 15 Jan.1968.
(See also 83)

75-1 **Forgiveness of Sin**, address to Student Christian Movement, Aston University, 18th. March, 1968.

75-2 Published in <u>Impetus</u>, Summer 1968, No.13, pp.226-231.

75-3 Sermon: on the theme of '*Forgiveness*', St Luke's-tide Service in Hereford Cathedral, 22nd. Oct., 1968.

76-1 **Ministry to the Bereaved**, 26th. March, 1968.

76-2 Published in ed. G.Cope, **Dying, Death and Disposal**, (Institute for the Study of Worship and Religious Architecture - University of Birmingham), 1970, pp.40-48.

76-3 **Ministry to the Bereaved II**, address in Manchester Cathedral, 16th. Nov., 1972.

76-4 **Ministry to the Bereaved III**, similar to 76-3, address in Manchester, Oct., 1975.

77-1 **Guilt and the Doctor**, address to General Practitioners, Post-graduate Centre, Selly Oak Hospital, 26th. May, 1968.

77-2 **Vicarious Guilt Feelings**, October 1976.

77-3 **Vicarious Guilt Feelings**, different address (written 22nd. March 1979) given to the D.P.S.Spring School, 29th. March, 1979.

77-4 Published in <u>Theology</u>, November 1979, LXXXII, No.690, pp.436-440.

77-5 Published in <u>Newlife,</u> The Prison Chaplaincy Review, August, 1980, pp.10-15.
(See also 146 Sermon: St Mary's, Swansea, 27th. March, 1974).

78-1 Prayers: St John Baptist, Longbridge, 16th. June, 1968.

78-2 Repeated in Mind Week, St Martins-in-the-Bullring, 24th. Oct.,1971.

79 **Psychiatry and Religion**, address at Severall's Psychiatric Hospital, Colchester, 24th. Sep., 1968.

80 **The Wholeness of Man**, eight statements presented for discussion at a local I.R.M. meeting at Oxford, 1968.

1969

81 J.M.'s Index Sheet on Fly-leaf of Folder Labelled 1969-1971.

82-1 Review: ed. R.C.de Bold, and R.C.Leaf, *'L.S.D., Man and Society'*, (Faber and Faber, 42s.)

82-2 Published in New Christian, 1st. May, 1969, p.17.

83 **The Family of the Mentally Afflicted Patient**, given to the London Medical Group, St Thomas' Hospital Medical School, 13th. May, 1969: and repeated to the L.M.G. at University College Hospital Medical School, 13th. Nov., 1969. (See also 74).

84 **Medicine in the Open Society**, given to Christian Action at Swanwick Conference Centre, 31st. May, 1969.

85 **Pastoral - What does it Mean?,** address to The Scottish Pastoral Association, Dumfries, 13th. June, 1969.

86 Published in Contact, (Edinburgh), June, 1970, No.31, p.22.

87 **Two Approaches to Healing**, address given to the Methodist Committee on Healing, Gravelly Hill, Birmingham, 2nd. July, 69.

88 Published in Guild of Health pamphlet No:28, **Two Approaches to Healing**, 1970.

89 **The Use of Understanding of Group Behaviour in Pastoral Care**, written 10th. Nov., 1969 for the *Expository Times*.

90-1 Published as No V **The Use of Understanding of Group Behaviour in Pastoral Care** in the series on *'The Social Sciences and the Work of the Churches'*: this text has no insertions.

90-2 **Group Behaviour in Pastoral Care**, in the Expository Times, April, 1970 Vol. LXXXI, No.7, pp.196-200. There is a typed addition of three insertions attached to pp.200/201.

91-1 **Evil and Me**, address B.B.C., St Augustine's Church, Edgbaston, 22nd. Feb., 1970.

91-2 Second draft, re-named **On Dealing with Evil**, Feb., 1970.

92 **Concepts of Healing**, Notes on Dr R.A.Lambourne's. 'Concepts Map', to be found in ed. J.M.Wilson, *Explorations in Health and Salvation*, (Theology Dept., University of Birmingham - 1983: re-issued 1995), for address to Methodist Committee on Healing, Richmond College, 8th. April, 1970.

93 **A criticism of The Cogwheel Report, 1967**, an internal document for the staff of Rubery Hill Hospital, 12th. June, 1970.

94 **Psychiatry in the Community**, outline of theme for conference arranged by South Birmingham Group of Psychiatric Hospitals, Post-graduate Centre, Selly Oak Hospital, 17th.-18th. Oct., 1970.

95 Sermon: *'Luke 4, 18'*, St Mary's, Bearwood, for St Luke's Day service, 18th. Oct.,1970.

96-1 Letter: from C.L.Mitton, Editor of Expository Times, asking J.M. to review Harmon L.Smith, *'Ethics and the New Medicine'*, (Abingdon Press), 1970.

96-2 Enclosure: publisher's blurb on Harmon L.Smith, *'Ethics and the New Medicine'*, (Abingdon Press), 1970.

96-3 Review by J.M. written 21st. Nov., 1970.

96-4 Review: as published in the Expository Times, April 1971, LXXXII, 7.

97-1 Letter: from T.Beeson, European Editor of Christian Century, to J.M. asking for a review of K.Leech, *'Pastoral Care and the Drug Scene'*, (S.P.C.K.), 1970.

97-2 J.M.'s review.

97-3 Review: as published in <u>Christian Century</u>, 16th. Dec.,1970.
98 **Loneliness**, address at St Chad's, Rubery, 20th. Dec., 1970.

<u>1971</u>

99-1 **Individual Conviction and Professional Cooperation**, report by J.M. for the
<u>I.R.M</u>. <u>News-letter</u> on a day conference, 28th. Jan., 1971.
99-2 As published in the <u>I.R.M. News-letter</u>, No.18, April, 1971.
100 **Serious Personality Disorders and the Lay Counsellor**, Carr's Lane Counselling
Centre, 4th. Feb., 1971.
101-1 **Participation and Objectivity**, address to Association of Residential Group
Workers at Birmingham Medical Institute, 9th. March, 1971. (See also 66).
101-2 As published in <u>Community Schools Gazette</u>, Sept., 1972, Vol.66, No.6, pp.284-
292.
102 **To Cure sometimes, to Relieve often, to Comfort always**. An extract from the
<u>Rubery News Letter</u>, 11th. March, 1971.
103 **The Pastoral Role: a Psychiatrist's View**, paper given on an Extra-mural course,
University of Birmingham, *'Further Training of Clergy'*, at Queen's College, 21st. April
1971.
Published in ed. M.A.H.Melinsky, **Religion and Medicine 2,** (S.C.M.Press), London,
1973, pp. 82-92.
104-1 **Crisis Theory**, paper for the D.P.S.Spring School, 26th. April, 1971.
Repeated to Norfolk School of Agriculture, 16th. Sep., 1971.
104-2 Cyclostyled text for students' use.
104-3 Reflections on **Crisis**, paper to the Selly Oak Colleges, 23rd. March, 1976.
104-4 Published in <u>Theology</u>, Nov 1976, Vol LXXIX, No.672, pp.343-350.
104-5 Text for students' use, published by the <u>Institute of Religion and Medicine</u>.
105, A letter: **The N.A.M.H. Guidelines** to the editor of <u>The British Journal of
Psychiatry</u>, Aug., 1971, 119, pp.226-227.
106 **Morale,** lecture in a series of four (104-1, 106, 107-1 108) to Norfolk School of
Agriculture, 15th. Sep., 1971.
107-1 **Maturation**, lecture to the Norfolk School of Agriculture, 15th. Sep., 1971.
107-2 Another text with alterations.
108 **On Losing one's Life - Failure and Death**, Norfolk School of Agriculture, 16th.
Sep, 1971.
109-1 Reviews: Owen Brandon, 1). *'Victory through suffering',* 2). *'This Way to Life,'*
                    3). *'Living with your Conscience'*, (Guild of Health), Sept.1971.
109-2 Letter: from Mary Kidson, organising secretary of I.R.M., acknowledgement of
                    the review, etc.
109-3 Letter: from Maurice Kidd, chaplain of Guild of Health, to J.M. in response to
reading draft review before publication.
109-4 Letter: from J.M. to Maurice Kidd in reply to 109/3.
109-5 Review: as published in <u>I.R.M. Newsletter</u>, No. 19, Feb.,1972.
110 Sermon: *'Where there is no vision the people perish.'* St James' Cathedral, Bury St

Edmunds, 17th. Oct., 1971.

111 **Discovering the Value of Listening**, address in St Francis Hall, University of Birmingham, 31st. Oct., 1971.

112-1 **The Nature of Prejudice**, address at R.C.Chaplaincy, University of Birmingham, 13 Nov.1971.

112-2 **The Nature of Prejudice**, paper 112-1 as published in One for Christian Renewal Folder, April, 1974.

112-3 Same address (revised form) given to C.P.Residential Social Workers, March/April 1973.

112-4 Notes for an address on '*Prejudice*' at the Lickey Church, 7th. Oct., 1981.

112-5 **Identity, Discrimination and Prejudice**, a chapter (written March 1979) in **'Cities, Race and Faith'**, (University of Birmingham), 1980.

113-1 **A Healthy Society? I** address at University of Aston, delivered in three parts: 11th. Nov., 1971, 22nd. Nov., 1971, 29th. Feb., 1972.

113-2 **A Healthy Society? II**, University of Aston, Dec., 1972.

113-3 **A Healthy Society?**, address during an act of worship at the end of MIND Week, 1973, Southampton and District Association for Mental Health, 4th. Nov., 1973.

113-4 **A Healthy Society** (Revised), draft for the I.R.M. Study Notes, Jan., 1975.

114 J.M.'s Index Sheet on Fly leaf of Folder labelled 1972-1973.

115 Notes on follow-up meeting of Industrial Christian Fellowship held at 210 Pentonville Rd. on 14th. Jan., 1972, written by J.M. on 19th. Jan., 1972.

116 **Keeping People Alive**, Extra-mural Lecture in the University of Birmingham Medical School, 15th. Feb., 1972.

117-1 **What is going to Replace our Mental Hospitals?**, written for publication in:

117-2 Health Magazine, (London), March 1972, Vol.9. No.1, pp.12-13.

118-1 **Custodial or Residential Care for the Long-stay Patient?** written for publication in:

118-2 The Lancet, 22nd. April, 1972, Vol.1, No.7756, pp.894-895.

118-3 Reprint of Lancet article.

118-4 Hospital Chaplain, Dec.1972, Vol.II, No.41, pp.9-15.

119 **The Doctor's Role in Society and its Future**, paper read to a conference of family doctors in Birmingham, 24th. May, 1972.

120-1 **Involvement and Identity in a Large Community**, two papers given on this subject by J.M. and Councillor Dick Knowles to the West Midlands Metropolitan Council Planning Group, March 1972. This is J.M.'s paper.

120-2 **Community Councils**, joint paper by J.M. and Councillor Dick Knowles, given to the W.M.M.C.P.G., May 1972.

120-3 **Identity in a Large Community**, fuller paper than 120-1 given to the W.M.M.C.Working Party on the morning of 8th. June, 1972, in anticipation of a parallel paper by Councillor Dick Knowles in the afternoon.

120-4 Duplicate of 120-1, dated 28th. May, 1972.

120-5 Duplicate of 120-3, dated 8th. June, 1972.

121-1 **What is a Whole Man?**, 'Precis' of an address written 30th. May, 1972, and sent in advance of delivery to the Rev Harold Tonks, Carr's Lane Church.

121-2 Letter: accompanying 'Precis' from J.M. to Harold Tonks.

121-3 **What is a Whole Man?,** the address as delivered at Carr's Lane Church, 23rd. June, 1972, and published as 121-4.

121-4 I.R.M.Study Notes, No.9, April, 1975.

121-5 **The Experience of Wholeness**, read at Selly Oak Colleges, 25 March 1975, and published as 121-6.

121-6 I.R.M. Study Notes, New Series, No.10, April, 1975.

121-7 **The Wholeness of Man**, address given at a clergy training day in the University Hospital of Wales, Cardiff, 4th. Dec., 1975. Published in Contact, (Edinburgh), 1980, No.66.

121-8 Cyclostyled copy of address, marked 'Mastercopy'.

121-9 **Treating the Whole Person**, address given to local I.R.M., Nottingham, 9th July, 1976. Repeated to The Hospital Chaplains Fellowship, Oxford, 13th. July, 1976.

122 **Notes on Centripetal and Peripheral forms of Social Organisation**, written for an Industrial Christian Fellowship study group, July, 1972.

123 Review: *'Can Man Survive?'* A kit for groups, One for Christian Renewal, 1st. Sept., 1972.

124-1 **Notes on a Model for Social Theory**, draft 1, 6th. Oct., 1972.

124-2 Duplicate of 124-1.

124-3 Letter: to J.M. from Miss Mary Robinson, Dept. of Applied Social Science, University of Nottingham, in reponse to 124-1.

124-4 Letter: to J.M. from Lord Cunliffe in response to 124-1.

124-5 **Notes on a Model for Social Theory**, draft 2, April, 1973.

124-6 **Notes on a Model for Social Theory,** draft 3, August, 1973.

125 **The Problem of Setting Standards**, paper for the Central Council of Education and Training of Social Workers, Nov.1972.

126-1 Review: Paul W. Pretzel, *'Understanding and Counselling the Suicidal Person'*, (Abingdon Press).

126-2 Review: as published in the Expository Times, Dec.,1972, Vol.84, No.3, p.93.

1973

127-1 **Issues of Wholeness and Healing**, a synopsis in preparation for 127-2.

127-2 **Issues in Wholeness and Healing**, lecture at Selly Oak Colleges in a course on 'Medicare', 16th. Jan., 1973.

128 Report: on one month's Residential Course for doctors and nurses on leave from developing countries, Selly Oak Colleges, 8th. Jan. – 3rd. Feb., 1973.

129 **Mental Health is Everybody's Business**, paper given at the Westminster Pastoral Foundation, 22nd. March, 1973.

130-1 **Strategy and Tactics of Health Care**, paper given to the Methodist Healing Fellowship, Swanwick Conference Centre, 25th. April, 1973.

130-2 **The Concepts Map: Strategy and Tactics**, Notes for a seminar with D.P.S. students.

131 Obituary: R.A.Lambourne, written April 1972 for publication. Published in Contact,

(Edinburgh), Spring 1974, No.44. And in <u>The British Medical Journal</u>, 1972, Vol.2, p.536.

132 Chairman's opening remarks to the D.P.S. Spring School of 1973, typed on a card.

133-1 Letter from C.L.Mitton, editor of <u>Expository Times</u>, to J.M. accompanying a book for review, and enclosing:

133-2 The publisher's (Macmillan) Press Release.

133-3 Review: Dr S.Bradshaw, *'Drug Misuse and the Law'*, (Macmillan), written 1st. Feb., 1973.

133-4 As published (cutting) in the <u>Expository Times</u>, May 1973, LXXXIV, No.8.

134-1 **The Gestation Period of Identity Change**, draft 1, May, 1973.

134-2 The Gestation Period of Identity Change, draft 2, May, 1973.

134-3 Revised draft for publication, 10th. March, 1974.

134-4 **The Gestation Period of Identity Change**, published in <u>The British Journal of Psychiatry</u>, Nov., 1974, Vol.125, pp.472-474. See 144-1 and 144-2 for reprints.

135-1 **The Role of the Hospital Chaplain**, paper given to Hospital Chaplains at Brindle Lodge, Preston, June, 1973.

135-2 Published in <u>Hospital Chaplain</u>, (Quarterly magazine of the Church of England Hospital Chaplains' Fellowship), March,1974, No.46, pp.16-28.

136 **Farewell Speech** to friends at St John's Church, Longbridge, on retirement, 17th. June, 1973.

137-1 **The Authority of the Pastor**, address given to a Course for Clergy, Bolton Parish Church, 16th. Oct., 1973.

137-2 *'Master Copy'*, copies like this are used for study on the D.P.S.course. Published, <u>Contact</u>, (Edinburgh), 1975, No.49 pp.25-31.

138-1 **Aspects of Community Care**, draft 1 for paper given to the South Warwickshire Group Homes Association, Warwick, 22nd. Nov., 1973.

138-2 Cyclostyled copy for students' use.

138-3 Copy with corrections and additions.

139-1 **Therapeutic Communities**, address at Swanwick Conference Centre to the Annual Conference of the Association of Chaplains to Children in Residential Care, 28th. Nov., 1973.

139-2 Cyclostyled copy for students' use.

139-3 Published in <u>The Community Schools Gazette</u>, May, 1974, Vol.68, No.2, pp.80-87.

139-4 Reprint from <u>The Community Schools Gazette</u>.

139-5 **Is the Therapeutic Community the Prescription for Health Service Sickness?**, paper read to local group of the I.R.M., Carlisle, 13th. May, 1975.

139-6 **The Changing Forms of Therapeutic Communities**, report on Conference at Swanwick, 10th.-12th. June, 1975.

140 J.M.'s Index Sheet on flyleaf of Folder labelled 1974-1975.

141-1 **Human Perspectives and Human Environments**, paper given to local I.R.M., Coventry, 26th. Feb., 1974.

141-2 **Human Perspectives and Human Environments**, revised draft given to D.P.S.Spring School, 25th. March, 1974.

142 **Strategy and Tactics of Health Care: Reflections on the Concepts Map**, written

March, 1974, revised April, 1974 for publication in ed. D.W.Millard, <u>Religion and Medicine 3</u>, (S.C.M.Press), London, 1976, pp.83-91.

143 **Caring in the Community**, Trefeca, Talgarth, 9th. March, 1974.

144-1 **The Gestation Period of Identity Change**, reprint in French: **La periode de gestation du changement d'identite.** Original text see 134.

144-2 Reprint in English. Original text see 134.

145 Notes of a paper for an Urban Ministry Project, Morden, 11th. March, 1974.

146 Sermon: on '*Guilt*', St Mary's Swansea, 27th. March, 1974. See also 77.

147-1 Review: ed Frank Cioffi, Freud: '*Selection of Critical Essays*', in series 'Modern Judgements', (Macmillan), published in:

147-2 <u>The Expository Times</u>, April 1974, LXXXV, No.7.

148 Record of a small I.R.M. house group, 1965-1973.

149 Letter: **Inequality and the Health Service**, to the editor, <u>The Lancet</u>, published 29th. June, 1974, Vol.1 for 1974, No.7870 p.1342.

150 **Health, Healing and Salvation**, address at Westbury on Trym, 6th. June, 1974.

151 Letter: to editor of <u>The British Medical Journal</u>, cutting as published on 19th. Oct.,1974, Vol.4, No.5937, p.163.

152-1 Sermon: '*You cannot serve health and illness*', Luke 16,13, St Lawrence's Church, Ludlow, 20th. Oct.,1974.

152-2 Sermon: '*What is Health?*', Luke 14, 15-24; Col.3, 1-17, Worcester Cathedral, 12th. Oct., 1975.

152-3 **What is Health?,** paper given to Hospital Chaplains of Trent Area Health Authority, Nottingham, 23rd. March, 1977.

152-4 **Search for a Christian Understanding of Health**, Chapter 8, no date, no place.

153-1 **Man, Medicine and Morale**, address to local I.R.M., Bristol, 25th.Oct., 1974.

153-2 Published in <u>Contact,</u> (Edinburgh), 1976.1, No.52, pp.21-28.

153-3 Revised version, 2nd. May, 1975.

153-4 Address for I.R.M. at the British Medical Association meeting, Leeds, 6th. July, 1975.

153-5 **Morale and the Importance of Failure**, a different ending (from top p.7) to 153-4, address given to I.R.M. Wolverhampton, 13th. Oct.,1976.

154 **On Teams and Groups**, a discussion paper, written 27th. Nov.,1974.

<u>1975</u>

155-1 **The Right to Strike in the Caring Professions**, reflections on an I.R.M.conference, (London, Jan., 1975), written 22nd. Feb., 1975.

155-2 **The Ethics of Strike Action**, comments on the replies to the I.R.M.'s letter of 2nd. Oct., 1974. ?Dicussion at King's Fund, 24 Nutford Place, W1, 21st. Jan., 1975.

156 Comments on a paper sent by Lawrence Reading from St John's College, York, 5th. Feb., 1975.

157-1 **A Brain of Brains**, written for The Teilhard Review, 8th. March, 1975.

157-2 As published in <u>The Teilhard Review</u>, Oct., 1976, Vol. II, No.3, pp.95-98.

158-1 Review: E.G.Loomis and J.Sig.Paulson, '*Healing for Everyone: Medicine of the*

Whole Person', Written for <u>Health and Healing</u>, (Magazine of Guild of Health), 1975.

158-2 Covering Letter: from J.M. to Miss Christophers of the Guild of Health suggesting they should not publish his review, 14th. Feb.,1975.

159 Biographical note for the <u>I.R.M. News-letter</u>, No.31, March, 1975.

160 **Amateurs in Health Care**, paper for local I.R.M., Huddersfield, 9th. April, 1975. Repeated for local I.R.M., Wakefield, 22nd. June, 1976.

161-1 **Too Much Noise Makes You Deaf**, paper given to A.G.M. of the I.R.M., Exeter, 9th. July, 1975.

161-2 J.M.'s **Presidential Address**, as published in the <u>I.R.M.News-letter</u>, No.32, Sept., 1975, given on 9th. July, 1975.

162 **Evolution and Human Values**, dated 17th. July, 1975.

163 **Retrospect and Prospect**, article addressed to members of the I.R.M., written for publication in <u>Contact</u>, (Edinburgh), Oct., 1975.

164-1 **The Medical Machine-Minder**, first draft, written Nov.,1975.

164-2 **The Medical Machine-Minder**, draft 2, written for publication in:

164-3 <u>Health and Social Service Journal</u>, 14th. Feb., 1976, pp.300-301.

1976

165 J.M.'s Index Sheet, on Fly-leaf of folder labelled 1976-1977.

166 **Caring Competence**, Report on I.R.M. Nurses' conference at Queen's College, Birmingham, 2nd.-4th. Jan., 1976.

167-1 **'Brain Death' or 'Heart Death'?**, Reflections on an ethical dilemma. Written Feb., 1976 for publication in <u>The Expository Times</u>.

167-2 The article in proof.

167-3 Article as printed in <u>Expository Times</u>, Aug., 1976, LXXXVII, No.11.

168-1 Review: Rosemary Haughton, *'The Liberated Heart'*, (Geoffrey Chapman), 1975.

168-2 As published in <u>Theology</u>, March 1976, Vol.LXXIX, No.668, pp.113-114.

169-1 Review: Bernard Haring, *'Manipulation: Ethical Boundaries of Medical, Behavioural and Genetic Manipulation'*, <u>St Paul Publications</u>, (Clough), written 6th. Dec., 1975 for:

169-2 <u>The Expository Times</u>, April, 1976, LXXXVII, No.7.

170 **Patients and Staff**, paper given to a conference of this title organised by The King's Fund, London, 12th. May, 1976.

171 Sermon: at the family communion, St Andrew's, Bedford, 13th. June, 1976.

172 **Health as the Context of Medicine**, King's Fund Lunch-time talk, 15th. June, 1976.

173 **The Problem of Abortion**, paper written for <u>The Church in Society</u>, a study series of The Church in Wales, 23rd. June, 1976.

174 Review: Jack Dominian, *'Depression: What is it? How do we cope?'*, (Darton, Longman and Todd), London, 1976. Cutting from <u>Expository Times</u>, August 1976, LXXXVII, No.11.

175-1 **Health and the Community**, written 31st. July, 1976.

175-2 Published in <u>The Christian Education Movement Review</u>, Nov., 1976, pp.6-9.

175-3 **Health in the Community**, lecture in the series 'Sickness and Society' at the

Institute of Christian Studies, London, 29th. Oct., 1977. Published in <u>Chrism</u>, XXI, 6 May, 1978.

175-4 A re-print from <u>Chrism</u>.

176 **The Sources of Violence**, draft contribution for 'The Advisory Commission for Church and Society' paper on '*Violence*', Church in Wales, 15th. Sept., 1976.

177 **On Being Responsible**, Notes taken by a listener at a conference address printed in <u>The Hospital Chaplain</u>, Sept., 1976, 56, pp.9-10.

178-1 **Homosexuality**, notes written for the A.C.C.S., Church in Wales, Oct., 1976.

178-2 **Homosexuality**, letter written to the Editors, <u>Theology</u>, March 1980, Vol.XXXIII, No.692, pp.131-133.

178-3 Letter: to the Editors of <u>Theology</u>, Sept., 1980, Vol.LXXXIII, No.695. p.364.

178-4 Review: P.Coleman, '*Christian Attitudes to Homosexuality*', (S.P.C.K.), London, 1980, published in:

178-5 <u>Theology</u>, March 1981, Vol.LXXXIV, No.698. pp.154-156.

178-6 Sermon: '*Dealing with Evil*', Remembrance Day, Monnington Parish Church, 9th. Nov., 1980.

179-1 **Health is for Everybody**, address to Stroud Healing Mission, 16th.Oct., 1976.

179-2 **Health is Everybody's Business**, notes for address at Chesterfield, 3rd. Nov., 1976.

180 **Neighbourhoods and Communities**, extended notes for an informal address to an I.R.M.dinner, St Peter's, Saltley (Birmingham), 26th. Oct., 1976.

181 **How far does the Evangel impinge upon Counselling Practice?** address to Association for the Promotion of Pastoral Counselling, Birmingham, 27th. Nov., 1976. Published in <u>Contact</u>, (Edinburgh), No.57.

182 Intercessions: Mission Sunday, 5th. Dec., 1976.

183-1 Review: Dr Jack Dominian, '*Authority*', (Burns and Oates), 1976, written for <u>Expository Times</u>.

183-2 Covering note for the book between editor, Rev C.S.Rodd, and the reviewer.

183-3 Cutting of the review as published in <u>Expository Times</u>, Dec., 1976, LXXXVIII, No.3.

1977

184 **Hospital Chaplaincy Work - Ethical Issues**, written (Jan.,1977) by invitation for ed. Duncan, Dunstan and Welbourn, **Dictionary of Medical Ethics,** (Darton, Longman and Todd), London, 1977. The article was pirated, edited and published without ascription under two other names: J.M. received an apology and a free copy of the dictionary from John Todd.

185-1 Review: Philip Rhodes, '*The Value of Medicine*', (George Allen and Unwin), 1976. Published in <u>Theology</u>, March, 1977, Vol.LXXX, No.674. Also in

185-2 <u>Social Service Quarterly</u>, Spring 1977, Vol.L, No.4, p.311.

186 **Leadership**, notes for address to Free Church Federal Council, 10th. Feb., 1977.

187-1 **The Nature and Existence of Evil**, draft 1, written for the I.R.M. Working Party on 'Exorcism', March, 1977.

187-2 **The Nature and Existence of Evil**, draft 2, May 1979.

187-3 **The Nature [and Existence] of Evil**, draft 2, May 1979, different type-set.

187-4 Sermon notes, '*Evil into Good*?', given to Mother's Union, Llyswen, 13th. Oct., 1981. See also 178-6.

188-1 Review: Melvyn Thompson, '*Cancer and the God of Love*', (S.C.M.Press), London, 1976, written 8th. Feb., 1977.

188-2 Covering note from the Editors.

188-3 As published in Theology, March, 1977, pp.158-159.

189 **Challenge to Structures of Health Care**, written as a discussion paper for the Consultation on Religion and Medicine, Deutsches Institut für Artzliche Mission, Tübingen, Germany, March, 1977.

190 **Education for Pastoral Ministry**, preliminary comments on Foundation Syllabus (?Church in Wales), 20th. April, 1977.

191-1 **Little Bends in the Truth**, I.R.M. Sheffield, 18th. May, 1977.

191-2 Draft 2, for D.P.S. course, Sept., 1978.

191-3 **Wholeness and Truth**, manuscript with corrections.

191-4 Cyclostyled copy for student use.

192-1 Sermon: service in Derby Cathedral to celebrate the centenary of the Manor Hospital, 3rd. July, 1977. Published as

192-2 **Caring Institutions**, in I.R.M. Newsletter, No.39, Winter 1977, article begins on p.2 of 192-1.

193 Review: Robert Dingwall, '*Aspects of Illness*', (Martin Robertson), cutting from Social Service Quarterly, Summer 1977, Vol.LI, No.1.

194 Letter: on **Perfection**, to the editors, published in Theology, Sept.1977, Vol.LI, No.1.

195-1 **The Accreditation of Counsellors**, draft 1, Aug., 1977.

195-2 Draft 2, Sept., 1977.

195-3 Covering letter to Michael Wilson from J.M. asking for comments, and explaining why he was moved to write the paper.

195-4 Draft 1 (better copy).

195-5 Reprint of published paper in British Journal of Guidance and Counselling, Vol.VI, No.2. July, 1978, pp.129-139.

195-6 **Accreditation**: a reply to Mathers from Louis Marteau, same journal, pp.140-145.

196 Sermon: '*Who Am I?*', in the United Reformed Church, Summertown, Oxford, 22nd. Nov., 1977.

1978

197 J.M.'s Index Sheet on Flyleaf of Folder labelled 1978-1980.

198 **Genetic Determinism and Human Survival**, a report (unpublished) on an I.R.M. Day Conference, 2nd. Feb., 1978.

199 **The Context of Stress**, paper given at Spode House (Staffs) Conference Centre, 17th. March,1978.

200 **Issues of Prevention**, paper given at the Sheffield City Polytechnic, 24th. May, 1978.

201-1 Review: E.N.Jackson, *'The Many Faces of Grief'*, (S.C.M.Press), London, published in:

201-2 The Expository Times, Vol.LXXXIX, No.10, July, 1978, p.317.

202-1 Review: *'Statutory Registration of Psychotherapists'*, report of a Professions' Joint Working Party, Chairperson Paul Sieghart, 6th. Aug.,1978.

202-2 Letter: from J.M. to Dr B Hopson, Dept of Psychology, University of Leeds, 6th. Aug.,1978.

203-1 Review: Yorick Spiegel, *'The Grief Process'*, (S.C.M.Press), London, 1978, published in:

203-2 Theology, Nov.1978, Vol.LXXXI, No.684, pp.461-462.

204-1 **Depersonalisation in Caring Relationships**, paper to the Manchester Medical Group, Manchester, 13th. Nov., 1978, published in:

204-2 The Journal of Community Nursing, July, 1981, Vol.5, No.1, pp.12 and 15.

205-1 Reviews:

1) Murray Cox, *'Structuring the Therapeutic Process: Compromise with Chaos, The Therapist's Response to the Individual and the Group.'*

Murray Cox, *'Coding the Therapeutic Process: Emblems of Encounter, A Manual for Counsellors and Therapists.'* (Pergamon Press) Oxford, 1978.

205-2 Published in The British Journal of Guidance and Counselling, Vol.7, No.2, July, 1979, p.242.

205-3 Review: different text to 205-1, written 30th. May, 1979, for publication in:

205-4 Crucible, October-December, 1979, pp.185-186.

206 Report: to Ruri-decanal Conference at Bronllys, 15th. Nov., 1978, then an address to St Mary's, Hay-on-Wye, 19th. Nov., 1978, on 'Partners in Mission Consultation', St Michael's College, Llandaff, Church in Wales, 29th. June – 2nd. July, 1978.

1979

207-1 **Sustaining, Healing and Growing in Marriage**, draft 1, Feb., 1979.

207-2 **Reflections on the Marriage Relationship**, draft 2, given as lecture in the series 'The Family in Contemporary Society', arranged by Diocese of Bristol Education Committee, March, 1979. Repeated at Swindon, 13th. March, 1979.

207-3 **Sustaining, Healing and Growing in the Marriage Relationship**, a fuller text with more references.

208 Sermon: *'Deliver us from Evil'*, written for delivery on 3rd Sunday in Lent at St Mary's, Hay-on-Wye, March, 1979, but not delivered!

209-1 Review: Elliott Jaques, *'Health Services, Their Nature and Organisation, and the role of patients, doctors, nurses, and the complementary professions'*, (Heinemann). Published in:

209-2 Social Service Quarterly, Spring 1979, Vol. LII, No.3, pp.105-106.

210-1 **Horse Therapy for severely handicapped children**, written personally for Joe Royds, manager of The Riding Fund, 11th. May, 1979.

210-2 **The Case for Continuity**, published by The National Society for Mentally Handicapped Children, May, 1979.

211-1 Review: Roger Grainger, '*Watching for Wings: Theology and Mental Illness in a Pastoral Setting*', (Darton, Longman and Todd), London, 1979, written 11th. April, 1979.

211-2 Note of agreement to review, between Rev C.S.Rodd, editor of Expository Times and J.M.

211-3 **Clown and Leader of Clowns**, review 211-1 published in Expository Times, Sept., 1979, Vol.XC, No.12, p.382.

212 **When we say People are Breaking Down, are they really Breaking Through?**, paper read in conference on Religion and Mental Illness at Norfolk and Norwich Ecumenical Centre, 26th. May, 1979.

213-1 Review: J.B.Nelson, '*Embodiment: an Approach to Sexuality and Christian Theology*', (S.P.C.K.), 1979, written 26th. July, 1979, published in:

213-2 Theology, Jan 1980, Vol.LXXXIII, No. 691, pp.73-75.

214 Review: Dr M.Rawlings, '*Beyond Death's Door*', (Sheldon Press), 1979, written 9th. June, 1979 for and published in Contact, (Edinburgh), No.64.

215-1 **Authority**, a draft note for the I.R.M. Working Party on 'Exorcism', a variation on the first part of

215-2 **Authority, Equality and Randomness**, D.P.S. Spring School, March, 1980.

215-3 **Development of the Idea of Authority**, notes, March, 1980.

215-4 **Wholeness and Authority II,** a later draft, undated, unplaced.

216-1 **Families: On Not Solving Problems**, delivered at Manchester on 27th. Oct., 1979 at the Third 'Caring and Curing Conference' on the theme 'Stress and Reconciliation', published in Contact, (Edinburgh), No.72.

216-2 Cyclostyled text for students' use.

1980

217 **Church and Psychiatry**, paper given at Swindon in March, 1980, revised draft.

218 Review: P.Speck, '*Loss and Grief in Medicine*', (Bailliere Tindall), 1978, written Jan., 1980 for and published in the I.R.M. Newsletter, No.46, Spring 1980.

219-1 Review: ed. K.M.Boyd, '*The Ethics of Resource Allocation in Health Care*', April, 1980, written for publication in:

219-2 Contact, (Edinburgh), 1980, 2, No.67, pp.27-28.

220 J.M.'s Index Sheet on Flyleaf of Folder labelled May 1980-Dec.1983.

221 Review: Susan Sontag, '*Illness as Metaphor*', (Allen Lane), 1979, written 26th. Aug., 1980 for the Journal of Medical Ethics.

222 Letter: personal to Mrs Goulder, Secretary of 'Save the John Conolly' hospital committee, 5th. Sept., 1980.

223-1 Review: Ruthe S.Kempe and C.Henry Kempe, '*Child Abuse*', (Fontana, Open Books), 1978, written Sept.1980.

223-2 Letter from M.Jacobs, reviews editor of Contact, (Edinburgh) to J.M. regarding review.

223-3 Contact, (Edinburgh), 1982,2, No.75, p.31.

224-1 Review: ed. D.W.Shriver Jr,. '*Medicine and Religion: Strategies of Care*', (University of Pittsburgh Press), written Sept., 1980 for:

224-2 <u>Health and Social Service Journal</u>, 21 Nov.1980, Vol.LXXXX, No.4720, pp.1507-1508, cutting.

225 **Bread and Word**, paper written Dec.,1980 for D.P.S.Spring School, 1981.

1981

226-1 **Life and Death: some Current Issues**, written July 1981 in IV sections for

226-2 The Advisory Commission on Church and Society, Church in Wales, Sept., 1981.

227 **The Making of Idols,** given to local I.R.M., Birmingham, 1st. Oct., 1981.

228-1 Review: Frank Lake, *'Tight Corners in Pastoral Counselling'*, (Darton, Longman and Todd), 1981, written Nov.1981 for publication in:

228-2 <u>Theology</u>, May 1982, Vol. LXXXV, No. 705, pp.225-227.

229-1 Review: Dr E.N.Jackson, *'The Role of Faith in the Process of Healing'*, (S.C.M.Press), 1981, written Dec.1981, and published as:

229-2 **Forces and Healing**, <u>Expository Times</u>, April 1982, Vol.93. No.7 pp.220-221.

229-3 Comment from the editor, C.S.Rodd, on the review which does not recommend the book.

1982

230 Review: Dr Pierre Solignac, *'The Christian Neurosis'*, (S.C.M.Press), 1982, written 5th. March,1982 for the <u>Expository Times</u>.

231 Sermon: *'Be ye therefore perfect . . .'*, Mothering Sunday, written 21st. March, 1982 but not delivered.

232-1 Review: Carl Djerassi, *'The Politics of Contraception'*, (W.H.Freeeman), written 13th. April, 1982, for publication in:

232-2 <u>Contact</u>, (Edinburgh), 1983. 2, No.79, p.30.

233-1 Review: Working Party Report from The Linacre Centre, *'Euthanasia and Clinical Practice: trends, principles and alternatives'*, (1982), written 19th.May, 1982, for publication in:

233-2 <u>The Expository Times</u>, Jan., 1983, Vol.94, No.4, p.120.

234-1 Reviews:

1) Paul and Linda Badham, *'Immortality or Extinction?'*, (Macmillan Press) 1982.

2) Dorothy Rowe, *'The Construction of Life and Death'*, (John Wiley and Sons), 1982. Written 21st. June, 1982 for publication in:

234-2 <u>Theology</u>, Jan.1983, Vol.LXXXVI, No.709, pp.56-57.

235-1 Review: Frank Wright, *'Pastoral Care for Lay People'*, (S.C.M.Press), 1982, written 21st. Sept.,1982, for publication in:

235-2 <u>Hospital Chaplain</u>, March, 1983, No.82, p.17.

236-1 Review: ed. M.E.Marty and K.L.Vaux, *'Health, Medicine and the Faith Traditions: an enquiry into Religion and Medicine'*, (Fortress Press), 1982, produced by 'Project 10' (U.S.A.), written 28th. Dec.,1982 for publication in:

236-2 <u>Expository Times</u>, June 1983, Vol.94, No.9, p.281.

1983

237-1 **Waiting**, address to the Brecon Clerical Association, 7th. March, 1983, written Feb.,1983.

237-2 **Waiting and Reality**, address to D.P.S. Spring School 1983, published in:

237-3 D.P.S.Spring School Papers, 1983, pp.15-19.

238-1 Review: Jean Vanier, '*The Challenge of L'Arche*', (Darton, Longman and Todd), 1982, written for:

238-2 Theology, Nov.,1983, Vol.LXXXVI, No.714, pp.469-470.

239-1 Review: Frank Lake, '*With Respect: a Doctor's Response to a Healing Pope*', (Darton, Longman and Todd), 1982, written 12th. Feb., 1983 for:

239-2 The Modern Churchman, 1983, New Series Vol.XXVI, No.1, p.76.

240 **Rules for Mental Health**, no place or date.

241-1 **Ethics of New Life: Possibilities, Choices and Problems**, draft section, written 29th. April, 1983, for The Advisory Commission on Church and Society, The Church in Wales.

241-2 Final printed draft of 241-1.

242 **Kaleidoscope,** (formerly entitled **'Mind, Health and Community'**), a description of the course which J.M. took for the Diploma in Pastoral Studies, in the University of Birmingham, c.1970 until 1983. Guide-lines for Stephen Pattison who took over tutorship of the Course in Sept.1983 when both J.M. and Michael Wilson retired from the University. Written May 1983.

243 **Reconciliation**, paper for Dept. of Mission, Selly Oak Colleges, 9th. June, 1983.

244-1 Reviews:

1) Gladysann Bryce, '*Divorce and Spiritual Growth*', (Anglican Book Centre, Toronto), 1982.

2) ed Ian Gentles, '*Care for the Dying and Bereaved*', (Anglican Book Centre, Toronto),1982. Written 11th. June, 1983 for:

244-2 Theology, Jan., 1984, Vol.LXXXVII, No.715, pp.74-75.

245-1 Review: Kenneth Leech, '*What Everyone Should Know About Drugs*', (Sheldon Press), 1983, written 18 June 1983 for:

245-2 Hospital Chaplain, Dec.,1983, No.85, p.19.

246 Sermon: "*. . .unless you turn and become like little children. . .*", St Mary's Church, Hay-on-Wye, 31st. July, 1983.

247 **Prognosis and Prophecy: Faith and Uncertainty in Medicine and Religion**, notes for summing up at end of I.R.M.Conference, Salisbury, June, 1983.

248-1 **Mental Health,**

248-2 **Anxiety,**

248-3 **Morale,**

Three contributions written for and published in ed A.V.Campbell, **'A Dictionary of Pastoral Care'**, (S.P.C.K.), 1987, pp.162-163, 169, 16-17.

249 Review: P.G.Liddell, '*A Handbook of Pastoral Counselling*', (Mowbray), London, 1983, written for The I.R.M.News-letter, No.63.

1984

250 J.M.'s Index Sheet on Fly-leaf of Folder labelled January 1984.

251-1 Review: ed Michael Wilson, *'Explorations in Health and Salvation: a Selection of papers by Bob Lambourne'*, (University of Birmingham), written Jan.1984 for:

251-2 Theology, July, 1984, Vol.LXXXVII, No.718, pp.311-312.

252 Reviews:

1) Martin Parsons, *'Learning to Cope with Old Age'*,

2) Christine Atkinson, *'Learning about being a Step-parent'*,

(Mowbray's Enquirer's Library Series), 1984, written Feb.,1984 for Hospital Chaplain.

253-1 Review: Martin Israel, *'Healing as Sacrament'*, (Darton, Longman and Todd), 1984, written 12th. March, 1984 for:

253-2 Expository Times, Nov., 1984, Vol.96, No.2, p.58, **'Meditations on Healing'**.

254-1 **Power, Salvation and Suffering**, a comment on the 1983 C.M.S. Annual Sermon, 20th. March, 1984.

254-2 *'Power, Salvation and Suffering,'* the sermon by the Rev Dr Charles Elliott.

254-3 Letter from Charles Elliott (Christian Aid) dated 28 March 1984 to J.M. in response to 254-1.

254-4 Letter: from Simon Barrington-Ward, Gen Secretary of C.M.S., dated 11th. April, 1984, to J.M. in response to 254-1.

255 **Vicarious Suffering**, paper given to local I.R.M. in Barnstaple, 27th. April, 1984.

256 Sermon: *'Communication i.e. prayer'*, St Mary's, Hay-on-Wye, 17th. June, 1984.

257 Review: Doris Stickney, *'Water Bugs and Dragonflies: explaining death to children'*, (Mowbray), 1984, written for and published in Hospital Chaplain, June, 1984, No.87, cutting.

258-1 Review: Mary R.Glover, *'The Retreat, York: an early Experiment in the Treatment of Mental Illness'*, (Sessions of York), 1984, written 24th. July, 1984 for:

258-2 Hospital Chaplain, March,1985, No.90, p.19.

259-1 Reviews:

1) Alastair V Campbell, *'Moderated Love: a Theology of Professional Care'*, (S.P.C.K.), 1984,

2) Jane H.Thompson, *'Spiritual Considerations in the Prevention, Treatment and Care of Disease'*, (Oriel Press), 1984.
Written 30th. Aug., 1984 and published in:

259-2 The Times Literary Supplement, 23rd. Nov., 1984, No.4, 260, p.1356.

260-1 Review: Roger Grainger, *'A Place like this: a Guide to Life in a Psychiatric Hospital'*, (Churchman - Worthing), 1984, written 6th. Dec., 1984.

260-2 Letter to the Editor from J.M., **Perfection and the Kingdom of Heaven**, 9th. March, 1985. Both 260-1 and 260-2 are published in

260-3 The Modern Churchman, 1985, New Series Vol.XXVII, No.3, pp.51 and 61.

1985

261-1 Some reflections on Eileen Inglesby's draft paper (261-2), written 19 Jan. 1985.

261-2 *On Being a Clinical Teacher*, a draft paper by Eileen Inglesby, written for Michael Wilson 16th. Jan.,1985, who asked for J.M.'s comments.

262-1 Review: Paul Rowntree Clifford, *'Politics and the Christian Vision'*, (S.C.M.Press), 1984, written 28th. March, 1985 for publication in:

262-2 Contact, (Edinburgh), 1985.2, No.87, pp.30-31.

263-1 Review: Jessie van Dongen-Garrad, *'Invisible Barriers: Pastoral Care with Physically Disabled People'*, (S.P.C.K.), 1983, written 4th. April, 1985 for publication as:

263-2 **Concern for Wholeness**, Expository Times, Nov. 1985, Vol.97, No.2, p.62.

264-1 Review: Alastair V Campbell, *'Paid to Care: the Limits of Professionalism in Pastoral Care'*, (S.P.C.K.), 1985.

264-2 Published in Hospital Chaplain, Sept., 1986, No.96, p.22.

265 Review: Jack Dominian, *'The Capacity to Love'*. (Darton, Longman and Todd), 1985, written 30th. April, 1985, for publication in Theology, March, 1986.

266-1 Review: W.H.Vanstone, *'The Stature of Waiting'*, (Darton, Longman and Todd), 1982. 'Book of the Quarter', written 22nd. May, 1985, for:

266-2 Religion and Medicine, Vol.1, No.2, Aug., 1985, pp. 76-78.

267-1 Reviews:

1) Digby Anderson, *'The Kindness that Kills'*, (S.P.C.K.) 1984,

2) Charles Elliott, *'Praying the Kingdom'*, (Darton, Longman and Todd), 1985.
Written 29th. Oct.,1985, for publication in:

267-2 Contact, (Edinburgh), 1986,1, No.89, pp.32-33.

268-1 Review: Averil Stedeford, *'Facing Death: Patients, Families and Professionals'*, (William Heinemann Medical Books Ltd.), 1984, written 23rd. Nov., 1985 for:

268-2 The Modern Churchman, 1986, New Series Vol.XXVIII, No.2, pp.74-75.

1986

269-1 Reviews:

1) Michael Jacobs, *'Swift to hear: Facilitating Skills in Listening and Responding'*, (S.P.C.K.), 1985,

2) Patrick Casement, *'On Learning from the Patient'*, (Tavistock Publications), 1985,
Written Jan., 1986 for:

269-2 Theology, July 1986, Vol.LXXXIX. No.730, pp.324-326.

270-1 Review: Ralph Wendell Burhoe, *'Toward a Scientific Theology'*, (Christian Journals Ltd., Belfast), 1981, 'Book of the Quarter', written 12th. Feb., 1986 for:

270-2 Religion and Medicine, April, 1986, Vol.2, No.1, pp.145-148.

271-1 Review: Lisa Sowle Cahill, 'Between the Sexes: Foundations for a Christian Ethics of Sexuality', (Fortress Press), 1985, written 30th. April, 1986 for:

271-2 Theology, Sept.1986, Vol.LXXXIX, No.731, pp.412-414.

272-1 Obituary: **Kenneth Soddy R.I.P.**, written 3rd. July, 1986 for:

272-2 Religion and Medicine, October, 1986, Vol.2, No.2, p.201.

273-1 Address by Canon John Morris at the Memorial Service for Margaret Mathers, St Mary's, Hay-on-Wye, 17th. July, 1986.

273-2 A Time of Celebration for James and Margaret Mathers in the University of Birmingham, 27th. March, 1987, a description of intent for the day's programme.

273-3 A Celebration of the lives of James and Margaret Mathers. A Thanksgiving Service in St Francis Hall, University of Birmingham, 27th. March, 1987.

273-4 Obituary, <u>The Times</u>, 19 Nov 1986.

273-5 Obituary, <u>The Bulletin</u>, University of Birmingham, No.557, 27th. Nov., 1986, p.3.

273-6 Obituary, by Dr Gladys E. Strang of Edgbaston, Birmingham, not dated.

273-7 <u>Contact</u>, (Edinburgh), 1988, 3, No.97, Memorial Number to James Mathers 1916 - 1986, containing:-

Editorial

James and Margaret Mathers, address at Memorial Service (Epilogue),

Articles of J.M.:

36 Vandalism

157 A Brain of Brains

187 The Nature and Existence of Evil

256 Sermon: St Mary's, Hay-on-Wye

265 Review: Jack Dominian, Capacity to Love

Critical Assessment of Writings By Stephen Pattison et al.

Selected Bibliography (incomplete).

274-1 Tape and Transcript of the James Mathers' Memorial Lecture by Professor Anthony Dyson, 27th. March, 1987.

274-3 Pastoral Studies Spring School Papers, 1987, containing pp.1-15 a copy of Professor Dyson's text. The copy in this book is my compilation from all these originals.

275 A folder containing some of the papers and the correspondence from the I.R.M. Working Party on Exorcism, 1979.

JAMES AND MARGARET MATHERS

(Complete paper, from which the address at the Memorial Service at St.Francis Hall, University of Birmingham, 27th March, 1987, was a selection).

Michael Wilson

The spectacle of a heroic but simple person is always a heartening one. Such persons were James and Margaret, both severally and together. Self-effacing almost to a fault, they have nevertheless enriched the lives of hundreds directly and an infinite number indirectly — by courageous exploration of what it means to be human, and living their questions with faith and gaiety.

Margaret grew up in Birmingham, and was at school here at the King Edward's High School for Girls. She took her degree in English in London and then began a Teacher Training Course. While still a student she became dangerously ill with diphtheria, an experience which influenced her to train as a Nurse at University College Hospital, London. This change of career probably better suited her gifts for caring for others. She joined what is now the Queen Alexandra's Royal Army Nursing Corp (Q.A.R.A.N.C.) in World War II and was posted to India.

James' parents were both missionaries in the Belgian Congo and died when he was young. He was brought up by his Great-Aunt, whose sister is known to their Birmingham and Hay friends as the old lady who lived with them, and who died at the age of 97. James was at school at Christ's Hospital, Horsham, and then went on to qualify in Medicine at St.Andrew's University in 1938. He joined the Royal Army Medical Corps (R.A.M.C.) in World War II and was also posted to India — and thence to Burma. It was in India that James and Margaret met, and they were married in 1944 at Poona.

After demobilisation James tackled postgraduate work and study in Glasgow and Loughborough, successfully taking the St.Andrew's Diploma in Psychological Medicine in 1949. Meanwhile they founded their family, Peter being born in 1946, and Alison in 1949. They came to Birmingham in 1950 when James joined the staff of Hollymoor Psychiatric Hospital, where he was to be Deputy Superintendent. It was five years later that James also experienced serious illness, being off work for a year and undergoing major lung surgery for Tuberculosis. Both James and Margaret had therefore experience of serious illness and of receiving skill and care.

In 1958, when he was 42, James was confirmed as a member of the Church of England in St.John's Parish, Longbridge. Both he and Margaret were rooted in regular parish worship from which they drew strength and a sense of purpose for their lives. Early in the 1960's Margaret was invited by the Vicar to become a Churchwarden. After due thought she said it seemed to her too early for a woman to take office in that church: but ask her in another ten years and it might seem right. Before the ten years were up, they had moved.

James became a member, of the Parochial Church Council (P.C.C.) and of the Church Assembly, it was as a sidesman that I first met him when I preached at St.John's. "I'm James Mathers" he introduced himself after the service: "you and I share a lot of the same prejudices!"

Looking back on the way his faith and work were related, he wrote:
My concern with religion and medicine seems to have come to me fairly late in life. In retrospect I think that since my student days I was more interested in trying to surround myself with healthy people than any disorder or disability they might have; and my discontent with the kind of medical service I found myself working in was only matched by the discontent I felt when, occasionally, I ventured into one or another church in search of spiritual refreshment.
It wasn't until I was over forty that I was able to swallow my pride sufficiently to be confirmed in the Anglican church (it took some very healthy people to persuade me): and in many respects my discontent — both with ecclesiastical and medical institutions — remains!

James was made Medical Superintendent of Rubery Hill Hospital, when Hollymoor and Rubery were divided in 1960. He was at once concerned with implementing the Mental Health Act of 1959; his liberal approach to patients' welfare and his willingness to delegate authority to staff became clear. James was very approachable and was able to give people a sense of worth, and set their feet in a large room. Asked by a Diploma of Pastoral Studies student "What is your first priority as a Medical Superintendent?" he replied "My first task is to see that those who come here ill already, are not further damaged by the Institution." He will always be remembered as the doctor who permitted the unlocking of the doors at Rubery.

One day he was going round the hospital, and as he entered a ward a patient reached the end of his tether and smashed a large plate glass window. Two male nurses rushed to restrain him and restore the kind of order deemed appropriate for a Medical Superintendent. James calmly waved them aside to let the 'prisoner' free and said to him: "I realise you're feeling angry and frustrated about something and you've made your point. If you feel you can tell me what you want to say I'm ready to listen and there's no hurry. But if you can't find words and want to break more glass, would you mind" (taking him gently by the arm) "coming over here and breaking one of these small panes of glass?"

James's first act on return from the hospital each day would be to unburden himself by sharing the day's problems and frustrations with Margaret. Her experience as a nurse was invaluable. They rarely did anything without consulting one another, and it is difficult for someone who knew James in his public sphere, to realise that he was always a *representative* of the James/Margaret dyad. They were truly one flesh, and a great deal of James's unruffled calm was Margaret's gift to him.

At the time of 'the trouble' (as Birmingham friends call the fracas at Hollymoor), a bureaucrat who had presumed to override the unassuming doctor must have been shocked to find that he had hit steel — Margaret was part of the courageous and long-lasting stand on principle. As we have seen, she was a woman of considerable qualifications and already embarked on a professional career when she chose with all contentment to give her life to marriage and a family. The reading from Proverbs 31 describes Margaret well: she was an excellent homemaker, and her skills of nursing and education were well used in bringing up Peter and Alison. But above all it was in her 'being there for the family' which gave them cohesion and security. She loved them enough to leave them free to come and go. Proverbs 31 yes, but there is also more to say of Margaret who combined self-giving with considerable independence.

When James was 55 he was made a Fellow of the Royal College of Psychiatrists, and then opted to retire from the National Health Service in order 'to relate to people as people, not patients' (he wrote), and to devote more time to reading and thinking — one result of which was the publication of some outstanding book reviews, useful to many people. Margaret was interested in Kilvert and so it was Hay-on-Wye they chose as the area to which to retire. Margaret researched and lectured for the Kilvert Society. She was a voracious reader and loved poetry. Late in life she developed a gift for painting, which captured in oils the local buffs, moors, rivers and trees in lovely landscapes. James was always good with his hands — when he had tuberculosis his occupational therapy was weaving — and at Hay he set up a carpentry workshop in the cellar where he made frames for Margaret's pictures, also wooden bookrests, easels, toy puzzles and xylophones (among other things). He was also musical and played the recorder. In Northfield he would appear on Saturday mornings to play his recorder with a group of children in the Parish: and when he came to our house he would play duets with Jennifer. In Hay he played with other friends. He was a great participator in all that was going on.

Much could be said and written about James's extra-hospital work. He was essentially an explorer of what it is to be human. 'He who wishes to see a vision, a perfect whole, must see it in minute particulars'. His thinking and writing are often original, and he would pursue a question for years with great determination. "Oh I'm glad you've got that" he exclaimed one day in conversation "I've been trying to get you to see that for at least three years". Many of us found him a source of ideas for our own writing. He read widely and in addition to his own subject — psychiatry (especially mental health in a social context) — he was particularly interested in Evolution, Ethology and Social Science. A transdisciplinary thinker like Gregory Bateson really thrilled him, or a deeply human person like Laurens Van der Post. He was almost apologetic for his many published papers, regarding them only as jumping off points for further exploration. *"But"* he was fond of quoting *"the map is not the territory"*.

James was a great — I deliberately choose the word — educator, infuriatingly permissive, tantalisingly suggestive, and authoritative from his wide experience of human involvement. He described this role of teacher as 'looking over a student's shoulder together with him or her at what was being studied'. His style was rooted in work with a Therapeutic Community — and I remember his describing a Ward Meeting when some question of discipline was raised and all looked to him as the psychiatrist for an answer: but no answer came. How embarrassed he felt by his own long silence: when slowly and unexpectedly bits of answers were put together by the patients and nurses themselves and a responsible consensus discovered.

I've never known any teacher who could so polarise the group of Diploma of Pastoral Studies students here in the University — year after year. Some thought him the bees' knees and flourished in his stimulating and exploratory sessions (which he called Kaleidoscope after the toy which breaks up existing patterns and forms new ones): others found him a complete waste of time. It was, perhaps, a misfortune that students encountered him in their first term while still hankering for a more authoritarian approach, rather than later in the course. James was authoritative, but not authoritarian — unless you failed to pick up the key to his method: he was exploring too. He was bored when asked to take a mainly informative session, even more bored by having to think up examination questions, and positively shattered when he had to correct examination papers (thus making it possible for me to have a sabbatical).

The prototype course for the Diploma of Pastoral Studies was run at James's hospital by Eric Fenn and Bob Lambourne in 1963. James became an Honorary Lecturer in Pastoral Studies in the Department of Theology here in Birmingham, and was also widely sought as a speaker at conferences or as a preacher at St.Luke's-tide, on many subjects related to health, mental health, healing, caring, counselling, ethics and hospital chaplaincy. He was much in demand by statutory and voluntary societies including the Institute of Religion and Medicine (I.R.M.) of which he was elected President 1974/5. He ran a stimulating discussion group of doctors, clergy, teachers, nurses and social workers at his house for many years. He was an external assessor for several residential social work courses. He was also on many working parties such as those on 'Cities, Race and Faith', on various ones for the Birmingham Council of Churches, a participator in Diocesan and I.R.M.studies on exorcism, a member of an international group of doctors and clergy at Tübingen — and after his retirement helped the Church of Wales on matters of medical ethics.

Of all his ideas, a fundamental one becomes clear from our description of his family life — the idea of we-relationships, both in forming children's self-identity, and in a mature humanity. "All things are yours, not by possession but by participation". We catch a glimpse too of Margaret as a shaper of James' thought. And deeper, the Christian basis for their understanding of God's purpose for themselves, others and the world. Guntrip wrote:

> *Consciously cultivated spirituality is apt to be precious and artificial. We are most genuinely spiritual when we are thinking least about it but are just immersed in living a genuinely personal life, and going on growing in it.*

This is true of both Margaret and James. There was no false piety about them. They were faithful in local church worship and prayer, but were not indifferent to its quality. James was interested in ritual and how it was performed, and when Series I and II were introduced experimentally, he was a member of the group who met in the parish church to think out and act out the best arrangements. Because they cared they were able to carry out small things without disdain, and large things without pomposity. If this account of their life and work seems anthropocentric, it is, but only safely so because rooted in the greater context of love of God and Christ.

Three of the biblical images of discipleship gather their well-differentiated contributions into one whole:

James was typically leaven. He could be relied upon to enter a discussion with a searching contribution (usually relevant but not always) which disturbed some underlying assumption that the rest of us were taking for granted. He worked in the depths of any discussion with 'the burning fire of thought', and was himself open and not afraid of being wrong.

Margaret was typically salt. She was the perfect enhancer of James' and others' pursuits, who brought out the taste of any occasion. When visiting their home she did everything possible to make James' and our conversation time as fruitful as possible. Lunch beautifully prepared and served, no washing-up allowed, door-bells and phones answered; then joining us for tea and adding her own 'no nonsense' comments on any ideas we shared with her. This was typical of her self-effacing service, which spread from the home into local church and surrounding events, and through which she expressed her Yes to God.

James and Margaret together illustrate the third image, "Light". Although both were so self-effacing, there was never any doubt about the source of their light. The Bible says nothing about waving your light about, but only 'Let it shine' — and they did. Both would, I am sure, be genuinely surprised that I describe them as 'conspicuously' excellent Christian laity, thoroughly involved in the community's life, and well able to discern the drift of a situation measured by Christian values.

It was when they retired to Hay-on-Wye for the last fifteen years of their lives that both were content to become local residents without title or status or professional role. They were free to develop their gifts, to care for the elderly Aunt and one another. Both were locally involved in the life of the town, in parish church, AlmsHouse Trusteeship, and a 'Study Group' and made many friends. For ten years or so James continued his forays away from home to lecture here, to speak at Conferences, to support the Institute of Religion and Medicine, and to support the Study group at Tübingen. It is right, therefore, that Memorial Services should be held both in Hay and in Birmingham. Today we remember James and Margaret together, and give thanks to Margaret for making it possible for James to undertake such creative public service here and more widely. His support during the twelve years when I tutored the Diploma of Pastoral

Studies Course (D.P.S.) was unstinting and vital to my sanity.

During her last illness Margaret was patient and brave. James, who could hardly boil an egg, adapted to shopping and caring for her. She died at home. James on the other hand, when colleagues stressed the importance of autonomy and dignity for people dying at home or in a hospice, would say he thought that in today's society we must prepare for the loneliness and indignity of dying in a desert not an oasis. And so it transpired. Following surgery, he died in an Intensive Care Unit surrounded by those he had described as the medical machine minders. This was his last exploration of the experience of being out of control, an experience for which he had prepared through reflection and prayer.

In his book, 'A Mantis Carol', Laurens Van der Post describes a bushman who through various vicissitudes came to live in New York and work in a circus. Separated from his own soil and people, deprived of his stories and language, he resisted all the pressures of a money economy, material possessions and competitiveness, retaining his dignity, his humour and his sense of bushmanhood: Van der Post longed for some kind of award, some kind of Order whose investment would be introduced by a citation like the following:

> *For valour in the field of life, distinguished conduct in the battle of being, and steadfastness in defending its quality and textures against aberration and distortion by the prevailing hatred, malice and envy of our collective time, ensuring thereby an example of how being for sheer being's sake, and pursuing it to its own end, is the true glory of life on earth, and the unique source of its renewal and increase of meaning and light in the darkness ahead.*

On behalf of us all I would like to invest James and Margaret Mathers jointly with this Order, for valour in the field of life and distinguished conduct in the battle of being.

"What, After All, is Health?":

James Mathers as Critical Pastoral Theologian
The James Mathers' Memorial Lecture
Birmingham 1987
Professor Anthony Dyson

(Samuel Ferguson Professor of Social and Pastoral Theology, University of Manchester)

INTRODUCTION

It is plainly premature to attempt a reflective and comprehensive estimate of James Mathers' contribution to pastoral theology, to pastoral practice and issues of health care in the Christian churches and in the wider society. When the time is right for such an appraisal, I know for certain that the task must be completed by someone other than me. For though I was acquainted with the man, and though I am acquainted with some of his writings (in both respects to my own great profit), there are others who knew James Mathers' life and thought better than me and who must be persuaded to venture upon that task of mature appraisal for the edification of us all. Furthermore, I do not have the knowledge to explore how his life-experience bore upon and shaped his espousal and interpretation of the Christian faith. Nor do I have the knowledge to examine the hugely productive interplay of influence between Bob Lambourne, Michael Wilson, James Mathers and others. Those tasks too must be taken up by other people. Thus, although I am painfully conscious of my disqualifications for these weightier and necessary responsibilities, I feel privileged to enter upon a more provisional and tentative undertaking which will try to capture _some_, and only _some_, of James Mathers' principal themes and relate these to one of my own main concerns, namely the question of the reconstruction of pastoral theology as a critical intellectual discipline which will serve both church and society. I do this to honour his memory in a city to which, and among people to whom, James Mathers gave so much of himself. I should say that in this paper, I quote from some fifty articles or book reviews, though I have consulted more than that. But nonetheless the paper makes no claims to completeness of coverage, nor reference to all the material which must exist. I quote widely from James Mathers' writings on the grounds that today you are mainly here to listen to _his_ words rather than mine. I owe a debt of gratitude to Hugh Melinski for pointing me to, and supplying me with, some of the material. I use gender inclusive language myself and for the sake of consistency, since I am quoting James Mathers a lot, I've adapted his own words to follow the same convention.

CHALLENGES TO PASTORAL THEOLOGY.

In an article which I wrote in 1983 called *'Pastoral Theology - Towards a New Discipline,'[1]* which is published in Contact, I try to set out some of the general, and more specific challenges, which now have to be faced and which are now addressed in the tradition of pastoral theology which we have inherited in the Roman Catholic and Protestant West. I am going to take my description of those challenges as I saw them and see them as a framework in which to set James Mathers' inspiring contribution to the subject.

First, pastoral theology has to involve itself in the wider debate about the authority of the bible and tradition, and of the meaning and content which may be given to the notion of revelation, in relation to other sources of knowledge to which pastoral theology refers. I shall show that James Mathers deals, admittedly fragmentarily, but nonetheless incisively with this question.

Second, Pastoral Theology is involved with the question of the historical Jesus and of the extent to which he may be regarded as an historical and/or theological norm for pastoral theology and practice. Mathers *does* utilise the gospel tradition about Jesus to no small extent, though I judge there to be some problems about the way he does so, in respect to the limitations imposed upon us by the historical-critical study of the Bible. I will however, set this matter on one side as too big a theme to pursue here. Nevertheless I observe that James Mathers certainly uses the gospel tradition to powerful effect, in, for example his article *'The Context of Anxiety'.*

Third, pastoral theology has to take account of the related issues concerning the time-bound character of theological statements, asking how far pastoral theology is determined by prevailing cultures and what interpretative procedures we should use in relation to this. Here Mathers has much that is implicit, if little that is explicit. But he quotes with approval Lambourne's comment on the shifts of theological emphasis that are required in the West, *'which may be need to be shifted again in a few decades with cultures other than those of the West.'* [2]

Fourth, pastoral theology will be required to register a great interest in the debates in the sciences about the nature and determinance of the self, or selfhood. I shall not pursue this theme in what follows, though it deserves exploration in Mathers' writings. An indication of his sensitivity to this question can be found in a pungent response to Jane Thompson's use of the phrase about the human being as a 'tri-partite creation of body, mind and spirit.'[4] Mathers replies that Thompson talks as if the three were logical categories of equivalent status. *"In fact"* he says *"they constitute a hierarchy of levels analogous to that of chemistry, organic chemistry, and biochemistry, and when this is not recognised, mind and spirit tend to be created and treated as things, like bodies, in a way which confuses rather than clarifies."*[5] Again, writing on hierarchy, Mathers talks of

> *The all too common mistake of a blanket condemnation of hierarchy. In fact, hierarchies of arrangement are a necessary feature of any kind of order throughout both human and other nature: it is only the persistence of a particular pattern of hierarchy when it is inappropriate that deserves to be anathematized.*[7]

And in an as yet unpublished article called *'Reflections on the Marriage Relationship,'*[3] he explores to begin with both neurological, ethological and other scientific discussions of that field.

Fifth, on the challenge to individualistic pastoral theology, James Mathers made a massive contribution to present day discussion of this theme and I shall explore this at length in what follows.

Sixth, the shape and content of pastoral theology has been profoundly influenced by the increasing professionalisation of the clergy over the last hundred years. But this very professionalisation has itself become confused because the nature and function of the clergy has become unclear. The picture being rightly and properly muddied by rising lay self-conciousness. James Mathers addresses this theme with some passion and I give a brief account of his views.

Seventh, pastoral theology is held by some to be embued with a Pelagian optimism about humankind and requires, they say, the injection of a more transcendental and judgmental quality. It will be clear from much of what I say about James Mathers that he does not deserve the "Pelagian" label. In his book review of Edgar N. Jackson's *'The Role of Faith in the Process of Healing'*, Mathers makes it abundantly clear that he knows the difference between an anthropocentric and a theocentric mode.[6]

Eighth, feminist analysis has succeeded in demonstrating beyond reasonable doubt the love, and the androcentric character of Christian tradition in theology and church practice in a way which must surely question many of the assumptions, pastoral beliefs, practices, rituals and personal interventions in people's lives. From what I have read, James Mathers barely raises these questions, though he says much which is indirectly sympathetic to these questions being put. And in what follows, I shall try to draw attention to some of the implications of the feminist question.

INDIVIDUALISM, MUTUALITY AND INCLUSIVENES

Here I get on to the substance of my lecture about his thought. A constant theme in James Mathers' writings is the critique of individualism in pastoral care, in theology, in medicine and in other fields. And I will give a number of examples of this to illustrate the different perspectives from which James Mathers views this phenomenon.

First, in a general sense, for example, he criticises two authors and I quote - 'whose books make the implicit assumption that persons are separate one from another'. But it is, he says 'an assumption which is increasingly called in question'. 'There is no person without encounter with other persons' says Paul Tillich. 'It is bodies which are enclosed by a covering of skin; by contrast *persons* are centres of agency within a network of living relationships.'[8]

Again, in a general sense, James Mathers criticises Marty and Vaux's book *Health, Medicine and the Faith Tradition's*, because, and I quote 'underlying most of the book is a basic assumption that health is to be sought by focusing on the individual: perhaps future studies will redress the balance and deal with health as a corporate phenomenon.'[9] On the other hand Mathers commends Martin Israel's book *Healing as Sacrament*, for its holistic orientation. For Israel contends, says Mathers, 'that a true theology of healing starts on a simple individual plane, extends to involve human society, and finally takes in the whole created universe.'[10] Though, I suspect Mathers would not be *entirely* happy with that particular formulation.

Now going on to look at his critique of individualism in the context of sexuality and marriage. James Mathers comments approvingly of Lisa Sowle -Cahill's claim that, I quote,

> . . . 'the primary framework in the Christian tradition for the evaluation of sexual behaviour has been a <u>communal</u> love rather than an individual one. Sex, like other gifts of God is primarily for the furtherance of his Kingdom and only secondarily for the comfort of the sexual partners'(my underlining).[11]

Mathers probes deeper to ask whether the couple's fulfilment must be more than a matter of 'co-operative sensual gratification'. He quotes, 'to be ethically adequate as *genuine* fulfilment requires the procreation of, and care for some new living thing, be it a child or a lifestyle or an artistic creation'. If this were the case, 'fulfilment would have just as important a communal relevance'[12] as it ever did. Another striking account of the communal reference of marriage is found in the unpublished essay which I mentioned: *Reflections on the Marriage Relationship*. Mathers asserts that, 'the family is something more than just a collection of individuals, it is also a network of relationships between them, binding them into a whole of some kind.'[13] Mathers goes on, *'the one flesh of a marriage will only mature, if together the couple become able to leave the exclusivity of that one flesh behind and centre their joint life in a wider grouping. First, in their family and then in successively wider social fields, until finally their caring concern is with so wide a humanity, spreading over past, present and future generations, from an individual to a cosmic perspective, that they have difficulty in distinguishing their love for their fellows from their love for God.'[14]

James Mathers' approach to the theme of individualism and love is also sharply focused in a book review of Jack Dominion's *'The Capacity to Love.'*[15] Mathers writes:

> *'Love is of course manifested only in relationship and it is disappointing to find Dominion emphasising that self-love is the key to all personal loving'.* 'Personal loving', Mathers continues, *'is not a code to be cracked with a key, it is a dance wherein self-discovery and the discovery of the other are so mutually intertwined that neither one can be a key to the other'.*

Mathers continues, 'Dominion talks of dependence and independence, even of mature dependence but never of *inter*dependence'.

> *'It is a pity that he limits his considerations to the traditional individualist frame of reference. Notions of wholeness, perfection, suffering and anxiety take on a new depth of significance both theologically and otherwise, when considered from a corporate stance'.*

I quote: 'the notion of perfection in this connection', which Mathers uses, 'brings forth a distinctive interpretation'. 'For Jack Dominion', says Mathers, 'the injunction to be perfect in Matthew 5:48 is a command not a request and is interpreted as addressed to the individual as if he or she were a social isolate'. Mathers argues that 'surely what we are to see is a corporate perfection since we are inescapably related to each other. It must be sought in other selves as much as in our own.'[16] He makes a similar point elsewhere, I quote: 'the achievement by anyone of us of true personhood is always the achievement (for better or worse) of all those people with whom we are or have been in relationship. Personality is a social or corporate achievement.'[17] It is in this context that James Mathers situates his exegesis of the Johanine phrase, 'that they may all be one'. The interpretation of that is not an ecclesiologial interpretation in the ecumenical sphere. Love finally leads not to a 'depletion of individuality' as Dominion suggests but to a corporate perfection of 'all'.

The emphasis against individualism and on mutuality and sociality, this time in suffering, is an account in a striking way in James Mathers' comments on Melvin Thompson's book, *'Cancer and the God of Love'.* Mathers writes: 'my only slight disappointment was in the theological chapters where... the author surveyed the problem of suffering only in an individual and not a social context. He spells out the possible ultimate meanings of disease, either as leading to despair or disintegration, or as calling human beings to struggle against it, or as a matter of indifference'. 'But', James Mathers asks, 'Is there not a fourth possibility: that disease may sometimes be *suffered*, in a sense of, *put up with*, neither in despair, nor struggling against - *but as a task to be done for others?*[18] I would like help with the exegesis of that statement. Elsewhere, James Mathers wants to propose that, and I quote, 'all suffering, or nearly all, whether we realise it or not, is borne not only on the sufferers account, but also vicariously for others... there is a solidarity in suffering.'[19]

In more than one place, Mathers' rejects the human atomism which could lead to the view of society being the kind of grouping that, I quote:

> *'from which disorderly elements could be extruded or exiled'. Thus he says, 'we are biologically as well as ethically committed to recognising humankind as one society. There is no place outside society to which we can consign elements or members, whom we choose to label deviant or disordered. . . . For the future, the social organism, society, must learn to live with, and re-interpret the significance of, its own waste products.'*[20]

A striking phrase. This reminds me of the idea of an unredeemable remnant, who because continuously unemployed and therefore unemployable are therefore morally blameworthy, an idea recurring in British social and religious history over the last two hundred years; earlier in the century, the Booths, thinking about the unemployable in London, and of course the current debate on unemployment. Mathers pursues the same theme theologically when he puts forward the interpretation, which it seems to me has much in common with the bias to the poor of Liberation Theology, that during his life, Jesus made special emphasis upon *peripheral* members of society as those who would in particular carry his authority. I quote:

> *'it really seems as if Jesus ... was enabling us to see for the first time the possibility of a more flexible kind of society, constantly discovering newness of life, wherein the persons worth paying attention to, worth endowing with authority, were all around us were all of us, especially those whom we prefer to ignore or don't seem to fit in or conform to our ideas of what is good.'*[21]

James Mathers recognises that this challenge to individualism highlights the corporate and institutional and *political* implications of Pastoral Care.[22] There is an example of this in the institutional dimension, we may note Mathers' observation on the British Medical Association in a particular context, I quote, 'The B.M.A. insist on the sacrosanct nature of the individual doctor, individual patient relationship, and thus deny themselves room to be influenced by other ethical requirements for the *common* good'. So, he says, 'medical persons should urgently seek to broaden their focus of concern from the single individual, seen as if in isolation, to a more realistic ethical focus on the common good.'[23] This attitude to medicine is based on the individualistic approach of an objectivist kind of science whose advances and advantages are not unlimited. 'We need', says Mathers, 'to supplement it with an approach which has a more corporate, participant, and therefore subjective bias.'[24]

As I draw this section on individualism to a close, may I refer to a set of variations by Mathers on an original theme from Pierre Teilhard De Chardin, which I discovered quite inadvertently reading through these difficult texts, in which he captures, from different angles, the subject of a communal view of the individual in society. I quote first Pierre Teilhard's theme in French, then in English, followed by five of the Mathers' variations.

'*Ma* matière ce n'est pas *une partie* de l'Univers que je posséderais *totaliter*; c'est la *totalité* de l'Univers possédée part moi *partialiter*"
'*My* matter is not a *part* of the Universe that I possess *totaliter*, it is the *totality* of the Universe possessed by me *partialiter*.'[25]

These are the variations:

1. 'We are all partly responsible, but not necessarily to blame for, all the suffering in the world, rather that each of us being wholly responsible for only a small individualised fraction of it.'[26]

2. 'This means that we see ourselves as partly responsible for the whole of the Body and no longer wholly responsible for that part of it which is centred on ourselves.'[27]

3. 'We are all partly responsible for the whole of the created order and not as we prefer to think wholly responsible for only a part of it.'[28]

4. 'It means accepting that we are, each of us, partly responsible for the whole of society's health instead of, as to often at present, imagining we are wholly responsible for a fragment of it.'[29]

5. 'In a truly healthy society, each person would see themselves as partly responsible for the whole of it, rather than wholly responsible for part of it.'[30]

James Mathers of course, sees many theological foundations on which to ground this move from individualism to mutuality and wholeness. He speaks approvingly of the Institute of Religion and Medicine's theological orientation, as one of I quote: 'emphasis on the corporate or communal aspects of whatever faith we possess.'[31] Again I quote, 'the Christian will be reminded that since what he or she is seeking is the Kingdom of God, and his righteousness, his holiness, his wholeness - he or she must always pay as much attention to wholes as to parts.'[32] Another tack: 'St. John and St. Paul between them make it plain, that by his resurrection, (Jesus') charisma, his authority, is re-embodied in his resurrected body, of which we are all members or potential members.'[33] The third theological tack: again, by experiencing repentance or change of mind, (the New Testament *metanoia*), we move in the direction of reconciliation (with God and one's fellows) 'which is to say that it leads away from an egocentric context to a sociocentric or a God centred one.'[34]

'REVELATION, AUTHORITY AND THEOLOGY'

At first it seems that James Mathers in this connection is taking a conventional, liberal, Protestant view of the theological task, thus he writes in one place, I quote,

> *'The good news maybe unchanging, the human expression of it is not and any such expression must be tentative and provisional. All attempts to fix it for the future, for instance in the making of creeds, run the risk of leading us into idolatory (It is what comes out of one's mouth that defiles a person).'*[35]

But, further, Mathers says,'The theologian should not neglect what David Jenkins has called the secular sources of reality'. He says:

> *'The pastor should have a chance to revise his or her theology in the light of his or her secular experience. We badly need more natural theology to help us make sense of present day society, and since society is undergoing rapid change, natural theology will have to change rapidly too. The old certainties of the faith must be continually re-interpreted if they are to remain relevant.'*[36]

But I think on reflection, that James Mathers' theological position is in fact more radical than this. Its direction may be gleaned from two brief remarks about counselling. Mathers speaks of the 'listening and watching attitude, primarily so that God's revelation may be heard or seen,'[37] and elsewhere he observes that, 'Christian counselling focuses on the present and the future, rather than on the present and the past.'[38] Thus Mathers places emphasis upon the *presentness* and the futurity of revelation, to correct what he suspects to be the widespread exclusive emphasis upon its pastness. This is more apparent in the following passage:

> *'We cannot expect to grow in our understanding of God unless we deliberately pay wide-ranging attention to the natural and human context in which God manifests Godself. Contrary to common practice we should learn to pray with our eyes open, to watch and pray.'*[39]

So Mathers unambiguously asserts in another place, 'Scripture is not the only source of revelation.'[40]

One of the principal reasons, I suspect, for James Mathers stress on the presentness of revelation, and on the need to restate doctrine, springs from his espousal of a rather interesting critical theory of the history of belief and doctrine. One element in this theory is that spiritual movements ebb and flow in history, thus underlying continuity is difficult to find. I quote:

> *'The flexibility and excitement of the early Church . . . disappeared after Christianity became the official religion and leadership became institutionalised. Subsequently, of course, new charismatic leaders arise . . . and a similar sequence of events follows.'*[41]

Not a simple view of continuity but of ebb and flow.

But Mathers goes further than this. What seems to be a truth in one generation maybe a falsehood in another. In his paper on prejudice Mather's argues that the intense tribal loyalty of the Jews helped their survival as a nation, and gave them a strong sense of their own identity. But Christians, whose history begins in Judaism, had to break out, of what in a larger context was seen to be a pattern of death, namely tribal prejudice. Michael Wilson comments that, I quote, 'doctrines which are handed on as if they were merely for intellectual acceptance, or as measures of conformity, may actually restrict our growth, by denying us understanding of the life experience which they contain.'[42]

As far back as 1976, James Mathers made his position clear, 'the Christian must be true to his or her understanding of God today, in the faith that this will make possible a different and deeper understanding of God tomorrow.'[43] But more than this, I quote:

> *'An understanding of history, which includes traditional doctrine is of great service in the pursuit of ethical endeavour, but it should not be determinative of it. The Christian's field of action lies in the present and the future not in the past. He or she seeks newness of life, both for others and of self. Health, Salvation, the inbreaking of the Holy Spirit are always unpredictable, no amount of extrapolation forward from past experience will make them otherwise.'*[44]

This stress on presentness and on today's natural theology becomes clearly visible in what I judge to be one of the last pieces James Mathers' wrote, a review of Robert Wendell Burhoe's *'Towards a Scientific Theology'*. Burhoe seems to talk pretty interchangeably with 'God (or Nature)' as the 'system of reality and power that created the life upon it', and 'also created, sustains and judges human life including our religions.' Mathers comments that, 'the strength of (this) book lies in its acceptance of currently established scientific fact as a basis for building theology - our understanding of God in our generation.'[45]

Mathers' discussion of Burhoe bears out what he says in another place when expressing his doubt about the practice of testing the significance of modern understandings of the world against long-held certainties about the value and meaning of Scriptural texts and the teaching authority of the Church. Mathers turns this process of testing on its head. Thus:

'modern understandings of the Creation have each in their own time, to be fought for and rigorously tested, but effective testing comes from other scientists rather than from religious tradition. Whenever, in history, the authority of the Church and the Bible has been in conflict with such modern understandings, it is always the latter which has proved the stronger and the former which have had to be re-interprete.'[46]

And as I conclude this section, I can sense James Mathers' wry sympathy but perhaps frustration with Bob Lambourne's characterisation of revelation. In a review of Michael Wilson's *'Explorations in Health and Salvation,'* (the collection of Lambourne's Essays), Mathers' quotes as follows: (to bring all three in, - the Trinitarian friends – laughter!) I quote, 'As always the central notion is a biblical one, namely, that God gives new self-revelation, does a new thing, gives a new perception of reality for tomorrow, when his people obediently do what they can already see to be right in the light of yesterday's revelation.'[47]

HEALTH AS AN ESCHATOLOGICAL CONCEPT.

The notions of health and wholeness as James Mathers employs them are rich indeed. In a theological perspective they may both be judged *eschatological* in character. I quote, . . . 'a healthy society is a visionary concept, a work of the imagination, far removed from current realities.'[48] Its realisation depends upon the sharing of the common vision. It is, Mathers insists again and again, 'an inclusive society' this healthy society, embracing us, our friends and our enemies. The wholeness which we seek does not arise through the expulsion of the individual. I quote: 'Tomorrow's greater good could emerge from the reconciliation of today's good and today's evil, rather than from the expulsion of today's evil.'[49] The wholeness we seek must *include* evil, and sickness and death. 'Evil is an essential part of goodness, sickness an essential part of health, death an essential part of life.'[50] So, 'the concept of wholeness is not a scientific one.'[51] He goes on, 'perhaps we should be glad that such a vision of wholeness and health seems to recede as our experience grows for nothing is so fatal to human endeavour as actually to reach one's ultimate objective.'[52]

This theological stress of the inclusiveness of the healthy society is contrasted, for Mathers, with Frank Lake's theological stance in his book *'Tight Corners in Pastoral Counselling'* where, for example, Lake writes, 'it was the priests and the ecclesiastical lawyers . . . who crucified Christ *and put themselves beyond the reach of His offer of forgiveness.'*[53] By contrast with Lake's apparent exclusiveness Mathers argues thus, in another place, I quote:

'Since we are all to some extent persons and relationships, we can only move in a healthy direction, if all persons are moving towards the same goal'. As Christians, this means I take it, that we cannot move faster

towards spiritual health than those who reject us. Love your enemies, not
merely out of blind obedience to an unrealistic commandment, but
because only so will we make any progress towards the Kingdom.[54]

The dynamic, always in complete, corporate and eschatological character of health is
made clear in Mathers' essay, on '*Psychiatry and Religion*':

> '*What after all is health?' he says (which is my title). 'A person is not*
> *healthy if they are badly adjusted to their environment . . . (which*
> *includes their social environment, and other people).. . . And if their*
> *environment is itself unhealthy, as is usually the case, they are not*
> *healthy if they are well adjusted to it. They can only be perfectly healthy*
> *if they were well adjusted to a perfectly healthy environment. This is not*
> *likely to obtain except in the Kingdom of Heaven'. So all our human*
> *notions of health must be understood as a dynamic, as movement*
> *towards an optimum, which is more or less remote from present*
> *reality.*'[55]

And as you well know, in relation to health and wholeness, James Mathers is
often critical of experts, I quote . . . 'professional care-givers, however skilled they may
be in problem-solving are not better guides to wholeness than anyone else. Health is not
a matter for experts'. 'It is only problems with which experts deal, and wholeness is not
a problem.'[56] The same is true in the Church. I quote: 'The teaching would seem to be
that the pastoral function was to be exercised as a general responsibility of all believers.
There is certainly very slender historical warrant for the present-day notion that the professional healers of disease, whose special concerns still seem to be individual and
private, rather than public and corporate, have anything to contribute to the understanding of the pastoral role.'[57] Mathers' standpoint becomes concrete when he says, I quote:
'I have tried to avoid suggesting that I believe in counselling as a specialist occupation.'[58]
The Christian counsellor 'is called to see his or her encounter with another person, as one
between equals, rather than between oneself as strong and the other as weak.'[59]
Moreover, as Mathers recounts Casement's argument in, '*On learning from the Patient*',
I quote: 'It is the patient and not the therapist who knows best what the patient needs.'[60]

In his review of Jean Vanier's book on L'Arche Communities, which Vanier
founded, James Mathers draws attention to its aim: 'To break down the barriers that too
often exist between assistants and the handicapped members and to stress the contribution which those we label as handicapped, can make to the health and wholeness of the
rest of us'. Thus L'Arche's objective is, I quote: 'to foster the growth, of a *Christian*
community'. 'This implies having a special concern for those on the margin of society,
but not with the aim of changing them . . . so much as respecting and nourishing their
proper contribution to community, as spiritually conceived.'[61] In another connection
Mathers boldly insists that, 'the unemployed, the deviant, the delinquent and the mentally
ill ought to be those whose voices are most carefully listened to in the development of

health care strategy, instead of being those with voices who are most ignored.'[62] In theological support of this point of view, Mathers argues that Jesus taught that, quote, 'he was present especially with those peripheral members of society whose authority is usually unacknowledged - those who are hungry, or foreigners, or poor, or sick, or imprison. . . . '[63] 'All in all', says Mathers, 'every single one of us has a responsibility to make a contribution to the strategy of healthcare.'[64] Now, however much others might wish to qualify James Mathers' critique of experts and professions, he may not be accused of a rabid populism, his position is all of a piece with his theological under-standing of community, which I have expounded at some length earlier. It is an under-standing of interdependence to which autonomy is also essential. A difficult combination.

FEMINISM, ACTION, MUTUALITY AND THE ESTABLISHMENT OF JUSTICE.

I have just noted how for James Mathers, the healthy society is one which embraces all who are judged deviant, handicapped or *other* in any way. I have noted how for Mathers, the true state of goodness must somehow include evil. I have already noted how on the psychotherapeutic levels, Mathers rejects those approaches which try to get rid of the human surd. For example, he recalls Martin Israel's view that 'evil has to be isolated, exorcised and then redeemed'. Mathers himself observed that, 'it is possible, even if difficult in practical terms for evil to be redeemed *in situ* without exorcism.'[65] Again criticising Frank Lake, I quote: 'To help disturbed people to *become aware* of repressed feelings implies an informational transaction: we communicate with them' – 'a process which makes for full (mental) life'. This is not the same as helping them to, 'discharge excessive quantities of excitation' . . . 'which implies movement towards the extinction of the tension of instinctual needs - which would mean death.'[66]

Mathers points towards, therefore, a pastoral and political theology which takes into itself struggle, action, growth and evil. Which can learn from what Beverley Wilding Harrison in her book, '*Making the Connections*', describes as 'our (that is women's) need for a moral theology, shaped and informed by women's actual historical struggle.'[67] Thus Wilding Harrison goes on, 'in a Christian perspective, the locus of divine revelation is in the concrete struggle of groups and communities to lay hold of the gift of life and to unloose what denies life.'[68] This points in turn she says to the 'need to incorporate the full meaning of the human struggle for life into our understanding of God.'[69] Underlying these theological prescriptions is Harrison's belief that feminism must call the Christian ethical tradition and the Christian pastoral tradition to accountability for what she calls 'minimising the deep power of human action in the work of, or the denial of, love.'[70] We must overcome that body-aimed dualism which issues in the assumption, quote: 'that we are most moral when most detached and disengaged from life-struggle.'[71] By contrast, Jesus was not involved in a 'headlong race towards Golgotha, towards crucifixion, as if he sought suffering as an end itself to complete the resolution of the divine-human drama once for all. . . . His death is the price to be paid for refusing to abandon the radical activity of love, of expressing solidarity and reciprocity with the excluded ones in His community.'[72] In criticising that false understanding of sacrifice, which as Nietzsche also realises, is against life, in favour of human action in community, Harrison also has to point out the unproductive results when that human action is characterised by the exercise of power by some and by powerlessness for others. She says 'it is notable that our God Language is power-preoccupied, while at the same time it is fixated on human power-lessness.'[73] So, many inherited images of the God relationship displace and overwhelm images of human self-direction altogether. But 'dependence on divine control, and fear of self-direction is in itself conducive to reproducing oppression.'[74] So much modern theology has confirmed earlier images that have seen domination and subordination as both morally right, and theologically desirable forms of relationality. So she says, 'This leads to a state of affairs where approaches to action orientated to *obedience* have a strong tendency to convey that good action is a mode of *doing* for others, rather than *acting with* them'.

So pastoral theology has painfully to learn, as systematic theology and ethics are painfully trying to learn, that so many of its dominant interests, images and assumptions, are profoundly vulnerable to the feminist critique, which is of course, a thoroughly ethical critique. Until, and unless, this learning is taking place, we have seriously to reckon with the objection that Christian pastoral theology, or at least our understanding of health, is in significant respects deeply oppressive to women and profoundly distorting to humankind, producing alienations in rationality and sensuality, theory and practice, selfhood and Godhead, corporate well-being and individual injustice.

A paragraph to conclude. James Mathers' writings abound in critical tensions, individual and corporate, clerical and lay, treating a disease and treating a patient, seeing/hearing, and looking/listening, God as active, God as receptive, therapy and growth, dependence and autonomy, institutional bureaucracy, and personal identity. These tensions and others arise for Mathers because he writes from a standpoint which is both pastoral and prophetic. I conclude by quoting James Mathers in one of his briefest but most searching observations as far as the quest for health is concerned. He is speaking in the context of the need for pastoral training to be continually brought under critical scrutiny and its unconscious implications challenged. For he says, 'Though the pastoral task is important, it is not pre-eminent. The prophetic function should be the call to priority'. Because as he remarks simply, but with telling thoughts, 'In the long run this prophetic function is more likely to preserve the flock and to promote faith'. With due modesty and without undue palaver, James Mathers was and is for us, in Church and Society, a prophetic, pastoral theologian, pastoral prophet and a prophetic pastor whose vision we should allow to disturb us for quite sometime to come.

References
1. A.0. Dyson, 'Pastoral Theology: Towards a New Discipline', <u>Contact</u>, No.78, 1983, pp. 2ff.
2. Review of ed., Michael Wilson, **Explorations in Health and Salvation: A Selection of Papers by Bob Lambourne**, <u>Theology</u>, 87, 1984, p.3ll.
3. J.Mathers, 'Reflections on the Marriage Relationship', (unpublished).
4. Review of Alastair V. Campbell **Moderated Love** and Jane H. Thompson, **Spiritual Consideration in the Prevention, Treatment and Cure of Disease,** <u>TLS</u>, 23rd. November, 1984, p.1356.
5. Ibid.
6. <u>Expository Times</u>, 93, 1982, pp.220ff.
7. Review of Lisa Sowle Cahill, **Between the Sexes,** <u>Theology</u>, 89, 1986, p.413.
8. Review of Paul and Linda Badham, **Immortality or Extinction?**, and Dorothy Rowe, **The Construction of Life and Death,** <u>Theology</u>, 86, 1983 pp.56ff.
9. Review of eds., M.E. Marty and K.L.Vaux, **Health/Medicine and the Faith Traditions,** <u>Expository Times</u>, 94, 1983, p.28l.
10. <u>Expository Times</u>, 96, 1984, p.58.
11. <u>Theology</u>, 89, 1986, p.413.
12. <u>Theology</u>, 89, 1986, p.414.
13. See note 3 above.
14. See note 3 above.
15. <u>Theology</u>, 89, 1986, p.l55.
16. Ibid.
17. 'The Authority of the Pastor', <u>Contact</u>, No.49, 1975, p.27.
18. <u>Theology</u>, 80, 1977, p.159.
19. 'Vicarious Suffering', <u>Contact</u>, No.88, 1985, p.23.
20. 'A Healthy Society?', <u>Contact</u>, No.55, 1976, p.16.
21. 'The Authority of the Pastor', op.cit., p.30.
22. Review of Carl Djerassi, and W.H.Freeman, **The Politics of Contraception,** <u>Contact</u>, No.79, 1983, p.30.
23. 'Reflections on the IRM Conference on the Right to strike in the Caring Professions', <u>Contact</u>, No,48, 1975, p.34.
24. 'Vicarious Suffering', <u>Contact</u>, No.88, 1985, p.25.
25. Pierre Teilhard de Chardin, **Science et Christ,** (Paris), 1965, p.34, and **<u>Science/Christ,</u>** (London), 1968, p.13.
26. 'Vicarious Suffering', <u>Contact</u>, No.88, p.23.
27. 'How Far does the Evangel Impinge upon Counselling Practice?', <u>Contact</u>, No.57, 1977, p.9.
28. 'The Wholeness of Man', <u>Contact</u>, No.66, 1980, p.4.
29. Strategy and Tactics of Health Care' in ed., D.W.Millard, **Religion and Medicine 3**, (London), 1976, p.86.
30. 'A Healthy Society?', <u>Contact</u>, No.55, 1976, p.18.
31. 'IRM: Retrospect and Prospect', <u>Contact</u>, No.50, 1975, pp.3f..
32. vid.sup. 27, p.8.
33. 'The Authority of the Pastor', op. cit. p. 30.
34. 'The Context of Anxiety' in ed., M.A.H. Melinksy, **Religion and Medicine: A Discussion**, (London), 1970, p.17.
35. 'How Far does the Evangel?', op.cit. p.5.
36. 'The Pastoral Role: A Psychiatrist's View' in ed., M,A,H, Melinsky, **Religion and Medicine 2**, (London), 1973, p.90.
37. 'How Far does the Evangel?', op. cit. p.6.
38. 'How Far does the Evangel?', op. cit. p.7.
39. 'Too Much Noise Makes You Deaf', <u>IRM Newsletter</u>, No.32, September, 1975.
40. Review of Martin Israel's **Healing as Sacrament,** <u>Expository Times</u>, 96, 1984, p.58.
41. 'The Authority of the Pastor', op. cit. p.29.
42. Michael Wilson, **Health is for People,** (D.L.T.), London, 1979, p.68.
43. **'Brain Death' or 'Heart Death'?**: Reflections on an Ethical Dilemma, <u>Expository Times</u>, 87, 1976, p.331.

44. Ibid. p.332.
45. Review of Ralph Wendell Burhoe, **'Toward a Scientific Theology'**, Religion and Medicine (IRM), April 1986, p.148.
46. Review of Peter Coleman, **Christian Attitudes to Homosexuality**, Theology, 84, 1981, pp.155ff.
47. op. cit. 2 Review of ed,, Michael Wilson **Explorations in Health and Salvation,** p312.
48. vid .sup. 20 'A Healthy Society?, p.14.
49. vid. sup. 28, 'The Wholeness of Man', p.4.
50. Ibid. p.5.
51. 'The Wholeness of Man', p.3.
52. 'A Healthy Society', p.l4.
53. Review of Frank Lake, **Tight Corners in Pastoral Counselling**, Theology, 85, 1982, p.227.
54. 'Psychiatry and Religion', p.15.
55. Ibid. p.14.
56. 'The Wholeness of Man', p.6.
57. 'The Pastoral Role', p.83.
58. 'How Far Does the Evangel?', p.10.
59. Ibid. p.6.
60. Review of Patrick Casement, **On Learning from the Patient**, Theology, 89, 1986, p325.
61. Review of Jean Vanier, **The Challenge of L'Arche**, Theology, 86,1983, p.470.
62. vid. sup. 29, 'Strategy and Tactics of Health Care', p.87
63. Ibid.
64. Ibid. p.85.
65, Review of Martin Israel, op.cit., p.58.
66. Review of Frank Lake, op.cit. p.227.
67. Beverley Wilding Harrison, **Making the Connections**, (Boston), 1985, p.6,
68. Harrison, p.8.
69. Ibid. p.9.
70. Ibid. p.11.
71. Ibid. p.13.
72. Ibid. p.18.
73. Ibid. p.35.
74. Ibid. p.37.

Also Consulted

Review of James B. Nelson, **Embodiment**, Theology, 83, 1980, pp.73-75.
Review of Gladysann Bryce, **Divorce and Spiritual Growth** and ed,, Ian Gentles, **Care for the Dying and the Bereaved,** Theology, 87, 1984, pp. 74ff.
Review of Yorick Spiegel, **The Grief Process,** Theology, 81, 1978, pp. 461ff.
'Our President.' (biographical note), IRM Newsletter, 31 March 1975.
Review of Susan Sontag, **Illness as Metaphor**, Journal of Medical Ethics, 7, 1983, pp.45ff.
'Custodial or Residental Care for the Long-Stay Patient?', The Lancet, 22nd April 1972, pp.894ff.
Review of ., Digby Anderson, **The Kingdom that Kills** and Charles Elliott, **Praying the Kingdom**, Contact, No.89, 1986 pp.32ff.
Review of K.M.Boyd, **The Ethics of Resource Allocation in Health Care,** Contact, No.67, 1980, pp,27ff.
Review of Maurice Rawlings, **Beyond Death's Door**, Contact, No.64, 1979, p.26.
Review of Rosemary Houghton, **The Liberated Heart,** Theology, 79, 1975, pp.113ff.
Review of Roger Grainger, **A Place Like This: A Guide to Life in a Psychiatric Hospital,** The Modern Churchman, 27, 1985, p.61.
Review of Pierre Solgnac, **The Christian Neurosis**, Expository Times, 93, 1982, p.348.
Review of Jack Dominian, **Depression**, Expository Times, 87, 1976, p.348.
Review of Edgar N. Jackson, **The Many Faces of Grief**, Expository Times, 89, 1973, p.317.
'Becoming a Participant Observor', The Teilhard Review, 22, 1987, pp.44-49.

JAMES MATHERS: CRITICAL ASSESSMENT

By: Stephen Pattison, Peter Bellamy, Brian Easter and Michael Wilson.

CONTACT No. 97 1988:3

This edition of CONTACT contained a selection of papers and reviews by the late James Mathers. … The following article is a short and probably premature attempt at putting Mathers' work in some sort of critical perspective and assessing its significance. … The content of this article is based on a conversation between four people who knew James Mathers from their own associations with pastoral studies at Birmingham. Michael Wilson was a close friend and colleague; Peter Bellamy and Brian Easter were pupils and friends; Stephen Pattison was simply an acquaintance, but also an admirer of Mathers' work and personality.

James Mathers made a remarkable and unique contribution to the development of pastoral studies at Birmingham University where he was an honorary lecturer, and so to the emergence of pastoral studies in the UK as a whole. He was part of an influential triumvirate of medical doctors-cum-theologians (Mathers, Wilson and Lambourne) who contributed crucially to the burgeoning dialogue between religion and medicine and other caring professions in the 1960s and 1970s. A humble, unassuming and gentle man with a sense of quiet irony, Mathers was a stimulating and sometimes frustrating teacher in the Socratic mode, modified by his extensive training in group psychotherapy. It is perhaps as a teacher that he will be best remembered. It is necessary to underline Mathers' personal flexibility and responsiveness in personal encounter because his writings so often adopt the tone of the self-assured, authoritative psychiatrist (though this never disguises Mathers' persistently questioning mind). Mathers was a prolific, clear and fluent writer and he wrote many papers and reviews, particularly after his early retirement from the superintendency of a large psychiatric hospital in Birmingham. Living in the country, he had time to reflect on a life filled with rich experience gained in the army, psychiatry and the university. His critical and creative talents are as well, if not better, displayed in his many book reviews as in his articles. It is almost as if the less words he had, the more effective he became in using them. Mathers appears to have had no desire to write a book-length work; the pursuit of one main idea in a paper or review was his *metier.*

Like his colleagues in pastoral studies at Birmingham, Mathers' writings are characterised by catholicity of concern, interest and research. Mathers read widely and was eclectic in his use of insights from many sources, psychoanalysis, evolutionary theory, biblical studies. His approach is broad and holistic, but it tends to focus round certain constant themes, eg., institutions, their organisation and effect on persons, communities and their health, authority in caring and other relationships, morale, social integration of badness, the significance of biological and scientific discoveries for understanding human relationships. Although his work is not systematic and it has no one clear organising principle, it seems that Mathers proceeded from a practical problem or situation by way of a kind of free association of ideas drawn from many different disciplines and sources to try and find new understandings and resources for dealing with things. The ultimate criterion for evaluating the usefulness of an idea or concept would appear to be whether or not it leads towards human flourishing in today's world. Mathers might well have expressed his concern for truth as being the practical business of 'making and keeping life human in the world' (Lehmann). He was essentially uninterested in impractical, antiquarian and inhumane aspects of the Christian tradition; he had no time, for example, for those aspects of Christianity which dwell upon or produce feelings of guilt, inferiority or inadequacy. At the same time he was shameless in press-ganging religious images, concepts, and figures into service if they appeared to be pointing in the direction that he wanted humanity to go. Mathers emerges, then, as a slightly undisciplined and pragmatic, if inspired and insightful thinker who might certainly be held up as a good exemplar of the liberal humanist Christianity of the middle part of the twentieth century. Liberal humanism is not an adequate description on its own, however. Mathers was also a sacramentalist in the broadest sense of the term. Perhaps it was his enormous sense of the essential goodness of the world and human beings which led him conspicuously to ignore important theological themes such as sin and atonement.

There are, of course, considerable limitations to Mathers' thinking as evident in his writings. Like many other writers in the field of pastoral studies, he can be criticised for his unsystematic approach, his, to some extent, undisciplined eclecticism, and his theological ignorance and selectivity (he never trained formally as a theologian and this is perhaps reflected in a partiality for biblical themes with which he was familiar and neglect of insight derived from systematic theology). It could be argued that Mathers made a mistake in thinking that practical theology was best undertaken retrospectively in the context which made the questions he attempted to address significant. It could also be said that Mathers never really adequately explored his own personal ambivalence about the institutions which supplied his daily bread and stimulus throughout his working life, yet so often seem to have been life-denying to others. While Mathers longed for the freedom and health of the ordinary person, he himself occupied a privileged position in the organisations in which he served; nowhere does he really examine his own part in systems of oppression in his writings, though it is difficult to believe that he was unaware of this dimension in his personal life. In this connection, readers might like to reflect on Mathers' response to the patient described in 'Vandalism' above: is it liberating and compassionate or merely patronising? Though in many ways a perpetual and trenchant critic and rebel, Mathers never really rejected the very established roles and institutions which formed such an important part of his life, a fact evidenced in his election to a Fellowship of the Royal College of Psychiatrists. This relates to another possible limitation to his thought; one of the most prominent characteristics of all his writing is its anti-individualism and its emphasis on the communal and the corporate. But, curiously, this social concern and analysis seems to be divorced from any kind of political analysis. Social power structures are dealt with almost entirely in a functional and organic way. Perhaps this strange omission in one so alert and critical might be explained by a temperamental preference or personal experience. On the other hand, it may be that Mathers was simply unwilling to problematise his own position as an upper middle class professional too deeply.

It is difficult to assess the long-term significance of someone's work when it is still so close in time. Mathers certainly influenced the institutions of which he was a part in important ways. He had enormous personal influence on Diploma in Pastoral Studies students at Birmingham and strengthened the teaching team for that course, though he did not influence the shape of the course itself to any great extent. Mathers' friendship and dialogue with Wilson and Lambourne was of great significance; the writings of each of these thinkers must, in many ways, be read together as so many of the ideas of each contributed to the writings of all. In contributing so readily to conferences of caring professionals, eg., the Institute of Religion and Medicine, and to written symposia and journals Mathers clearly became a significant figure in many different worlds. It is difficult, however, to see him as a figure of enormous stature and importance in any of the fields to which he contributed. He never, for example, became a 'guru' in the area of running hospitals, which was, after all, supposed to be his area of primary professional expertise. Some might argue that his chief significance to the religious life of this country lies in his being truly a lay theologian – a lay person who took theology seriously and tried to work with it from a genuinely lay perspective. The accolade of 'lay theologian' cannot be denied to Mathers, but perhaps it does not really capture what was important about the man and his work. Mathers' interests were too wide and his devotion to theology too tenuous to make this a felicitous label. In one of his own papers Mathers refers to the business of 'learning to live constructively'. This is certainly what he did himself and what he tried to encourage others to do, by his writing and personal example. There is no neat role description for one who wants to learn to live constructively and help others to do the same, yet Mathers was such a person. His writing and teaching hang well around this nexus which may indeed be seen as being profoundly religious even if it is only loosely theological. Mathers was working at the practical task of living and caring in his own time. His writing was relevant to that time and so may date quickly and prove ephemeral.

Times have certainly changed since Mathers' professional life finished in the 1970s. The era of liberal interdisciplinary enquiry and loyal criticism within stable consensual institutions situated within an equally stable and consensual society has passed. Fundamental conflict and polarisation are the order of the day. Even the large psychiatric hospital which stimulated, nurtured and enraged Mathers has largely disappeared together with therapeutic communities and the psychoanalytic ideas which informed them. Perhaps, then, Mathers' thought will have no lasting influence. On the other hand, however, wherever people find themselves reflecting on human relationships, on actual interactions rather than techniques, on care rather than helping skills, on communities and groups rather than anonymous collectivities, they will find much in Mathers which must remain unsurpassed. Mathers' great talent was to take an everyday concern or situation of practical importance and to worry away at it until new light emerged upon it. The reader often finds himself or herself mentally exclaiming, 'Why didn't I see it that way before? Of course he's right!' Mathers is not a guide to the forbidding heights of the intellect, casting great thoughts on a wide canvas. He is a splendid miniaturist, a thorough explorer of the little valleys of ordinary experience in which most of us spend so much of our time. As such he is, in his writings as in his life, a stimulating and fascinating companion and friend. When will we see his like again?

INDEX

Chapter headings, and Contents in Page Order

(Under each sub-heading is the list of the paper/s from which the extracts are taken.)

PAGE NO:

SPACE FOR YOUR OWN NOTES

SPACE FOR YOUR OWN NOTES

SPACE FOR YOUR OWN NOTES